Keepers of the Forest

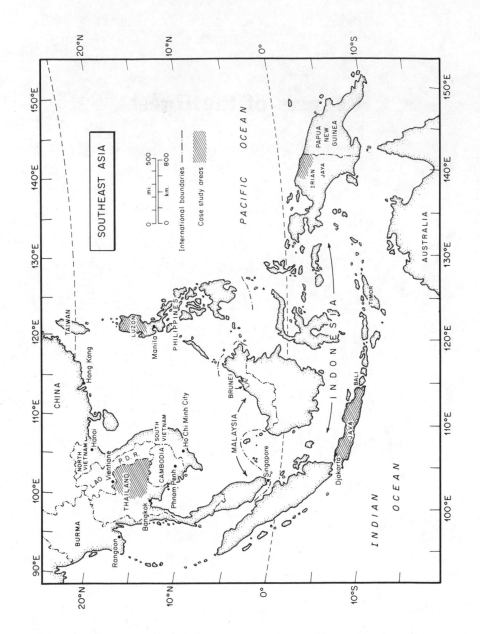

SOUTHEAST ASIA

International boundaries
Case study areas

Keepers of the Forest

Land Management Alternatives in Southeast Asia

Editor
Mark Poffenberger

 1990

Kumarian Press

© 1990 by Kumarian Press
630 Oakwood Ave, Suite 119, West Hartford, Connecticut 06110-1529

Printed in the United States of America

Library of Congress Cataloging in Publication Data

Keepers of the forest : land management alternatives in Southeast Asia
 / edited by Mark Poffenburger.
        p.   cm.
    Includes bibliographical references.
    ISBN 0–931816–81–5. — ISBN 0–931816–80–7 (pbk.)
    1. Forest management—Asia, Southeastern. 2. Forests and
forestry—Social aspects—Asia, Southeastern. 3. Agroforestry-
-Asia, Southeastern. 4. Land use, Rural—Asia, Southeastern.
I. Poffenberger, Mark, 1950–
    SD235.A785K44   1989
    333.75'0959—dc20   89–38879
                                                               CIP

Contents

Figures and Tables

LIST OF FIGURES

LIST OF TABLES

Contributors

Yaowalak Apichatvullop is a Professor of Sociology at Khon Kaen University in Thailand. She has conducted in-depth studies of human–forest management patterns in Northeast Thailand. She is currently a senior scientist with the Northeast Thailand Social Forestry Project.

Salve B. Borlagdan is a Research Associate at the Institute of Philippine Culture, Ateneo de Manila University. She is a community psychologist who has focused her research on strategies to enhance farmers' participation in managing water and forest land resources.

Mulyadi Bratamihardja is Chief of the Forest Products Division of the Indonesian State Forest Corporation (SFC). Before joining the SFC in 1974, he taught forest management at Bogor Agricultural University. He is currently director of the SFC's social forestry program on Java.

Romulo del Castillo is Professor of Forest Resources Management at UPLB. Since its inception he has acted as senior consultant to the Ford Foundation-assisted Philippine Upland Development program. He is a past Dean of the College of Forestry at University of the Philippines at Los Banos (UPLB) and has thirty years of experience teaching and conducting research on upland management issues.

Luzviminda B. Cornista is the Director of the Institute of Agrarian Studies at UPLB. For the past fifteen years she has conducted research and advised the Philippine Government on land tenure programs and policy.

Eva F. Escueta is a rural sociologist at the Institute of Agrarian Studies, UPLB. She has conducted extensive research on problems of land tenure and agrarian reform.

Yance de Fretes is a senior staff member with World Wildlife Fund's Irian Jaya program. From 1986 through 1989 he acted as project coordinator for the Mt. Cyclops Social Forestry program. He is currently on a two year study leave in the United States.

Jefferson Fox is a Research Associate with the Environment and Policy Institute at the East-West Center in Hawaii. He has considerable experience in Nepal and Indonesia in the application of information system methodologies to resource planning and rural development needs.

Christopher Gibbs is a resource economist with the Environment Department of World Bank. As a Ford Foundation program officer in the early 1980s, he assisted the development of the Philippines Uplands Working Group. He has experience in agricultural and resource management policy analysis in Asia and North America.

James A. Hafner is a Professor of Geography and Asian Studies in the Department of Geology and Geography, University of Massachusetts in the United States. His research since 1975 has included work for the United Nations on population resettlement and dam construction in Laos and Thailand, and studies of rural migration, resource use and development in central and northeast Thailand.

Arthur Mitchell is a primatologist currently completing a doctoral program at Yale University in the United States. His past work includes directing World Wildlife Fund projects on Siberut and Irian Jaya in Indonesia, including the development of the Mt. Cyclops park management program.

Elizabeth A. Omegan is a doctoral student in geography at the University of Hawaii. She is Research Director of the Montanosa Development Center at Sagada Mountain Province in the Philippines.

Edwin Payuan is the Chief of the Philippine Forest Management Bureau's Social Forestry Division. He has pioneered the Bureau's upland management programs for over sixteen years. He is currently on leave as a consultant to FAO forestry extension programs in Malawi.

Nancy Lee Peluso is a Visiting Lecturer with the Energy and Resources Group at the University of California at Berkeley in the United States. She has conducted research in Indonesia for seven years, focusing on rural resource use patterns and their historical, political, and economic contexts.

Mark Poffenberger is a Program Officer with the Ford Foundation's South Asia Office in New Delhi. During the 1970s he studied rural resource use patterns and demographic change in rural Nepal and Indonesia. From 1982 through 1987 he coordinated Foundation support to Southeast Asian social forestry groups.

Kamon Pragtong is Head of the Thai Royal Forestry Department Community Forestry Section within the National Forest Land Management Division. He has worked in community forestry program design and implementation for the past fifteen years, and holds a Masters degree in social forestry from Yale University.

Percy E. Sajise is a Professor of Plant Ecology at the University of the Phiippines at Los Banos (UPLB). He has directed the research program of the Institute of Environmental Science and Management for the past twelve years and currently acts as advisor to the Department of Environment and Natural Resources' Rainfed Resources Development Program.

Frances Seymour is a Program Officer with the Ford Foundation's Southeast Asia Office, and currently manages Foundation support for the Indonesian Social Forestry Program. She has considerable experience evaluating forestry sector programs in the Philippines, Indonesia, and Nepal.

Carol Stoney is an agroforestry specialist with Winrock International working with the Java State Forest Corporation's Social Forestry Program. She has ten years experience in agroforestry program design and implementation in Africa and Latin America.

David Thomas is a Program Officer with the Ford Foundation's Bangkok office. He presently coordinates support for Foundation–assisted community forestry programs and advises the Thai Royal Forestry Department. He has extensive experience in rural resource research and management programs in Thailand.

Foreword

DON'T LET THE TITLE of this book deceive you. It *is* about the management of a particular natural resource—forests—in a particular part of the world—Southeast Asia—and, in fact, foresters and Asian scholars will find much here pertinent to their particular interests.

The scope and implications of *Keepers of the Forest*, however, have universal application and vision. Southeast Asia leads the world in developing resource management practices that get more for less through increased involvement of the people who live in or around a natural resource. The wide range of social strategies found in Southeast Asia has much to offer for resolving the failed resource strategies of both other tropical areas and temperate areas as well.

You will find here history, data, case studies and an emerging theory of development that appeals to your intellectual appetite. The real reward, however, is somewhat different. Though the volume is the work of objective, disciplined scholars and scientists, it is the interwoven story, the poetry, that binds the chapters. *Keepers of the Forest* sings a tale that expresses how once upon a time there were traditional patterns of order and balance between a people's needs and the sustainability of their resources. Authority and accountability were close to the source of need and nature. Then came a period of disorder and destruction as resources were redefined to meet centralized, commercial goals of distant accountability and whimsical market forces. Now, with the rise of modern Asia, there is the emergence of redemption and restoration as traditional strategies are rediscovered and adapted to today's realities. In Southeast Asia both the pressures of the population-land ratio and the emergence of new desires and resources are being enfolded into new ways of fulfilling older vision.

As we recognize the earthbound wonder of our interdependent, global ecosystem, a new and concrete understanding of the universal resource drama may just become the most useful contribution of *Keepers of the Forest*. So enjoy this journey to Southeast Asia for all of its scholarly substance—and be prepared to carry its lessons right to your own backyard.

William R. Burch, Jr.
Director of the Tropical Resources Institute
School of Forestry and Environmental Studies
Yale University

Preface

IN SOUTHEAST ASIA, access to state forests, which comprise the majority of the region's total land area, is intensely sought by timber companies, development projects, and rural people. "Who are the rightful forest keepers?" is becoming a major political question in villages and national capitals, and an issue driving social conflicts and creating political instability throughout much of insular and mainland Southeast Asia. The title of this book, "Keepers of the Forest," is purposely ambiguous. Are the keepers the forest administrators in their offices, or the rangers in green suits and black boots with guns on their hips? Are they the logging companies who hold the lease rights to exploit? Are they the insatiable consumers of the developed world? Are they the forest communities who have lived in the forests from prehistoric times, or the migrant families that arrive daily in increasing numbers?

At the heart of forest mismanagement lie deep-seated differences between governments and rural people about who should control these lands and how they should be managed. Unless action is taken to resolve forest management conflict, unsustainable use practices will continue, leading to the ultimate destruction of the region's tropical forests.

In response to failing custodial and production forest management systems, during the last twenty years small groups of foresters, scientists, and community development specialists in Southeast Asia began developing methods to empower forest families and villages with the rights to manage public lands. Throughout this period the Ford Foundation has provided support to some of the region's forestry agencies, university-based scientists, and nongovernment organization community development specialists to explore means to improve these efforts through staff training, pilot projects, and diagnostic research. This book is an attempt to bring this experience together and share some of the learning that was collectively generated. The authors have attempted to provide their readers with a realistic assessment of problems and possible solutions to deforestation through cooperative action between state forest agencies and forest communities.

It is hoped others will take the next steps to further develop effective ways to bring forest control into the hands of forest communities, in an attempt to slow the destruction of one of the earth's most valuable natural resources. This book is dedicated to the growing body of progressive foresters who see forest communities as part of the solution to deforestation, rather than as part of the problem, and to the forest communities that are willing to take on management responsibilities, if given the chance.

Preparation of this anthology was generously supported by the Ford Foundation. The Department of Forestry at the University of California at Berkeley provided facilities where much of the book was compiled. William Carmichael, Norm Collins, John Gerhart, Tom Kessinger, Joe McBride, and Jeff Romm supported and encouraged this effort. The editor wishes to extend his gratitude to Marie Litterer of the Department of Geography at the University of Massachusetts at Amherst for her work in the final preparation of the graphics.

The editor wishes to thank Gary Mcdonald, Paul Green, Debra Ivens, I. D. Khurana, and K. R. Raghunathan for assistance in editing and preparing the manuscript for publication, and Nancy Peluso, Fran Korten, Jim Hafner, Mary Zurbuchen, and Tom Poffenberger for their guidance in developing the book. The authors are grateful to William R. Burch, Jr., for writing the foreword. We would also like to extend our appreciation to Krishna Sondhi and Jenna Dixon at Kumarian Press for their willingness to publish and bring this book to their readers.

Mark Poffenberger
New Delhi, India

Introduction:
The Forest Management Crisis

Mark Poffenberger

THE DEVASTATION OF the earth's tropical rainforests is causing world-wide concern. Equatorial forests contain an estimated 50 percent of all known animal and plant species. As the forests are destroyed, so are genetic resources that evolved over millions of years. Tropical forests play important, and only partially understood, roles in shaping our climate and atmosphere. Forest clearing, accelerating since 1860, is now considered a major cause of the global warming trend.[1] Ultimately, tropical deforestation threatens human survival.

A large part of the earth's people depend on firewood for fuel, and wood remains the primary raw building material. Forests are a major source of income and food for the world's poorest people. As tropical rainforests are depleted, the long-term potential of developing nations to generate income is eroded. Rural poor are forced to burn organic materials essential to sustain soil fertility, which further impoverishes the resource base of those nations.

Human clearing of forest land is an old process. The felling of the vast cedar forests of Lebanon began as early as 3,000 B.C.[2] Parts of Greece were largely deforested by the fifth century B.C.[3] Over the millennia, large forested areas in China, the Middle East, Europe, and North Africa were felled.

During the twentieth century, however, tropical forest clearing has accelerated at an alarming rate. In Southeast Asia, primary rainforests shrank from 250 million hectares in 1900, to less than 60 million hectares in 1989.[4] In Indonesia, a nation possessing 10 percent of the world's tropical forests, over 600,000 hectares are cut annually.[5] In northeastern Thailand over 60 percent of all forest land was cleared by loggers and migrant farmers over the past fifteen years. In the Philippine uplands, tribal peoples, indigenous farming communities, and settlers from the lowlands compete for forest land. Some scientists now predict the destruction of all tropical rainforests by the early twenty-first century if deforestation continues at its present rate.

Logging and population expansion are the primary forces driving deforestation in Southeast Asia. Governments in search of revenues have encouraged rapid timber exploitation in the past. Population growth floods the forests with migrants searching for farmland. Concern is mounting over the loss of the region's rich forest lands, yet there is no consensus regarding solutions to the problem. While some of the region's governments have greatly curtailed commercial logging in response to the devastation brought by timber companies, the Malaysian and Indonesian governments continue to lease extensive tracts of forest lands to timber enterprises. While forestry policies require companies to follow sustainable-yield logging practices, a lack of incentives, limited monitoring capacity, and corruption have led to overcutting and the permanent degradation of many leased areas. British forester Ducan Poore's recent study of commercial logging practices in tropical forest areas estimated that fewer than 1 percent of the concessions were being managed in a sustainable manner.[6] Throughout the region, logging roads have opened remote forest tracks, making them accessible to migrants who clear remaining vegetation through cutting and burning, further denuding the land. Frequently, after several years of farming, the fertility of former forest lands declines, forcing migrant farmers to move on to clear other areas, leaving their fields to be taken over by grasses and shrubs.

Foresters are concerned with the widespread "encroachment" of land-hungry people who seek forest lands to grow subsistence and cash crops. While the forestry establishment has supported the commercial exploitation of vast areas by multinational and local timber companies, government officials frequently blame peasant and tribal communities for forest destruction. Although there are many migrant forest farmers who have not yet developed ecologically sound agricultural practices for forest lands, and who cause much damage, there is also a wealth of experience and knowledge of forest ecology and sustainable use practices among the indigenous communities. Agroecological research studies reveal that many of the indigenous pastoral, swidden farming, and agroforestry systems of Southeast Asia are based on the efficient use of land and labor and cause little damage to the larger forest ecosystem.[7]

Besides foresters and forest inhabitants, other groups have their own forest use priorities. Politicians and administrators in government agencies often struggle to have forest lands transferred to their control. In some cases they seek to have the land reclassified for resettlement projects, industrial export zones, state plantations, or privatization. Citizens concerned about the environment raise their hands in protest over the irresponsible exploitation of forests. They hope to protect unique flora and fauna. They lobby for bans on logging operations and sometimes for the exclusion of forest communities. Social scientists bring still another perspective to the debate. Their concern is often for the people living near or in the forest.

Contending that commercial exploitation does not answer economic needs, many argue for the rights of indigenous tribal and farming communities. Each group has its own view, yet all have been relatively ineffective in developing alternative management systems responsive to diverse, and sometimes conflicting, national and local priorities.

Local forest management problems are characterized by the diverse and complex social forces changing the land in each locale. Lacking the tools and incentives to respond to varying local conditions and needs, forestry staff rely on standardised technical procedures, which limit the opportunities to involve communities in management. This lack of communication between forest users and forest administrators has often led to misunderstanding and conflict.

In the past, forestry agencies in danger of losing control of state forest lands have sometimes called in the police and army to reestablish their position. Such confrontations over land access have increased tensions between rural people and the government. Land disputes have repeatedly resulted in armed conflicts, periodically stimulating antigovernment separatist movements throughout the region. The Philippines, Thailand, Indonesia, Malaysia, and Burma have all experienced insurgency movements since independence, aggravated by the discontent of forest communities. As pressures on these lands intensify, the potential for violence grows.

It will be difficult to slow the process of forest degradation in Southeast Asia. Neither the nonagricultural economic sector nor existing agricultural lands have the capacity to absorb the growing rural work force. As a consequence, many rural poor will continue to need forest land for some time to come. Fortunately, if made available, there are millions of hectares of degraded and cleared forest land that rural communities could productively develop and manage. These lands could be used to absorb excess labor and take pressure off the remaining natural forest.

While some governments have tended to view their rainforest lands as vast unpopulated territories, a recent report by the Independent Commission on International Humanitarian Issues cites estimates of between 140 and 200 million tribal people living in or on the edges of closed tropical forests.[8] Many government forestry agencies, fearful of losing land control, hesitate to transfer authority to forest users and provide incentives for ecologically sound management. Governments are slow to recognize local management capacity and rights, yet the management ability of tens of thousands of forest communities is apparent in the great diversity of productive, ecologically viable agroforestry systems found throughout the tropics. Policies and procedures are needed which smooth the transition to the decentralized management of local forest lands.

With technical, marketing, and credit support, small agroforestry enterprises may achieve their latent potential. A wide range of forest products, including pharmaceuticals, bamboo, rattan, tannin, wood oils, fruits, and honeys, have considerable economic and employment potential. For example, in 1977 the Southeast Asia rattan industry alone was valued at $1.2 billion per year[9] and estimated to employ half a million people in collecting, cultivating, processing, and small-scale manufacturing. Market analysis suggests international consumption could be increased threefold if production could be increased and marketing linkages improved. Given the millions dependent on forests for construction materials, food, medicine, and cash income, the term "minor forest products," often applied to products such as those listed above, is both inaccurate and reflects a widely held timber bias within the forestry sector.[10] Further, the needs of small-scale forest industries have been increasingly neglected in recent decades. In 1940, for instance, minor forest products accounted for approximately 45 percent of all revenues generated from the forestry sector in Indonesia; by 1980, however, their contribution had fallen to less than 8 percent.[11] Leading forest management specialists recommend a worldwide effort to help shifting cultivators and migrant forest farmers adopt agroforestry technologies because they require low capital investments, afford a great deal of employment, and are likely to be environmentally acceptable.[12] By intensifying sustainable agroforestry production systems, millions of jobs could be created, reducing the pressures on remaining forest lands, while rehabilitating forests already degraded.

Deforestation can be slowed, even reversed, given the political will and the daring to break with nineteenth century management traditions. But time is running out and the forces stimulating degradation are firmly established. Deforestation will not be stopped by international conferences. Addressing the macroeconomic roots of forest mismanagement is only part of the solution; methods of effectively involving rural people in forest management must be urgently developed.

Most government attempts to work with communities have been paternalistic, based on the belief that project designers and programmers needed to package technologies, credit systems, and new institutions for rural people. Planners assumed outside implementors were needed to manage the projects and protect the people from themselves and their own lack of experience, in the hope that one day they could take over these responsibilities. Repeatedly, this approach has failed. This strategy has led to heavy rural dependencies on government projects and has stifled local initiative, encouraging planners to believe they know more than the communities about local problems, needs, and potential solutions. Finally, it has cost billions of dollars and wasted many years of human effort.

Most public agencies tend to be conservative and resistant to change. Change disrupts established procedures, delays routine operations, and results in additional costs. Change can also threaten the positions of agency staff, especially those with greater seniority. Within most public organizations there are vested interests in the way agency funds are used and resources managed. These interests can be threatened by a change in operations. In the past, change has been effected mainly through policy decisions by senior management. Yet policy decisions are no guarantee that the changes will be implemented. Policy change may have little or no effect on staff attitudes or in the development of more effective procedures and new management capacity. These are developed through learning, a process that must be created within the agency.

Many forestry agencies give little attention to understanding the social problems related to field operations. Junior staff may submit routine reports, but they convey little information about field problems and community relations. There are few upward communication channels and little sense among managers that information on community matters would be useful. In fact, field staff may fear that informing management of operational problems may be viewed as "trouble making" or "rocking the boat." The problem of over-extended forestry bureaucracies has been amplified by agency attempts to strengthen their authority by resettling forest dwellers and eroding their role in forest management. State bureaucracies sometimes view their own increased authority as a major organizational objective, and lose sight of their original responsibilities to manage forest resources to meet local and national economic and environmental goals.

The development era of the 1960s to the present has encouraged the growth of bureaucracies in the developing world. The underlying philosophy of this period equated economic growth and development with the expansion of government agencies and their services, whether in health, agriculture, education, or governance. It was assumed that the prime mover of development was the government, rather than the people themselves. However, while this strategy fell short of expectations, the costs continued to rise. By the mid-1980s, many developing nations suffered from heavy debt burdens that badly sapped their economic growth potential. Economic constraints have forced many of the region's governments to restrict expansion of forestry agencies and their programs.

Southeast Asia's forests require new, more effective management systems. This book examines the potential of collaborative schemes that bring foresters and communities together in using and protecting forests for the good of the nation and rural people. Experience from such programs in a range of social and ecological environments indicates that improving the land-tenure security of forest villages can result in increased community participation in forest management, greater long-term productivity, and reduced administrative costs. The ultimate outcome of decentralized forest management systems is yet to be determined, but existing forest administration regimes are clearly failing to fulfill their mandates. Community management represents a promising alternative approach to the administration of state forest lands.

The book synthesizes the work of scientists, foresters, and management specialists in the Philippines, Thailand, and Indonesia who have been involved in developing new forest management systems. In each country, groups of scientists and forest administrators are actively experimenting with new policies and procedures to transfer management authority to farm families and community organizations. These groups premise their work on the concept of participation. They assume that rural people who are given responsibility for the forest lands in their area, can develop management skills to administer those resources effectively.

This book is broadly divided into three parts. Part I examines the evolution of land conflict between governments and rural people in Southeast Asia. The political, demographic, and economic forces that shaped forest use patterns are discussed for Thailand, the Philippines, and Java. These chapters illustrate the diversity of contexts and the uniqueness of problems encountered in each setting, while pointing to underlying historical forces which breed tension throughout the region.

Part II focuses on learning techniques and tools that allow forestry managers and field staff to know communities better and to develop collaborative management systems. The chapters in this section discuss methods to stimulate learning in forestry agencies, diagnostic tools for understanding community needs, legal mechanisms for empowering communities through enhanced land-tenure security and greater forest usufruct rights, and agroforestry technologies to increase land productivity and sustainability. In Part III the authors describe their experiences in developing national and field-level programs to enable forest management bureaucracies to work more effectively with communities to manage forest lands.

NOTES

1. The Worldwatch Institute has estimated that up to 180 billion tons of carbon have been released into the atmosphere through forest clearing since the beginning of the Industrial Revolution, equal to all carbon emissions from fossil fuel burning during the same period. Carbon dioxide emissions are primary, causing approximately 50 percent of the greenhouse effect. While the clearing and burning of forests generates large amounts of carbon dioxide into the atmosphere, as forests are lost the earth's capacity to transform carbon dioxide into oxygen is diminished. See Simons, Marlise. "Man-Made Amazon Fires Tied to Global Warming," *San Francisco Chronicle,* August 8, 1988, pp. A-1, A-6.

2. Eckholm, Eric P. 1976. *Losing Ground: Environmental Stress and World Food Prospects.* New York: W. W. Norton & Co., p. 27.

3. Goudie, Andrew. 1986. *The Human Impact on the Environment.* Cambridge, Massachusetts: The MIT Press, p. 37.

4. Scott, Margaret. "The Disappearing Forests." *Far Eastern Economic Review,* January 12, 1989, p. 32.

5. "In Indonesia, a Ravaging of Forests." *International Herald Tribune,* October 6, 1987.

6. As quoted by Scott, Margaret, "The Disappearing Forests," *Far Eastern Economic Review,* January 12, 1989, p. 33.

7. Dove, Michael R. 1985. "The Agroecological Mythology of the Javanese and the Political Economy of Indonesia." *Indonesia* 39:35.

8. Independent Commission on International Humanitarian Issues. 1986. *The Vanishing Forest: The Human Consequences of Deforestation.* London: Zed Books, p. 29.

9. Siebert, Stephen F., and Jill M. Belsky. 1985. "Forest-product Trade in a Lowland Filippino Village," *Economic Botany* 39(4):522–533 citing Shane, M. 1977. "The Economics of the Rattan Industry," in W. Y. Wong and M. Shane, eds. *A Sabah Rattan Industry.* Transcript SAFODA, Kota Kinabalu, Malaysia, pp. 43–53.

10. Ibid, p. 522.

11. Peluso, Nancy Lee. 1986. "Rattan Industries in East Kalimantan, Indonesia." Unpublished paper commissioned by the FAO Policy and Planning Service Forestry Department.

12. Nair, P. K. R., and E. Fernandes. 1984. "Agroforestry as an Alternative to Shifting Cultivation," *FAO Soils Bulletin.* Rome: FAO, 53:12.

Part I

Historical Perspectives

Introduction

Mark Poffenberger

BY STUDYING THE evolution of forest use patterns and management practices we can better understand the forces currently driving deforestation in Southeast Asia. Historical analysis allows us to identify how past actions of governments and societies have affected forest use. A historical perspective on changing human environmental interactions can help illuminate destructive patterns and improve society's ability to resolve them.

In Part I the authors attempt to outline the ways governments, foresters, tribal peoples, migrant farmers, and loggers have historically perceived and managed Southeast Asia's forest lands. In Chapter 1, Poffenberger examines indigenous forest use patterns in Southeast Asia and proceeds to chart the growth of state control over the "public domain." The author reviews some of the underlying concepts and practices of early kingdoms, colonial governments, and modern independent states in extending central authority over the region's forests. He notes that while the influence of government policy over forest use has increased gradually over the past millennium, it has accelerated dramatically in the postwar period. Poffenberger suggests that the rise of state control has been at the expense of indigenous forest management systems. Although modern Southeast Asian governments attempt to control national land-use policy for vast areas of forest land, at the community level state administrative capacity remains limited. He concludes that the resulting conflict between state land management policies and locally operating forest use systems is a major cause of deforestation and mismanagement throughout Southeast Asia.

In Chapter 2, Peluso documents the consolidation of state control over Java's forests through the colonial era, Japanese occupation, and independence. She discusses the state's functions as government landlord, forest enterprise, and conservator, explaining how it legitimized its authority through law and policy and wielded its power through foresters and police.

Peluso found that in Java, perhaps more than anywhere else in Southeast Asia, the Dutch colonial state was able to control forest use effectively by strictly enforcing land-use regulations. This system proved profitable for the state and, toward the end of the colonial period, sustainable. While this system was justified under the concept of mutual benefit, which assumed that what was good for the central state would benefit all, evidence indicates forest communities suffered under state control and village forest enterprises languished.

Peluso also describes the rapid exploitation of timber and labor during the Japanese occupation and the turbulent postwar period. The disruption of state control during the 1940s resulted in over 500,000 hectares of forest being burned or taken over by squatters. Peluso cites the absence of state authority and the rise of new concepts of nationalism and human rights as reasons for the populist revolts of the 1950s and early 1960s against state control of forest lands. She notes that foresters in the early independence period considered alternative management systems more responsive to rural people, but soon sought to reestablish agency control, and in fact translated many Dutch forest laws verbatim into Indonesian. Criticized by labor unions, political parties, and competing state agencies with their own priorities, the forestry agency became increasingly defensive and centralized, resisting any attempt to change forest land control policies. With the demise after an attempted coup in 1965 of the communist party and labor unions supportive of local forest rights, advocates of decentralized forest land control were virtually eliminated and the state forestry agency consolidated its authority during the 1970s and 1980s.

In Chapter 3, Sajise and Omegan trace the changing patterns of land use and deforestation in the Cordillera Mountains of northern Luzon from precolonial times to the present. They discuss the social values and organization of the indigenous tribal peoples, their group solidarity and their perceptions of themselves as caretakers of the forest for the ancestors and their own descendants. The Spanish, who came to conquer with "cross and sword," brought new concepts of land and the state's role in its control. The authors review the emergence of commercial logging under the late-Spanish and American colonial governments and the growing concern of foresters and planners over deforestation. Sajise and Omegan describe how Philippine governments, like those of Indonesia and Thailand, responded to forest degradation with protectionist policies suppressing forest farmers and swidden cultivators.

The authors conclude by examining contemporary patterns of forest use and conversion. They note that indigenous land-use beliefs and practices, which stress sustaining the forest landscape, are being eroded by competing concepts of land as a resource for exploitation and revenue generation. This change of perspective, encouraged by the urban private sector and, for almost 400 years, by government policies, has brought about the deforestation of the Cordillera. To assure long-term forest productivity and sustainability, the authors recommend that local communities be included in land-use planning and that indigenous organizations and management systems be given greater recognition and authority.

In Chapter 4, Hafner examines the forces driving deforestation in Northeast Thailand during the twentieth century. According to the author, the Northeast was sparsely populated until the Lao people began settling the region in the early nineteenth century. During the first half of the twentieth century, the Northeast was viewed as pioneer territory, where Lao and Thais migrated to clear forests for dry rice cultivation. Forest policies of the 1960s supported forest conversion and extraction. High post-war population growth and agricultural systems requiring extensive land use pushed forest clearing beyond sustainable levels. Hafner suggests that government attempts to extend territorial control through the 1954 Land Act encouraged the clearing and claiming of unoccupied forest land throughout the Northeast. The 1975 amnesty for illegal residents of reserve forest lands brought a further influx of migrants hoping to gain land titles. Hafner concludes that efforts to halt deforestation were ineffective largely because of the lack of coordination between government policy makers and the failure of forest codes to acknowledge the social dimensions of indigenous forest use systems. He suggests that until policies and management systems can respond to social, institutional, and economic challenges, establishing a sustainably productive forest resource system will remain an unattainable goal.

Part I provides an analysis of the historical background of current conflicts over forest control. It reviews the policies and actions that have increased tensions between rural communities and forest agencies over the past century. As a group, the chapters reflect the diverse histories, forest policies, and rural contexts existing between and within the countries studied. Yet, within this diversity, patterns emerge revealing the growing authority of the state, the extension of its power through forest bureaucracies, and those agencies' inevitable confrontation with forest communities. It is these themes which appear pervasive throughout the region and across time, whether they are being played out in a Filipino, Thai, or Indonesian context.

CHAPTER ONE

The Evolution of Forest Management Systems in Southeast Asia

Mark Poffenberger

THIS CHAPTER EXPLORES evolving patterns of forest land use and control in Southeast Asia. As Southeast Asian states developed over the last millennium, government authority over the region's forests has expanded, while the rights of forest communities have eroded. This process has accelerated rapidly in recent years. As political, technocratic, and private-sector interests have extended further into the forest, conflicts with forest people have become increasingly common. Indigenous and state management systems clash over territorial authority and forest use practices, leading to poorly controlled, unsustainable forest exploitation and environmental degradation.

Current conflicts between forest peoples and governments over forest land use in Southeast Asia stem from different cultural presuppositions regarding resource management and control. Over the past several hundred years, states have systematically attempted to gain exclusive rights to vast areas of forest lands through legislation and policing measures, giving little or no recognition to the rights of populations inhabiting and dependent upon the forests.

In the Philippines, for example, 55 percent of the country's total land area is upland forest under the authority of the Forest Management Bureau (FMB). Over 7 million indigenous people and migrant settlers live inside state forest lands, with an additional 10 million on the periphery.[1] Human pressure on upland forest areas is exacerbated by the large population of lowland landless families, who are migrating into forested areas in increasing numbers.

In Indonesia, 74 percent of the entire nation has been designated state forest land. With a population of nearly 160 million in 1980 scattered unevenly across the 13,000 islands of the nation's 3,500-mile archipelago, the Indonesian government attempts to determine use and access policies, primarily from its base in Jakarta. Much of the state-claimed forest land is inhabited by swidden and sedentary farming communities, who are often perceived as encroachers. The acceleration of commercial logging and government and private development has increasingly brought indigenous communities into conflict with the Ministry of Forestry and with migrant farmers who use the logging roads to enter cleared forest lands.

In Thailand, as in Indonesia and the Philippines, deforestation has proceeded rapidly during the twentieth century. In 1938, approximately 72 percent of the country was forested, but by 1985 forest lands had declined to 25 percent.[2] With a staff of 7,000, the Royal Forestry Department (RFD) administers 40 percent of the nation's land area. Despite considerable postwar legislation to strengthen state control, Thai and Lao-speaking settlers cleared northeastern forest lands throughout the 1970s for timber and agriculture, while northern Thailand experienced periodic conflicts between tribal communities, settlers, and RFD field staff over forest land control.

While the governments of Southeast Asia have been relatively successful in claiming large areas of forest for the nation (often displacing local forest communities in the process), the states have been less successful establishing alternative structures to ensure sustainable forest use.

This chapter begins by reviewing some characteristics of indigenous forest management systems and their relation to early Southeast Asian kingdoms, and outlines the development of state forest control systems in the Philippines, Indonesia, and Thailand. The chapter concludes by summarizing some of the tenurial, economic, and political problems emerging from the juxtaposition of different systems of forest management.

FOREST COMMUNITIES AND EARLY KINGDOMS

In the first millennium A.D., much of Southeast Asia's population was probably located in scattered settlements of swidden cultivators and hunters and gatherers in upland forests. It appears that most of region was under forest cover until clearing and logging accelerated in the nineteenth century. In the Philippines, it is estimated that over 90 percent of the land was forested in the sixteenth century.[3] As Spencer notes, the broad river valleys of the region were probably lightly populated until flood control was established for wet rice cultivation.[4] The presence of malaria in lowland areas may also have encouraged the early settlement of upland forest lands.

Anthropologists studying Southeast Asian swidden farming communities over the past century have found communal management was common, especially for less intensively used lands such as uncleared forests used for hunting and gathering, lakes and streams for fishing, and quarries for mining. Forest lands cleared for swiddens were often held in common by residential or kin-based groups. Cultivators were given temporary use rights extending through the agricultural rotation cycle or cycles. As wet rice cultivation and intensified dryland farming spread, requiring a great deal of labor to build such permanent structures as walls, terraces, and irrigation systems, the concept of individual ownership and land sales became more common.

Many Southeast Asian cultural groups traditionally perceived their lands as something held in trust for their ancestors and descendants. Some communities viewed common land as inalienable, to be held by the group in perpetuity. According to one tribe in Irian Jaya, "the ancestors made these goods (the land) at the beginning of time . . . and their descendants must be handed these goods in unimpaired condition in the future."[5]

In both insular and mainland Southeast Asia, customary land law and the beliefs and values on which it is based still persist, frequently in opposition to government titling systems that rely on Western civil law procedures. Indigenous land law often provides the only functional mechanism controlling land access at the community level. MacAndrews notes that "from the colonial times to 1960, it is estimated that less than 5 percent of all land in Indonesia was titled under the Western titling system, leaving more than 95 percent of the land in the country untitled yet recognized under adat (customary law) ownership and control."[6] Indigenous tenurial concepts and practices continue to be widely accepted and used by rural people in many parts of the region, but they generally receive little recognition under national land laws.

The state's role in controlling land resources in Southeast Asia probably emerged during the first millennium A.D. and appears tied to the spread of sedentary farming communities in lowland areas. The earliest references to state territorial control discuss attempts by the Chinese and Vietnamese to establish their administrative systems in northern mainland Southeast Asia in the first centuries A.D. We can assume that their intent was to extract tributes and corvee labor. Since low population densities were the primary constraint on production, it was the control of people and their produce, not land, that was the source of economic and political power. Consequently, the precolonial kingdoms generally sought territorial expansion in the larger population centers located in river plains and coastal areas. Forest communities in the uplands and the interior of the region were rarely subject to prolonged campaigns and were generally outside the administration of the court.

Inscriptions indicate that some rulers tried to increase their prestige by claiming large land areas, but there is little evidence to suggest these kingdoms ever effectively controlled much of the land they claimed. According to Hutterer, "the principal means of demonstrating economic wealth and political influence of leaders were the ostentatious display of expensive foreign trade goods and the espousal of foreign religious ideologies."[7] Monumental remains from the precolonial period, including the massive religious monuments of Pagan, Angkor Wat, and Borobudur, bear witness to massive investment of human and material resources used to aggrandize the ruler before the gods and the court communities. By contrast, there is little evidence that similar investments were made to raise armies to extend territorial control.

Even in lowland areas, most farming communities were probably relatively autonomous; as distance from the court increased, central authority weakened. Concerning the Javanese kingdom of Majapahit, Casparis states, "One can easily envisage the situation in which the entire (state) pyramid disappears, but the villages continue to function. This was actually the case with large parts of Southeast Asia, where there simply did not exist any effective central authority."[8]

Yet the precolonial kingdoms of Southeast Asia were influential in establishing the concept of state domain and, in limited areas, administrative control. Javanese court inscriptions from the tenth century indicate the changing nature of rural society and tenurial arrangements in lands under the ruler's jurisdiction. Private ownership of wet rice land was by then well established, along with an elaborate class system. Inscriptions indicate that communities in some parts of Java were subject to the growing influence of the state. The king, his representatives, and land grantees taxed agricultural produce at one-sixth the yield, reflecting the traditions of ancient India.[9] Village councils were also required to provide corvee labor to build monuments, roads, bridges, and irrigation structures. The later kingdom of Majapahit held revenue rights to significant tracts of wet rice lands in the Solo and Brantas river basins and lower watersheds, as well as some forest lands used for hunting and wood products.

Forest products were the court's primary interest in forest lands. Exotic woods, resins, spices, and honeys were some of the products first sought by Indian and Chinese traders. By the first centuries A.D., millions of ceramic wares had entered the Philippines in exchange for rainforest products.[10] Because exported goods were largely derived from upland forest areas beyond the administrative control of the courts, coastal people and trading kingdoms established exchange relationships with the forest villages of the interior and contacts between them were common. Nevertheless, upland communities generally "remained unincorporated into the Buddhist, Muslim, Confucian, and Christian societies of the lowlands."[11]

EVOLVING PATTERNS OF STATE FOREST MANAGEMENT: THREE NATIONAL CASES

The forest land management policies and practices of individual Southeast Asian states evolved differently between the sixteenth and nineteenth centuries. In the Philippines, the Spanish introduced the concept of state ownership of forest lands over 200 years before the British and Dutch made such claims in Indonesia. Despite these claims, colonial powers were unable to exert administrative control over forest lands until the late nineteenth century. As Figure 1.1 indicates, Southeast Asian powers at the end of the eighteenth century truly controlled relatively small areas of territory, and much of the region in fringe areas was disputed or entirely unexplored.

In Indonesia, the early Dutch colonial government had little economic incentive to establish bureaucratic control over the extensive forest lands of Sumatra, the Celebes, and Borneo. They focused on the more profitable exploitation of the teak forests of Java, as the British did in Thailand and Burma. Until modern concepts of forest management were adopted in the

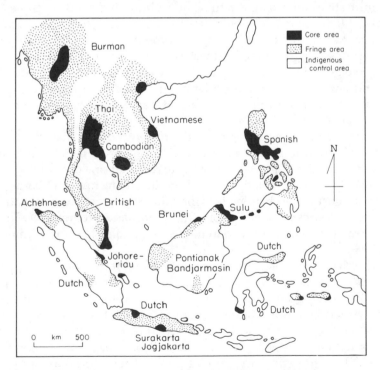

Figure 1.1. Areas of state control in Southeast Asia in the late eighteenth century

mid- to late-nineteenth century, forest lands were not generally viewed as an asset or management responsibility of the state; instead, only accessible teak stands and certain forest products were valued and administered, in much the same way as other export commodities. In the following pages the evolution of state forest control systems will be examined for the Philippines, Indonesia, and Thailand.

The Philippines

The beginning of the European colonial era in Southeast Asia can be dated from Magellan's arrival on the island of Luzon in 1521. At that time virtually all of the uplands were forested and inhabited by scattered tribal communities.[12] Magellan claimed the entire Philippine chain for the Spanish crown under what came to be known as the Regalian Doctrine. Although colonial land claims had little effect on forest communities during the early centuries of Spanish presence in Luzon, they established a precedent for state territorial authority. According to Lynch, "the legal effect of Magellan's gesture was to convert all of the indigenous forest occupants of the still unexplored archipelago into squatters."[13] Over the centuries, as colonial administrative authority grew, the land rights of indigenous peoples were eroded. Under Spanish colonial land laws, unless the natives "acquired documentation from the colonial government which recognized their ancestral property rights, their land was presumed to be owned by the Spanish sovereign."[14] In 1985, the Regalian Doctrine continued to provide a basis for land law in the Philippines. Undocumented land is still considered part of the public domain, regardless of how long it has been occupied or cultivated.[15]

As the colonial government and the religious orders that administered its policies tried to extend their control over forest lands, local people resisted. In 1745, an agrarian revolt occurred after one of the religious estates near Manila attempted to usurp land belonging to a neighboring town and "alter custom by charging fees for collecting forest products and grazing on unused estate land." From this point land progressively lost the "communal associations it had in medieval Spanish law and Filipino custom."[16]

The clearing of forest lands and the commercialization of agriculture were closely related. In central Luzon, the Spaniards organized the population into village and district administrative units (*bario* and *sitio*), each being visited by a priest-administrator. The priests encouraged wet rice cultivation to increase agricultural production and make the populations more sedentary. The spread of wet rice also accelerated the conversion of forest land to permanent agriculture.[17] Estate cultivation was pushed into the well-drained, sandy soils of the forested uplands, increasing immigration from the lowlands. These commercial activities led Marshall

McLennan to refer to the 1800–1920 period as the "great era of forest clear-ance in the central plain of Luzon."[18]

Demand for forest land and products increased rapidly throughout the nineteenth century. Extensive tracts of forest were cleared in Luzon, Cebu, Negros, and the Visayas to provide fuel for expanding colonial agribusiness. Sugar cane refining required large quantities of firewood. By 1850, wood was in such short supply in central Luzon that planters used cane husks for fuel. McLennan likens the deforestation of Luzon to that of England during the same period due to charcoal demands of the iron foundries.[19]

In response to rapid deforestation, the first Philippine forestry bureau was created in 1863. The bureau was given administrative control over much of the nation's land, a model followed by American colonial adminis-trators and later by the independent government. The agency implemented new forest laws and assessed land title claims, but this provided little ben-efit to small rural farmers, who were rarely able to bring a claim to court or contest it with the educated, wealthy elite. The bureau also issued cer-tificates to private companies for forest land exploitation, but its ability to monitor logging was limited. Lack of professional supervision took its toll on lands leased to timber firms. The island of Cebu was so badly deforested and eroded by 1870 that the bureau banned logging; but this soon stimulated a lively black market in timber, which the bureau could not control.[20]

In 1900, George P. Ahern was appointed the first American director of the Philippine Bureau of Forestry. His agency controlled over 20 mil-lion hectares of forest land. In the early years, the Bureau was involved in staff development, botanical studies, and mapping activities, and gave considerable attention to forest conservation problems. However, forest land administration was disorganized and grossly understaffed. The Ma-nila office was isolated from the field, morale was low, and red tape and bureaucratic delays were claimed to hold up requests for legitimate use. Frustration over ineffective state land administration was so high that by 1905 one American forester claimed that if there was a revolution in the Philippines it would be the Forestry Bureau's fault.[21]

Ahern was under political pressures to accelerate forest exploitation, generate revenues, and justify the Bureau's existence. In 1904, modern logging began in the Philippines with the granting of the first twenty-year renewable lease. Steam-powered logging equipment for cutting and trans-porting timber accelerated the extraction of hardwood. The Bureau's regu-lations required timber concessionaires to cut only those trees above forty centimeters in diameter, but the agency was unable to enforce compliance. In 1914, the Bureau reported that logging firms were virtually clear-cutting the forests. The foresters also learned how fragile the hardwood dip-terocarp tree species of the rainforests were and how irreversible was the damage caused by logging. They found that the forty centimeter dip-terocarp trees at high elevations were over 380 years old, making sustained yield logging virtually impossible.[22] Despite a growing body of data questioning the sustainability of commercial logging of the upland forests, those interested in expanding Pacific trade prevailed over the protests of some foresters. Logging roads opened tracts of land to lowland migrants. Over the next 60 years the combination of logging and migrant land clearing destroyed most of the Philippine forests.

Until recent political change allowed for open discussion of other causes, the problem of upland degradation in the Philippines was officially attributed to population growth and the spread of shifting cultivation. Foresters' fears that upland villages would accelerate forest destruction led to a series of legislative acts between 1966 and 1975 that further undermined the tenurial claims of local peoples. Due to upland discontent and the growing threat of insurgency, however, these acts were reversed in the late 1970s, with greater recognition given to the legitimacy of existing forest settlements. The development of such tenurial agreements as the certificate of stewardship contract (CSC) and the community forest lease (CFL) strengthened the tenure security of upland families and communities that received them. Still, the Forest Management Bureau lacked the capacity to implement the conciliatory policies on a wide scale: During the first seven years of the Forest Occupancy Management (FOM) Program (1974–1981), use certificates were issued on only 0.2 percent of the public forest land.[23]

However, the Forest Occupancy Management program gave foresters new experience in integrating upland communities into forest management systems. These early activities also led to the Integrated Social Forestry (ISF) program in 1982. ISF parcellary survey teams began demarcating public lands for the issuance of lease agreements and by 1985 had surveyed over 270,000 families; however, only 50,000 had received tenure leases. The Uplands Working Group of the Philippines, which advised the program, concluded in 1987 that to accelerate and improve its effectiveness it would be necessary to (1) make tenurial arrangements more compatible with the diverse local traditions and agricultural practices in the uplands, (2) decentralize and empower local institutions, and (3) focus the social forestry strategy more closely on the needs of upland people.[24]

The Aquino government has encouraged the ISF program by allocating a sizable budget to expand field staff and by creating additional supportive policies. Yet the vast land area involved and diversity of cultural groups and land-use practices make the task of rationalizing upland forest management immense. The question now confronting the Forest Management Bureau is how to rapidly create an effective system of decentralized community forest management.

Indonesia

In 1602, Dutch merchants founded the United East India Company (VOC), aspiring to maintain the "Spice Islands" (Banda and the Moluccas) as their private trading ground. Initially the traders had little interest in ruling the archipelago's vast forest lands, but over the next 200 years the foreign merchants gained nominal territorial control over the Indonesian island chain in an effort to monopolize access to commercial spices and forest products. By 1800, however, corruption and mismanagement so permeated the Company that it was dissolved and replaced by a formal Dutch colonial government. In 1813, during a brief period of British rule, Thomas Stanford Raffles claimed much of the Indonesian archipelago for the state.

The Agrarian Act of 1870 further extended state claims on forest lands by narrowly defining private and communal lands as land under constant cultivation. Tribal swidden lands lying fallow and forests used for hunting and gathering were thereafter viewed as state dominions. As Dove notes, "this law began what was to be a century and more of conflict between the state and the swidden farmers."[25]

Despite the state's claims to the vast majority of forest lands in Indonesia, the colonial forest bureau had limited ability to monitor or regulate forest use beyond the teak plantations of Java. During the 1930s, Dutch foresters increasingly recognized that they had overwhelmingly focused on production forests, which represented a small fraction of the lands officially under their management. While pressure was mounting to develop a national forest management policy, government officials realized that comprehensive land-use supervision by a central administration would be prohibitively expensive. The concept of community management of state forest lands was advocated by Haga in 1933, who proposed leaving the greater part of forests in Sumatra "to be managed by the local communities."[26] Other foresters also proposed recognizing community forest management rights in Sumatra: "The *margas* (local communities) should control the forests destined for local interests (wood production, agricultural reserves), and should be responsible for the forests they use. The Forest Service will save time and money which can be used for the intensive management of the forests of general interest."[27] Those foresters more concerned with commercial production disagreed, however, and found that involving local populations in logging "proved to be a desultory and unreliable business;" thus it was preferable to use modern technologies on large timber concessions requiring "large investments and highly paid experts."[28]

Althought forest management policy in Indonesia throughout the colonial era was based primarily on national control of production forests and profit maximization, Dutch and Indonesian foresters also experimented with a range of decentralized community management systems, especially in areas deemed to have little commercial value. Meys concluded in 1937 that for much of the state lands the "best solution is joint management by the Forest Service and the communities."[29] In 1937, after decades of debate, the colonial government decided to decentralize Outer Island forest management, largely to reduce administrative costs. The outbreak of the Second World War, however, kept the new policies from being implemented.

After independence, there was a movement to transfer land rights back to users. In 1960, the Indonesian government passed the Basic Agrarian Law (BAL) in response to growing rural unrest on Java and Bali, revoking some of the Dutch colonial tenurial laws. BAL accepted customary land rights under traditional law (*adat*) as a basis for making land claims, provided they did not conflict with national interests. The recognition of rights based on *adat* strengthened the position of forest communities, but ambiguous national interests have resulted in limited implementation of the law. Further, as Lynch notes, because BAL was based on the needs of the politically influential Javanese peoples, the rights of tribal communities in the outer islands like Kalimantan, Sulawesi, and Irian Jaya did not receive as much support.[30] Unlike the Javanese, many of the outer island forest communities were swidden cultivators. A recent report from the Ministry of Forestry makes the state's position on swidden communities very clear: "From the point of view of the Department of Forestry, the activities of the shifting cultivators only degrade forests lands, destroy forest timber and interrupt the activities of the concessionaires."[31] The general practice of the Indonesian government has been to resettle swidden farming communities outside forest areas, rather than to recognize their ancestral rights to forest lands and products.

The dominance of the modern state in controlling forest access is illustrated by the province of East Kalimantan. Vargas notes that, while BAL attempted to promote land registration, as late as 1983 "no Dayak village in East Kalimantan had received land titles."[32] In this region, even though Dayak communities are scattered throughout the forests, 42 percent of the province has been leased to logging concessions. Commercial loggers and the Forestry Department have disrupted tribal forest use and management systems. As a result, many of the estimated 2.5 million Dayak people of Kalimantan have been displaced in recent decades and forced into resettlement camps. The Indonesian Forestry Plan of 1985 proposed moving a million families of shifting cultivators to resettlement communities over a ten-year period. The history of such projects is depressing: costs for developing resettlement areas are high, and frequently many inhabitants leave the camps, often to return to their ancestral lands.

As development activities such as dam construction, road building, and transmigration accelerated in the 1970s, fueled by billions of dollars of oil revenues and foreign loans, conflicts between local communities and government officials over land use became more frequent. Possessing neither financial leverage nor political clout, local communities were usually ignored when national land-use decisions were made. Short-term profits became the primary rationale in land-use policy. Need for revenues put pressures on the forestry agencies to rapidly exploit timber reserves, far beyond their capacity to monitor carefully formulated selective cutting procedures. The rapid allocation of concession rights necessitated central control. Throughout the region, over-ambitious exploitation targets resulted in widespread forest degradation. Yet despite extensive field research documenting the ecological viability of many indigenous swidden farming and forest use systems, government officials primarily blame shifting cultivators for Indonesia's rapid rate of deforestation.

Ultimately, conflicts over Indonesian forest land in the Outer Islands result from economic development policies in which indigenous people have little or no role, and from government agencies' inability to understand indigenous land management and tenure practices or to respond to their diversity. Until forest communities and their indigenous use practices are incorporated into national forestry plans and use systems, conflicts and mismanagement will likely continue.

Thailand

Although Thailand remained independent throughout the colonial period, Europeans played an important role in the development of forest management concepts and practices in that country. By the mid-nineteenth century, European demands for commercial teak concessions in Thailand began to threaten the stability of the state by undermining the authority of the court. In 1873, King Chulalongkorn introduced a series of reforms to modernize state administration and put Thailand on an equal footing with the region's colonial powers. The young king had previously traveled in the Dutch and British colonies and studied their emerging forest administration systems.

King Chulalongkorn deplored the mismanagement of Thailand's forests. During the second half of the nineteenth century, natural teak stands were largely exhausted by the British, who were responsible for the deforestation of lower Burma during the same period.[33] Foreign logging merchants operated freely in both countries, bribing government officials for unregulated leases. Charles Bernard noted in 1886 that in Burma, and likely in Thailand as well, "vague, undefined leases of vast forests cause very great destruction and waste of valuable timber. . .and denude the country to its great and lasting loss."[34] In response, Chulalongkorn established a Forestry Department within the Ministry of Interior in 1896. A British forester named H. Slade was brought from India to train the Thai staff. Some of the Thai trainees were sent to the Indian Forestry

School at Dehra Dun. Later, decrees were issued to protect forest areas and regulate lumbering operations.[35]

From the outset, the new policies for regulating logging operations and policing protected forests created conflicts between the agency and local chiefs. Riggs quotes a late 19th century observer in Chiang Mai:

> In his work in organizing the Department, Slade naturally met with a good deal of opposition from the local northern chiefs, on whose preserves he had naturally to encroach to a large extent; but in the end, after a hard fight, he won his battle, and this victory weakened the position of the chiefs, who never regained their former prestige. Slade may be said, therefore, to have played an important part in con-solidating the Siamese Kingdom. . . [36]

The Forestry Department thus played a key role in extending the center's control over northern lands that in the past had only vaguely recognized the regal claims of Bangkok. The Minister of the Interior during that period, Prince Damrong, also noted that the Forestry Department, by efficiently handling complaints of foreign firms, made it unnecessary for them to rely on their consulates for arbitration and helped create a modern apparatus for policy implementation.[37] Further, the emergence of specialized technical departments such as forestry bureaus decreased the authority of territorial administrators by strengthening that of the central government.

By 1957, the Royal Forestry Department (RFD) had 1,885 personnel, making it the largest of the six units in the Ministry of Agriculture, with responsibility for 50 percent of Thailand's national territory.[38] Its field staff numbered little more than 1,000, however, and monitoring land use of the nation's forest was a monumental task. During the 1960s and 70s deforestation proceeded rapidly in Thailand, in part due to the RFD's limited ability to control loggers and migrant settlers in the North and the Northeast.

In an attempt to work more closely with forest communities, the RFD established the Forest Village program in 1975. Under the program, communities living on state lands were resettled in selected forest areas to supply labor for forest production. Because forest village projects required heavy capital investment to build community infrastructure, however, the program moved slowly and affected few forest communities. To accelerate the recognition of forest occupants' rights, a land certification (STK) program was established in 1982. Sympathetic Thai foresters, like their counterparts throughout the region, are gaining support for alternative policies that give communities legal management of tracts of forest. The challenge is to make those policies work.

CONCLUSION

State control and exploitation of Southeast Asia's vast forests grew slowly up to the mid-nineteenth century and accelerated rapidly over the past 150 years. While the kingdoms, sultanates, and colonial governments of Southeast Asia frequently claimed large areas of sparsely settled forests, it was not until forestry administrative systems were established in the latter half of the nineteenth century that national governments were able to begin to regulate and determine forest use. With a corresponding expansion of timber markets, exploitation technologies, and populations, forest clearing has accelerated sharply over the same period. Central government control of forested areas was part of the broader bureaucratization of societies throughout the region, a process involving the formation of modern nations and new economic systems within Southeast Asia. Evers argues that "Southeast Asian bureaucracy has attempted to appropriate an ever increasing share of societal surplus"[39] by increasing their numbers and authority, extending government activities into the corporate economy, and combining bureaucratic and private economic pursuits. This process is especially evident in the field of forest land management.

It is apparent that, although forest departments were given responsibility for forest management, use policies were often determined by political groups at the center and private-sector interests. Records show that some senior foresters working in Southeast Asia during the twentieth century were appalled by commercial logging practices and the resulting environmental damage. The Philippine Bureau of Forestry banned logging in Cebu as early as 1870, yet failed to control the severe deforestation taking place. In the early 1900s, the Director of the Bureau tried to pursue a conservationist strategy, his position supported by early studies indicating tropical forest exploitation was not sustainable due to the very slow growth of the commercial dipterocarp species. The Bureau came under immense political and private-sector pressure to accelerate commercial exploitation, however, and clear-cutting was widely practiced. Similar pressures were felt by the forestry departments of Indonesia and Thailand.

Groeneveldt, writing in 1936, discussed the catastrophic extent of forest destruction in the preceding twenty years due to clearing for agriculture and road systems and to fires. He urged government agencies to cooperate and "stop defending the interests of their own service"[40] in order to improve land-use planning and prevent the firing of forest lands. Many prewar Dutch foresters argued for decentralized management based on community control, yet these recommendations were never implemented.

Moreover, in the first thirty years of the postwar era, the leaders of Thailand, Indonesia, and the Philippines passed legislation to further strengthen state control. Many new agrarian laws denied recognition to forest communities, especially swidden cultivators, hunters and gathers, and migrant farmers. In fact, these groups were generally stigmatized throughout the period as destroyers of the forest and branded practitioners of "slash and burn" agriculture, "encroachers," and "backward tribals." Communist, Islamic, and ethnic separatist groups in Thailand, Indonesia, and the Philippines used upland forest areas as bases of operation, often gaining the sympathies of marginalized forest communities. As hostilities and social distance between forest communities and the state grew, the ability of forest departments to regulate forest use was further eroded, and responsibilities for protecting state claimed forest lands were often turned over to the military and police units.

Government needs for revenue generation and private-sector interests lead political leaders to direct forest agencies to adopt rapid exploitation policies. In both the Philippines and Indonesia, the demand for foreign exchange was an overwhelming factor in the aggressive extraction programs of the last two decades. Economists called for revenues to stimulate national economic growth, politicians needed funds to support their emerging bureaucratic machines and stabilize their regimes, while foreign and local entrepreneurs desired fast profits. All supported the growth of the timber industry and forest agency control. The development of international timber markets, transportation facilities, and more efficient harvesting technologies allowed for greatly accelerated exploitation. By 1978, Southeast Asia was responsible for nearly two-thirds of global hardwood log production.

In Indonesia, gross revenues from log exports rose from virtually nothing in 1968 to nearly $1 billion ten years later. Tropical timber industry brought badly needed foreign exchange to the region, but questions arose regarding the balance between costs and returns. Economic analysis indicates the timber industry has had a limited role in stimulating national economic growth. In 1978 the "investment cost per job created by one transnational timber company operating in Indonesia was $40,000, considerably more than the $4,000 required to create a job in traditional textiles industries or the $12,000 need to generate an opening in an electronics industry. By the end of the 1970s the logging industry had created 35,000 jobs in the Philippines and only 11,000 in Indonesia with a work force of 45 million at that time."[41]

Gillis postulates that one reason the Southeast Asian economies did not benefit as much as those of temperate wood producers was the different role the timber industry played within the domestic economy. In Canada, Norway, and the United States, for example, forestry is closely linked to construction and manufacturing industries, allowing timber extraction to stimulate job creation, capital income growth, technological development, regional development, and revenue generation. In tropical countries, where domestic markets are less developed and downstream processing industries limited, the benefits from timber extraction are mostly limited to revenues in the form of taxes and royalties.[42]

Due to limited scientific knowledge of tropical forest ecology and the regenerative processes of the ecosystems, the long-term effects of large-scale logging operations are not known. According to Gillis,

> What is known, however, is not comforting: the potential for heavy damage to the fragile ecosystem of the rain forest is substantial enough to counsel pause in implementation of further projects involving intensive harvesting practices. The costs of such damages are costs to society as a whole and, under present concession agreements, are not reflected in costs to harvesting enterprises or to consumers of tropical wood products. Future concession agreements that ignore these social costs will do so only at some peril to the continued existence of natural forests, and all that implies not only for future yields from timber, but also for non-forest agriculture, erosion, and climatic changes.[43]

The ecological complexities of the tropical rainforest and the lack of knowledge concerning its dynamics, combined with a dominant concern for short-term profits, have resulted in the failure of most replanting programs. Because procedures for reestablishing logged-over tropical forests are not well developed, it has been difficult for the region's forestry agencies to set stumpage fees that accurately reflect the costs of replanting. Further, past regulatory policies had little effect on improving timber concession management, often because they did not take forest department implementing ability into consideration. As Gillis notes, they were designed "as if administrative constraints were absent and information were costless."[44]

While the mechanized hardwood industry has been the major preoccupation of foresters and policy makers in Indonesia, and to a somewhat lesser extent in the Philippines, minor forest products have generally not had the same priority. In fact, the rapid growth of the timber industries has likely caused forestry agencies to give indigenous or traditional forest-based industries even less attention. Many small saw mills and other related industries have disappeared with the growth of highly capitalized timber activities. Nonetheless, tens of millions of forest families throughout the region are involved in informal forest production linked directly to the domestic economy. These individuals collect, process, and market lumber, fuelwood, charcoal, medicinal herbs, bamboo shoots, rattan, rubber, spices, coffee, fruits, and numerous other commodities. Since the beginning of the twentieth century, swidden farmers have increasingly adopted a commercial orientation, establishing smallholder rubber, coffee, and other export crop estates. There also exist many indigenous systems of minor forest crop production.

Approximately 90 percent of the world's rattan supply comes from Indonesia.[45] Most of the rattan is from natural growth, but Dayak communities have cultivated rattan in natural rain forests for some time. Sustained rattan production must expand if Indonesia's natural stock is not to be exhausted, as it was in Thailand and the Philippines. Current production levels in Kalimantan generate several million dollars annually, but local income could increase dramatically under intensified management. Income from forest-based medicinal plants, aloes wood, resins, and bird nests, could also be greatly increased by intensifying such minor forest production. Shifting policy support from large-scale timber extraction to sustainable multiple-commodity production would also allow the forest industry to break out of its current export orientation. The cost of forestry-sector job creation could be greatly reduced, and the integration of different ecomonic sectors advanced.

In the past, minor forest products have received less attention because they did not offer the state the rapid returns and high revenues available from large-scale exploitation. Further, smaller forest industries are more difficult to control and tax and require decentralized management and the development of local infrastructure. Such requirements have deterred forestry agencies as well as private investors. Yet, from the standpoint of long-term economic growth and sustained forest management, small forest industries based on decentralized agroforestry enterprises may have the brightest prospects of all production management regimes. As reserves dwindle in large-scale logging concessions, it appears likely that agroforestry production systems will gain importance. To prepare a solid foundation for such a transition, its implications for forest use policy, management systems, and technological research and extension must be considered.

While forestry bureaucracies continue to grow and fight to protect their authority, an increasing number of foresters recognize that some sharing of management responsibilities will be inevitable. Political representatives from forest regions lobby for the rights of local communities, and environmental coalitions are gaining influence. Foresters are also aware that much of their territory has little economic value to their agency and, in terms of organizational budget, represents a liability.

Although what remains of the region's large timber concessions may need to be administered through conventional production forest management systems, and the richest biosphere reserves and national parks require increasingly intensive custodial management, new approaches must be developed to manage much of Southeast Asia's forests. Southeast Asian forest agencies have never had the requisite field staff to effectively monitor either their reserve, protected, or production forest areas, and given growing population dependencies and budget deficits, this is unlikely to occur in the future. In Thailand, with only 7,000 full-time staff, many of whom are based in Bangkok, and a limit of 2 percent increase in staff annually, the RFD has limited field personnel and little hope of major increases in the future. In Indonesia, the agencies' own estimates of staff requirements for effective management indicate it is severely understaffed. For example, one agency report suggests that trained forest rangers and guards would need to be increased from 7,700 to 88,000 to provide adequate supervision for production forests. It was further recommended that the number of Indonesia's professional foresters be increased by twenty-three times.[46] Currently, approximately 50 percent of Indonesia's professional foresters work in Jakarta, which limits monitoring capacity.[47]

Delegating protection responsibilities and usufructs to communities provides a realistic option for improving access control without massive budget increases. Since the late 1970s, both the Philippines and Thailand have begun issuing forest use certificates. Although well intended, the certification programs are not yet well integrated into mainstream national forest management systems and have only had limited impact on community-agency conflicts over forest access. The certification programs are most significant as precedents for stronger community control.

To succeed, these new management systems must reflect the tenurial rights and needs of old communities and migrants. New management systems will need to give communities and local governments greater authority and autonomy in land-use planning. A 1976 survey of a range of social forestry programs indicated that community participation was the most important factor in determining project success, defined by income generation, growth of management capacity, and program sustainability.[48] The ultimate utility of decentralized community forest management systems is yet to be determined, but existing forest administration regimes alone are clearly insufficient to meet complex socio-economic needs and protect forest resources.

Over the past two decades forestry agencies have come into much closer contact with rural society. The ways in which foresters interpret their roles have also begun to change. Many foresters no longer look at the forest system in isolation from the people who surround it and inhabit it. Forestry agencies are finding that they need to interact and understand more about community institutions and leaders, crops and livestock, small industries and fuelwood needs. Forestry agencies now find themselves faced with a need to rethink management policies and practices, many dating from the colonial period, in order to create new forest administrative systems that respond to the needs of rapidly changing societies.

The successful decentralization of forest management responsibilities to community groups will ultimately be determined by a national political commitment to resolve the problem and increased agency cooperation with communities. Community-agency collaboration is still limited, and the broad-based adoption of joint management systems will probably not occur before the end of the millennium, if then. It should be remembered, however, that the process of growing state control over forest territory has been gaining momentum for over one hundred years and this trend will not be reversed overnight.

NOTES

1. Upland Development Working Group. 1987. "Upland Development in the Philippines." Unpublished paper, p. 6.

2. UNDP. 1986. "Plan of Action for Forest Development in Thailand." Bangkok: Project of the Government of Thailand, 2nd Rev., p. 2.

3. Roth, Dennis. 1983. "Philippine Forests and Forestry: 1565–1920," in Tucker, Richard, and J. F. Richards (eds.), *Global Deforestation and the Nineteenth Century World Economy.* Durham, N.C.: Duke Press Policy Studies.

4. Spencer, J. E. 1966. *Shifting Cultivation in Southeast Asia.* Berkeley: University of California Press, p. 27.

5. Colchester, Marcus. 1986. "Unity and Diversity: Indonesian Policy towards Tribal Peoples," *The Ecologist* 16 No. 2/3:101, citing Salisbury, R. F. 1962. *From Stone to Steel: The Economic Consequences of Technological Change in New Guinea.* London: Cambridge University Press, p. 61.

6. MacAndrews, Colin. 1986. *Land Policy in Modern Indonesia: A Study of Land Issues in the New Order Period.* Boston: Oelgeschlager, Gunn & Hain, Publishers, Inc., p. 20.

7. Hutterer, Karl. 1977. "Prehistoric Trade and the Evolution of Philippine Societies: A Reconsideration," in Hutterer, Karl (ed.), *Economic Exchange and Social Interaction in Southeast Asia.* Ann Arbor: Michigan. Papers on South and Southeast Asia 13:177–196.

8. Casparis, de J. G. 1986. "The Evolution of the Socio-economic Status of the East Javanese Village and its Inhabitants," in Sartono Kartodirjo (ed.), *Agrarian History.* Yogyakarta: Gadjah Mada University Press, pp. 12–13.

9. Ibid, p. 4.

10. Hutterer. "Prehistoric Trade and the Evolution of Philippine Societies: A Reconsideration," p. 181.

11. Steinberg, Joel et al. 1973. *In Search of Southeast Asia: A Modern History.* New York: Praeger Publisher, p. 25.

12. Roth. "Philippine Forests and Forestry: 1565–1920," p. 30.

13. Lynch, Owen. 1984. "The Ancestral Land Rights of Tribal Indonesians: A Comparison with the Philippines." Unpublished paper, p. 6.

14. Ibid., p. 6.

15. Ibid.

16. Roth, Dennis M. 1977. *The Friar Estates of the Philippines.* Albuquerque: University of New Mexico Press, p. 33.

17. Ibid., p. 31.

18. McLennan, Marshall Seaton. 1973. "Peasant and Hacendero in Nueva Ecija: The Socio-Economic Origins of a Philippine Commercial Rice-Growing Region" (Ph.D. dissertation, University of California) as cited by Roth (1983) p. 33.

19. Ibid., p. 32.

20. Roth. 1983. "Philippine Forests and Forestry: 1565–1920," p. 41.

21. Ibid., p. 44.

22. Ibid., p. 47.

23. Upland Development Working Group. 1987. "Upland Development in the Philippines," p. 5.

24. Aquino, Rosemary et. al. 1987. "Mounting a National Social Forestry Program: Lessons Learned from the Philippine Experience." Honolulu: East-West Center Working Paper, p. 57–58.

25. Dove, Michael. 1985. "The Perceptions of Peasant Land Rights in Indonesian Development: Causes and Implications," prepared for the ICRAF International Consultative Workshop on Tenure Issues in Agroforestry, 27–31 May, 1985, p. 1.

26. Goor, C. P. van, and Junus Kartasubrata. 1982. Indonesian Forestry Abstracts: Dutch Literature until about 1960. Wageningen: Centre for Agricultural Publishing and Documentation, p. 562:5569, citing Haga, B. J. 1933. "Indlandsche Gemeenten en Boschbeheer in de Buitengewesten" ("Indigenous Communities and Forest Management in the Outer Provinces"). Tectona 26:517–520.

27. Ibid., p. 561:5566, citing Japing, C. H. 1929. "Inlandsche Gemeenten en Boschbeheer in de Buitengewesten" ("Local Communities and Forest Management in the Outer Provinces"). Tectona 25:1583–1592.

28. Ibid., p. 179:3881, summarizing Ottows, A. 1952. "De Opzet van Bosexploitatie-Bedrijven in de Buitengewesten, meer Speciaal in Cost-Borneo" ("The Design of Forest Exploitations in the Outer Provinces, Especially in East Kalimantan") Tectona 42:175–281.

29. Ibid., p. 378:3875, summarizing Meyes, P. C. J. 1937. "Het Boschbeheer door Inlandsche Rechtsgemeenschappen in Rechtstreeks Bestuurd Gebied" ("Forest Management by Local Communities in Directly Governed Area"). Tectona 30:452–453, 602–616.

30. Lynch. "The Ancestral Land Rights of Tribal Indonesians: A Comparison with the Philippines."

31. Government of Indonesia, Department of Forestry and IIED. 1985. "A Review of Policies Affecting the Sustainable Development of Forest Lands in Indonesia," 2:13.

32. Vargas, Donna Mayo. 1984. The Interface of Customary and National Law in East Kalimantan, Indonesia. Ph.D. dissertation, Yale University, New Haven, p. 52.

33. Keeton, Charles Lee 3rd. 1974. King Thebaw and the Ecological Rape of Burma. Delhi: Manohar Book Service.

34. Ibid., p. 344, citing "Bernard to Durand, Memorandum on the BBTC's Leases, February 3, 1886," in Forest Proceedings of February 1886 2:4–5. Bound in Burma Proceedings, Vol. 2663, Burma Forests (Home Dept.) 1886.

35. Riggs, Fred W. 1966. Thailand: The Modernization of a Bureaucratic Polity. Honolulu: East-West Press, p. 138.

36. Ibid., citing Le May, Reginald. 1926. *An Asian Arcady: The Land and Peoples of Northern Siam.* Cambridge, England: W. Heffer and Sons, p. 62.

37. Ibid., p. 145.

38. Ibid.

39. Evers, Hans-Dieter. 1987. "The Bureaucratization of Southeast Asia," Comparative Study of Society and History, p. 680.

40. Goor, C. P. van, and Junus Kartasubrata. 1982. *Indonesian Forestry Abstracts: Dutch Literature until about 1960.* 377:3849, citing Groeneveldt, W. 1936. *"Boschvernieling in Ned-Inde, Speciaal in de Buitengewesten"* ("Forest Destruction in the Dutch East Indies, Especially in the Outer Regions'). *Kol. Studien* 20(4):28–67.

41. Gillis, Malcolm. 1980. "Fiscal and Financial Issues in Tropical Hardwood Concessions: Development Discussion Paper No. 10," Cambridge: Harvard Institute for International Development, p. 17–18.

42. Ibid., p. 6.

43. Ibid., p. 4.

44. Ibid., p. 9.

45. Jessup, Timothy C., and Nancy Lee Peluso. 1986. "Minor Forest Products as Common Property Resources in East Kalimantan, Indonesia," in *Proceedings of the Conference on Common Property Resource Management, April 21–26, 1985.* Washington, D.C.: National Academy Press, p. 510.

46. Government of Indonesia, Department of Forestry and IIED. 1985. *A Review of Policies Affecting the Sustainable Development of Forest Lands in Indonesia* 2:13.

47. Ibid., 2:86–87.

48. Brokensha, David, and Alfonso Peter Castro. 1984. *Fuelwood, Agro-Forestry, and Natural Resource Management: The Development Significance of Land Tenure and Other Resource Management/Utilization Systems.* Binghamton, N.Y.: Institute for Development Anthropology, p. 53–54.

CHAPTER TWO

A History of
State Forest Management
in Java

Nancy Lee Peluso

THICKLY CARPETING THE mid-section of the island from the coast near Tegal to the shores of Tuban and stretching inland in some places to the southern coast, hundreds of square kilometers of teak attracted the first Dutch mercantilists arriving in Java in the mid-seventeenth century. The strategies followed by the East India Company ("VOC" or "the Company") in seeking to control access to teak foreshadowed those of its successor, the Dutch colonial state. Unfortunately, the forests of Java proved not to grow as fast or as ubiquitously as early Dutch administrators assumed and many teak stands had been exhausted before the end of the eighteenth century.

This chapter examines the consolidation of state control over Java's forests. During Java's colonial period, the two stages in the consolidation process corresponded to the two periods of European (mainly Dutch) influence and rule: by the VOC from the mid-seventeenth century to 1799, and by the Dutch colonial state from 1814 to 1940. The second section of the paper examines the structural and ideological influences on peasant forest use and state management from the Japanese occupation of Java to the present. Before treating the evolution of state forest access control, however, I will outline its conceptual components.

FOREST ACCESS CONTROL

State forestry agencies have traditionally controlled land, trees, and labor to fulfill three custodial and productive functions as (1) a government landlord, (2) a forest enterprise, and (3) a conservation institution.[1] The custodial-productive agency is assigned to protect state property by guarding its territorial boundaries, protecting its capital goods, and preserving the ideal environment for their sustainable production. These roles are legitimized by law and policy; the duties are implemented by field-level foresters and forest police.

For purposes of analysis, we can divide the control of production forests into control of land, commercial control of species, and control of forest labor. Each component is significant, although in reality the elements are intricately interwoven. Forest management agencies derive their legitimacy from the control of land. Guided by state ideology, the agency monopolizes the right to make decisions about land use: what species will be planted, how many people will be employed, the organization of production, and so on. In many countries, land control as a basis of forest agency legitimation has its roots in the colonial periods. Precolonial rulers were more concerned with controlling populations and the products of the land and less able to enforce restrictions on land use in regions distant from the seat of government. Many contemporary Third World states have become more coercive than their colonial predecessors, enforcing boundaries and imposing controls on broad tracts of increasingly valuable land. As a result, the ideological, political, and economic importance to the state of forest land control has increased.[2]

Similarly, control of the species grown on forest land is linked to the legitimation and perpetuation of the state agencies. Forestry, as traditionally conceived, is the science of tree production and, more recently, of environmental protection. The planting, maintenance, and exploitation of trees on particular lands justify the forestry agency's "claim" to that land. The exploitation of trees on government land provides revenues to the state, finances the reproduction of the forest agency, and, at a national level, legitimizes the forestry agency's right to control certain species.

The control of forest labor, which is itself facilitated by control of land and species, of the production and exchange process in general, and of conservation and access ideology, ensures the profitable exploitation of trees and tree products on forest lands. Frequently, population growth, skewed distribution of rural resources, and the inability of industrialization to keep up with growth in the labor force create the ideal conditions for rural labor reserves, rendering access to temporary forest employment or reforestation land desirable. In Java, land, species, and labor controls restricting access have rendered capital accumulation by forest labor an impossible dream for most forest villagers, who start with little or no capital of their own.

STAGE 1: CONTROLLING TREES AND PEOPLE

Initially, the Dutch did not want to sell teak, but to use it to build ships critical to maintaining the power they had enjoyed throughout the seventeenth century. The strength of their navy had made the Dutch the most powerful traders in the world, and Amsterdam was the Singapore of seventeenth century Europe. The dense, durable teak was among the finest species in the world for ships' timber, and the tall, straight trees, more populous than people in some parts of the island, made majestic masts for the most formidable battleships.

The VOC's first attempts to acquire Java teak were neither easy nor uniformly successful. Establishing offices, hiring labor, and gaining access to fields and forests first required negotiation with and valuable gifts to the Javanese sovereigns and their officials.[3] The VOC was eventually able to acquire timber from forests in the vicinity of Japara, Rembang, Pekalongan, Waleri, and Brebes (see Figure 2.1). Contracts were made and deliveries of wood to the north coast port of Japara began. In 1677, a treaty with the Sultan of Mataram allowed the Company to establish a shipbuilding center at Rembang. The treaty put thirty-six villages in the Rembang region in the service of the Company for forest labor such as logging, hewing beams, and hauling timber (using draft animals, primarily water buffalo).[4] In later agreements, rulers in the teak regions granted the VOC rights to cut specific quantities of wood from the hinterlands, as well as access to forest laborers.[5] Contracts in the early eighteenth century with the Javanese king led to the cession of some teak districts to the VOC, putting local forest laborers at the VOC's virtual disposal.

Threats to the shipbuilding industry caused by excessive cutting along the north coast resulted in the VOC's mounting military campaigns to acquire more timber concessions from Javanese rulers.[6] The VOC tried to monopolize shipbuilding rights in the mid-eighteenth century, with varying degrees of success. Despite the monopoly, private (*i.e.*, non-VOC) enterprises exported teak and built ships. Java's north coast was heavily traveled by sailing vessels and Dutch efforts to monopolize teak were difficult; Raffles estimated an annual delivery of 50,000 to 60,000 beams to private concerns in Central Java alone.[7] Meanwhile, the official log quotas delivered from Central Java in the eighteenth century averaged about 10,000 to 15,000 a year.[8]

By 1796, forest destruction had become so widespread that the VOC formed a commission to investigate the state of the forests of Japara and Rembang. The commission recommended halting all forest cutting in the two regions and reducing logging quotas from Blora by 50 percent. Despite these recommendations, over-cutting of the forests continued.[9] The conflicting interests of VOC officials were partly responsible for the persistent forest destruction. In 1797, the governor of Northeast Java, P. G. van Overstraten, blamed the Residents, who received commissions on the "legal" cut and also sponsored "illegal" private woodcutting. The Resident of Rembang, for example, privately earned 40,000 rijks dollars per year from the cutting of teak forests in his residency.[10] Also, logging

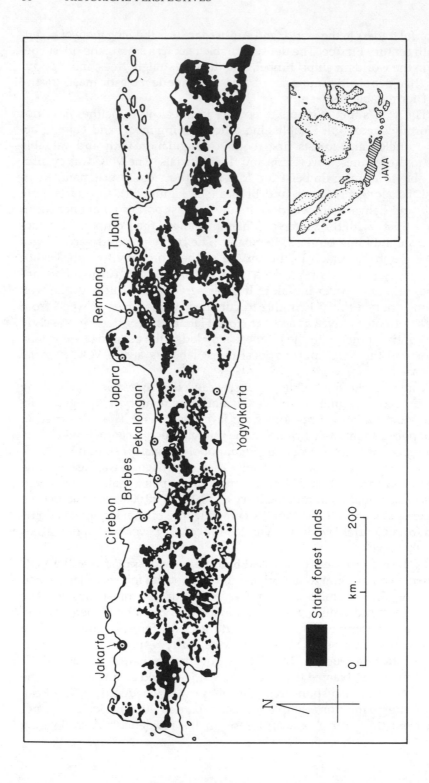

Figure 2.1. Declared state forest land on Java, 1938–1985

practices were inefficient and damaged the soil and only minimal efforts were made to replant.

Forest laborers were exempt both from the usual labor services (*heeren-diensten*) exacted from the peasantry by regional rulers and the sultan, and from head taxes. The compulsory forest labor services became known as *blandongdiensten;* the woodcutters were called *blandong*.[11] Local Javanese officials, called Regents, mustered the necessary numbers of teak-hauling buffaloes from the peasants in their jurisdiction. Dragging beams to the coast took three to five days from the closest forests. As the sites became more distant, particularly after 1776 when the king granted permission to cut in the forests of Blora, hauling logs and beams to Rembang or Surabaya took twelve to fifteen days; the walk back required another five. The effect on both the peasants and their livestock was devastating: Lugt reports the buffalo population in these locales fell drastically during this time.[12] This loss of animals affected both the Company's immediate capacity for transporting timber and the agricultural capacities of the peasants forced to use their animals.

As the coastal teak forests were depleted and the best trees had to be sought further inland, private firms gained a competitive edge on the VOC. Individuals rented forest villages not leased by the Company and bought timber that did not meet Company standards. Private contractors were willing to pay higher wages for hauling wood to the coast from distant inland logging sites.[13] Nevertheless, the end of an era was approaching. As the form of Dutch involvement in Java changed, so did the nature of colonial control and access to the island's forests.

STAGE 2: THE FORESTS OF JAVA UNDER THE COLONIAL STATE

The VOC was bankrupt by the end of the eighteenth century, largely because of the depredations and corruption of its own officials. As of December 31, 1799, when the VOC's charter expired, the Dutch state replaced the Company as proprietor and administrator. Under Dutch colonial administration, forest exploitation changed from the Javanese rulers' loosely organized delegation of tree-cutting rights and peasant labor to legislative and police control of land, trees, and labor by a highly organized, semiautonomous, field-oriented bureaucracy by the end of the nineteenth century.

When Governor-General Daendels arrived in Java in 1808, he organized the exploitation of Java's teak forests, passed edicts on appropriate forest management, and secured the government's monopoly on teak, forest labor, and shipbuilding. For the first time, a quasi-modern government forest service, the *Dienst van het Boschwezen*, was created, with rights to control land, trees, and labor. At the time, teak was most valued for profits or shipbuilding; thus the domain of this early forest service was limited to lands where teak grew or could grow.

Among other elements in Daendels's system that would retain at least philosophical importance through the ensuing two centuries were:

1. Declaration of all forests as the domain of the state (*Landsdomein*) to be managed for the benefit of the state;

2. Assignment of forest management to a branch of the civil service created expressly for that purpose;

3. Division of the forest into parcels (*perceel*) to be logged and replanted on a rotating basis; and,

4. Restriction of villagers' access to teak for lumber, allowing them to collect only deadwood and nontimber forest products.[14]

Daendels established the first regulations punishing all uses of the forest that were unauthorized by the state, thus criminalizing many customary uses of the forest. The maximum penalties for forest "criminals" were ten years in prison or a fine of 200 rijks dollars. Two-thirds of this fine went to the state and one-third to the person who reported the crime.[15] Though seemingly harsh, these regulations were difficult to enforce; there was not yet a forest police force and many parts of the forest were remote. Daendels issued edicts designating the technical aspects of forest management (21 August 1808) and appointed "*boschgangers*," or subdistrict forest managers, to oversee local operations and manage the laborers.

Forest laborers, their village lands, and the adjacent forest lands were placed under direct administration of a Board of Forests. Some 100,000 forest laborers were at the Board's disposal, each of whom received a small annual allowance of iron, salt, and gunpowder. Each woodcutter was also given one catty (approximately one and a half kilograms) of hulled rice a day. Partial advance payments for logs were made as an incentive, with the remainder being paid on delivery to the coastal log yards. These payments were administered through middlemen, however, and often were not received by the workers.[16]

Daendels' successor during the five-year interlude of English control in Java, Lieutenant-Governor Stamford Raffles, felt that the state was too heavily involved in costly forest management. He retracted all the forestry organizational reforms implemented by Daendels. Only in Rembang was a special forest superintendent appointed; in other residencies, the task of forest administration and oversight fell to the Residents.

Raffles sponsored a policy of reserving the largest and best forests for the state, allowing private entrepreneurs to lease and log the rest.[17] He was also more lenient in prosecuting forest "crimes," if for no other reason than to save money. Measures to replant were not mentioned in his *History of Java*.

When the Dutch resumed control of Java in 1816, they adopted some of Raffles's more profitable ideas. Despite their renewed attempts to regulate forest cutting, however, conflicting objectives from other government sectors caused further forest deterioration. During the Java War (1825–1830), for example, many teak beams and logs were used in Central Java to build forts and bridges and to block roads. Under the Cultivation System,[18] teak forests were heavily cut with no regard for logging regulations. The tallest, straightest trees were selected to build sugar factories, coffee warehouses, tobacco drying sheds, and housing compounds. An extensive road system was built through sections of the teak forest to deliver the prized logs to sawmills and wood-working centers. Luxurious teak homes were constructed for plantation managers and highly placed personnel. In addition, industrially processing the sugar cane, roasting the coffee, and drying the tobacco from the extensive government plantations required tremendous quantities of fuel. In Semarang residency in the 1830s alone, 60,000 logs were cut to build tobacco drying sheds, while in Pekalongan 24,000 cubic feet of firewood were required each year for sugar refining. Though the foundations of state forest management were being laid in this early period, the power of other government sectors was such that the forests' major "enemy" was the state itself.

LAWS AND FOREST MANAGEMENT

In the half-century after the Dutch regained control of Java in 1816, a number of regulations for forest management were made and retracted. The 1865 forestry laws,[19] usually credited with being the first forestry laws for Java, and the *Domeinverklaring* of 1870, which declared all unclaimed and forest lands as the domain of the state, were neither new nor unique legal developments; the underlying principles had been nurtured for at least fifty years in the Indies. The difference between these regulations and the declarations and treaties made by precolonial rulers and the Company lay in the idiom of control, of tenure, of rights to access, and rights to control access.

Some foresters argued then and now that the forests have always been "state" property, as they were considered the property of Javanese kings and sultans. However, the nature of these kings' property rights, and the simultaneous validity of local systems of usufruct, differed greatly from the systems imposed by the Dutch. To the Javanese rulers, land was important insofar as it bore profitable or useful fruits (food, wood) and was worked by subject populations.[20] The rights to harvest teak and use the labor of forest people were leased to the VOC; land was not. Nevertheless, while the Javanese rulers regarded their own positions as preeminent, in practice the Company was gaining control over land as well as the trees.

Private individuals' usufruct and ownership rights to teak were specifically defined (and denied) under the Dutch colonial state. For example, Daendels issued directives stating that teak trees growing on private property or on the private estates (tanah partikelir) could be cut for the owner's own use without government permission; however, if the teak were transported off their property or sold, a 10 percent tax was due the government.[21] Grazing, particularly in young stands, was also discouraged.

Two other aspects of this series of regulations concerned the forest villagers. One was the nature of changes in labor requirements, treated in the following section on labor. The other concerned the government's ambiguity towards allowing villagers to cut wood for household or other uses.[22] Finally, in 1865, it was decided that forest villagers could take branches, fallen wood, and the wood from forest thinnings for their own use, but in collecting these they had to be "under close supervision" and were restricted to particular forests.[23]

In 1849, the Dutch brought two German foresters and a German surveyor to Java and stationed them in Rembang. Within five years, the German general manager of this valuable teak forest had established a simple parcel system that fixed areas to be cut and replanted each year. These first "scientific" foresters were joined in 1855 by another German expert, who was made the inspector of forests in 1858. In 1857, four aspiring Dutch foresters from Java were sent to study forestry in Germany.[24] In 1860, the governor-general formed a committee to plan forest laws for Java and Madura. The committee included an official of the justice department, an inspector of estates (plantations), and a forestry inspector.[25]

To foresters then and now, the 1865 forest laws represent the first set of "real" forestry laws, primarily because of their technical content. They contain clear descriptions of appropriate forest management and the jobs of Forest Service employees. For the first time, nonteak forests (Wildhout-bosschen, literally, "wild" or "jungle" woods) were included in the category of state forest lands. Unlike the teak forests, they were placed under state management for environmental protection, not production.[26] By 1875, another set of forest laws, including regulations on policing and punishments for forest crimes, was enacted.[27]

The second phase of forest access control was well established by the end of the nineteenth century. The state was appropriating forest lands and, like the monopoly on the forest species of teak, forest land appropriation was "justified" by colonial law. The state forestry organization's conservation function was used to justify acquisition of watershed areas. Both land and species control were accompanied by a liturgy of colonial production objectives and conservationism. Changes in the system of labor control, however, were just beginning.

STATE FOREST MANAGEMENT AND LABOR CONTROL

Raffles had been unsatisfied with the Dutch form of the *blandongdiensten*, complaining that forest laborers, exempt from head and land taxes, "contributed nothing to government revenue but their labor." He decided that forest workers should be subjected to the same land rents as other peasants. Rather than paying land rents in cash, however, the forest workers' "wages" were to take the form of tax remissions. Forest labor was credited in value for taxes due.

Under Raffles's version of the *blandongdiensten*, woodcutters and timber haulers had to work eight out of twelve months a year, with an obligation to guard the forests during the other four months, in exchange for exemption from land rent. Half the "working men" of a village were supposed to be left free to work the rice fields. Whole *blandong* villages were remunerated through designated village heads and regents. Raffles thus created an efficient system for giving the government immediate control over all the resources of the forest settlements, at a cost (the value of their land rent) less than one-third the potential cost of wage laborers hired to cut and haul the wood.[28]

When the Dutch returned to Java in 1816, *blandongs* remained liable for land rents and continued to pay by laboring in the forest. Villagers were still required to provide the quotas of draft animals. All villagers had to help build logging roads. To work off his land rents, an owner of a team of buffalo had to deliver the equivalent of fifteen giant teak trees or thirty-five smaller ones to the log yards. Loggers were only provided daily rice rations if they worked far from their villages.[29] Thus, the state's production activities were subsidized by forest villagers' labor and their food production.

In 1865, the *blandongdiensten* system was abolished. Though a so-called free labor system was created, workers still needed cash to pay taxes on land, livestock, marriages, divorces, and irrigation water.[30] Moreover, as the state classified, mapped, and bounded state forest reserves, forest villagers were increasingly deterred from converting the forest lands to agriculture and from collecting forest products.

Villagers were now required by law to *purchase* wood for housing, an option few could afford. Nongovernment wood extraction or trade became a criminal act, a crime against the state, from the government's perspective. Under the pretence of liberating the forest people from oppressive systems of labor obligation, the state attempted to evict people from the source of their subsistence, limiting legal access to those who complied. This indirect labor control, enforced by the state's ever-growing demands on peasant incomes, was equally if not more oppressive than the *blandong* system. To people who made their living by converting the forest to agriculture, who grazed their cattle there, and who needed wood for housing and fuel, forest use was the most natural activity in the world.

Control of labor was more difficult in reforestation than logging. When German and German-trained Dutch foresters established the rotating system for teak harvest in "parcels," reforestation became the art of persuading people to plant trees on state land, an art in which local foresters had little training.[31] At the organizational level, managing forest laborers to sustain decent working relations was not emphasized in the same way as managing teak stands: Profits, wages, commissions, and bribes came from cutting big trees, not replacing them. Foresters working in their individual districts were so isolated, and communications so poor, that each developed his own strategies for handling routine management tasks, such as replanting clear-cut areas.

In 1873, W. Buurman began experiments with the *taungya* (or *Tumpang sari*, as it later became known in Java) system of reforestation in the forest district Tegal-Pekalongan. It is not clear, but seems likely, that Buurman learned of the *taungya* system through British colleagues in Burma, where the system is said to have originated. Between rows of teak seeds, peasant planters could grow rice, corn, tobacco, and other field crops for one or two years. The agricultural crops belonged to the planters; in addition they received a nominal cash fee.

Taungya was not widely known or applied in Java until 1883, when Buurman wrote a pamphlet describing the method and the local response. The system succeeded best where socio-economic circumstances were worst. For many of the same reasons that laborers flocked to work in remote forest districts, landless or land-poor peasants sought access to *taungya* land through Buurman's method. On very poor land the system failed, unable to attract labor even by high payments, requiring the forester to resort to other means of replanting.[32]

Foresters lauded the Buurman system for its economy and efficiency in replanting the forest; secondarily, it was seen as a means of providing land access to poor villagers. However, the temporary nature of reforestation land access helped create a new kind of forest-dependent rural proletariat. Whole families would follow the harvest of teak parcels and build houses of waste wood and teak bark, as dependent on forest labor opportunities as on forest land for their subsistence. By providing the laborers with barely enough cultivable land for household reproduction, the foresters were able to keep wages low. Thus, two methods of controlling forest labor were established by the end of the nineteenth century:

first, controlling access to forest products, either for wages (cutting timber) or use value (deadwood collection); second, controlling access to forest land for temporary subsistence farming.

THE CONSOLIDATION OF FOREST CONTROL

Several changes took place at the end of the nineteenth and beginning of the twentieth centuries. First, the Forest Service was moved from the Department of the Interior to the Department of Agriculture, Industry, and Trade, a move that symbolized, among other things, its concerns with land and commodities rather than people. Second, the forest police, formed in 1880 and originally under the Interior Department police forces, was made a part of the Forest Service. Third, the contracting-out of timber concessions to private contractors slowed down. The state began planning the harvest and replanting of specific forest districts. Those districts with plans, controlled by the state, were called *houtvesterij;* those controlled by private contractors and lacking state plans were called *boschdistrict.*

By 1900, the laws and procedures differentiating wood that might belong to the people and wood that belonged to the state were clear. All mature teak trees growing on state lands were the property of the state, which also had the right to tax any mature teak trees sold or transported from private property. Thinning wood could be purchased by local villagers but all pieces, like other types of government teak, had to be marked with a Forest Service stamp or were assumed to be "stolen."[33]

The forest police entered village houses without advance notice. They looked for standing wood (wood already used in construction) and concealed pieces such as door frames, roofing ribs, boards, and posts that had been "clandestinely obtained." Not infrequently, houses were demolished, the inhabitants punished, and the wood confiscated. The villagers resented the police and their malicious searching. Some said that the possession of a piece of teak was punished almost as severely as possession of illegal opium. Forest guards could even use the aroma of freshly cut teakwood as evidence of punishable theft. Some administrators attributed the high rates of theft to the high prices of teak, which drove people to steal it for their own use and for illicit sale. Yet, their proposed solution to the problem was to increase police activities, rather than lower prices or make teak accessible to the people. Some forest administrators and other observers did not approve of such severe restrictions on local people's access to the forest or of the methods employed by the forest police.[34] However, these liberal attitudes were little match for the increasingly efficient state machine for extracting forest products. Shipbuilding had long ceased to be the primary use for Java's teak, but teak exports had taken on an important role in providing state revenue. The interests of the Forest Service and the forest people were thus in direct opposition.

Subsequent sets of forest ordinances were passed in 1875, 1897, 1913, 1927, 1928, 1931, and 1934. The 1927 laws defined the state forest lands of Java and Madura as those "lands which are owned by the state, to which other people or parties have no right or control," and all other unclaimed surrounding land. After 1927, only minor changes were made, and the 1927 laws are still valid today. Not until 1927 were hydrological, climatological, and very broad social welfare aspects of upland or watershed forests written into law.

In the 1920s, government timber yards stocked with thinning wood were established near the big cities to sell lumber to local people.[35] The poorest people lacked both credit and cash to buy this wood.[36] As neither other hardwoods nor bamboo grew as abundantly in teak regions as in the rest of Java, however, other types of building materials were unavailable to most teak forest villagers.[37] They had to use teak for their household needs. The Forest Service also required villagers to purchase forest entry permits to collect firewood, in some areas limiting access to two days a week. In other districts, woodcutters were not paid in cash, but with tickets allowing them to collect a certain quantity of waste products from the forest.

Some observers in the 1920s questioned whether forest products generated actual revenues for the government. Critiques of government policy on forest exploitation and forest product distribution became more common during the 1930s, when the world economic depression drastically reduced the volume and value of wood exported. Nevertheless, teak cutting continued. Some foresters boasted that employment rates in forestry remained up during the Depression, disregarding the fact that wages dropped with the prices. Official reports claimed that labor demoralization rates were low. Other state enterprises profited, however; the railways, for example, had inexpensive fuel to run on.[38]

After an eight-year (1930–1938) administrative split of the Forest Service into the commercial Teak Enterprise (*Djatibedrijf*) and the Junglewoods Forest Service, an advisory commission was formed and a plan constructed for a united service to manage all state forest lands. This marked the end of the era of private forest exploitation on Java and the vesting of full authority for the production and sale of unprocessed timber products in the *Dienst van het Boschwezen*.

The Forest Service continued buying up what it called "critical" land, *i.e.*, land in watersheds, with steep slopes, or which was highly eroded. Where local ecology permitted, nonteak land was reforested in teak. Land exchanges were made to consolidate the forest lands: Where peasants were cultivating land enclosed by forest, efforts were made to exchange suitable plots of government land outside the forest. These complicated exchanges often did not satisfy all involved parties; disputes over the relative fertility, size, and location of exchanged lands were frequent.[39]

Although colonial concern was voiced for the welfare of people dependent on the forest, the actual forestry policies—like policies in other sectors affecting rural life—reflected a lack of commitment to meeting the basic needs of forest laborers and other forest villagers. Effectively, the state took away the primary means people had of helping themselves. However, the Germanic notion that external centralized state forest control benefited everyone would continue to pervade Indonesian forestry policy long after the Dutch had left.

THE SETTING FOR CHANGE: JAPANESE OCCUPATION

The Dutch colonial government in Java, and the mystique that had permitted it to rule for nearly 150 years, fell within ten days of the Japanese invasion in 1942. Some key changes took place under the Japanese which would influence the politics and patterns of forest use and state management until the present. The occupation initiated a quarter-century marked by political fervor and violence that echoed through the forests and forest villages. Through this violence, Javanese society was straining towards a new kind of solidarity. The physical revolution (against the Dutch) lasted for only four years; social revolution, with at least equal impact on the forests, raged for decades longer. The nature of forest access control and forms of resistance were swept up by—and mimicked—the political, social, and ideological revolution of the times.

Directly and indirectly, the Japanese occupation of Java from 1942 to 1945 had deleterious effects on the island's forests and forestry; the scars of this period are still evident in the distorted structure of today's forests. Few trees were planted during the Japanese occupation and the Indonesian revolution: many were cut. As a result, most teak plantations today are relatively lacking in thirty- to forty-year-old growth.

Chaos and destruction were begun by the foresters themselves, after they heard that Japanese occupying forces had landed and taken over in March 1942. Before Japanese control spread over the entire island, the Dutch embarked on a scorched-earth policy (verschroeingsaarde-politiek). The foresters wanted to extinguish any potentially useful elements of their legacy and proceeded to demolish their own infrastructure, devastating the sawmills at Saradan (East Java) and Cepu, burning down many foresters' houses and forest district offices, blowing up rail bridges across rivers in the forest, destroying forest maps, and igniting log-yards full of giant teak logs waiting for shipment.

To the Javanese forest villagers, it must have seemed initially that they were being freed from a steady, secretly violent form of oppression, of control over and intrusion into their everyday lives. Forest villagers responded vehemently to the sudden change in the forest custodians. They ransacked remaining log-yards, administrators' housing, and the forest itself. The worst destruction took place in some of the most valuable teak forests in the residencies of Semarang, Jepara, Rembang, and Bojonegoro. Some local village heads and regents took advantage of the confusion and ordered people to bring them money kept at the forest district offices. Alarmed by the state of the forest and their loss of control, some lower-level Javanese forestry personnel assumed command of their forest territories and issued orders for cutting and planting the forest. These self-appointed mini-commands lasted only until the Japanese arrived in each locale.

Finally, in June 1942, the Japanese Forest Service of Java, called *Ringyo Tyuoo Zimusyoo* (RTZ) was established. Becking, the head of the deposed *Dienst*, and a few Dutch forest district officers were retained initially as advisors to Japanese military leaders in the Japanese Forest Inspectorship territories (there were five of these in the whole of Java). Forest areas *(daerah hutan)* were under the jurisdiction of Indonesians, with a Dutch advisor overseeing two or three of them. Senior Javanese formerly employed in the lower ranks of the Dutch Forest Service were appointed to managerial positions. By mid-1943, all Dutch advisors except those at the experiment station, the main office in Bogor, and the inspection divisions were interned in concentration camps.[40]

Logs, firewood, and charcoal were in great demand for the trains, factories, and other war-related industries (manufacturing cement, matches, crates). All teak near railways and roads was cut and shipped, leaving holes in the well-kept Dutch forests. Timber and fuelwood production in 1943 and 1944 virtually doubled prewar wood production under the Dutch. In 1944, shipbuilding alone consumed an estimated 120,000 to 250,000 cubic meters of the longest and broadest teak trees to build 400 to 500 requisitioned ships of 150 to 250 tonnes apiece. The Solo River carried logs from Bojonegoro, Cepu, and Ngawi forest districts as it had not for over a century.[41]

In many forest locales, the Japanese created new forest villages by settling colonies of woodcutters to convert the forest to agriculture. In other districts, such as Cepu, the business of forest exploitation and replanting continued, but all wood harvests were taken for the war effort. No matter what form state forest management took, forest villagers who survived this chaotic three and a half years recall the rampant, and ubiquitous, cutting of trees. Everyone took part.

Except in a few instances, the Japanese all but ignored the critical routine tasks of sustained-yield forestry—planting, thinning, maintenance. There were no work plans. A few Indonesian forest district managers organized some replanting. In time their efforts were cut short by their Japanese superiors, most of whom had no training in forestry. At the end of this period, Becking estimated that teak production would have to be reduced by 30 percent over the next thirty years just to return the forest to its prewar quality level.[42]

The forest villagers bore the brunt of the Japanese excesses in the forest. Forced rice deliveries to feed the military and civilian bureaucracies were begun in 1943. Vast armies of forest laborers were put to work cutting timber under the Japanese forced labor system (romusha). On meager food rations, workers cut and hauled timber for the Japanese. Running away often meant a more rapid death than the starvation that killed many forest laborers. Some peasants risked death by planting crops for themselves in newly cleared forest areas. Sympathetic regents, village heads, or foresters risked allotting forest land to local people or to private Japanese companies, often without permission from Japanese authorities.

A total of 4,500 hectares of forest land were reportedly allocated to approximately 8,000 peasant cultivators in "created" forest villages. Much more land was occupied without official approval or taken over by the Japanese military for its own use.[43] Contemporary foresters complain that this practice of "lending" forest lands contributed to people's land hunger and to their propensity to cut down the forest for food production. It is equally likely that the Japanese period fueled people's beliefs in their rights of forest access. In any case, decades after the Japanese surrendered, their war production policies have led to contemporary disputes over land rights between the State Forest Corporation, the Department of Agrarian Affairs, and individual farmers.

FORESTRY IN THE NEW REPUBLIC

Soon after Soekarno and Hatta declared the Republic of Indonesia an independent nation in 1945, British troops landed on Java to rescue over 100,000 European prisoners of war, to oversee the repatriation of the Japanese troops, and, according to an agreement with the Dutch, to help the latter reestablish their authority in Indonesia. The Indonesians resisted the return of Dutch authority and the British attacked and occupied various government buildings, including the Forest Service's main office in Bogor. As a result, the Indonesian Forest Service (Jawatan Kehutanan) moved to Yogyakarta, where it remained for the duration of the revolution.

Like the Japanese war planners, the Republican (Indonesian) government needed wood to fuel trains and feed people; villagers continued to clear forest for agriculture and to cut any wood they needed. Sheer lack of service personnel and forest labor prevented the foresters from reimplementing the Dutch-German management system. The forest police had resumed patrolling the forests, but lacked the manpower and often the will to prevent forest raiding by impoverished villagers. Eventually, village leaders and the army were enlisted to assist the forest police.

A contradiction began to emerge in deciding how to manage the new nation's forests. On one side there were the long-term technical and economic objectives of so-called scientific forestry. Upland forest reserves protected lowland agriculture and lowland reserves were huge storehouses of current and future state capital. On the other hand, the people's needs for construction and fuel wood and land for grazing or agriculture were an important concern. Many younger nationalists felt the needs of forest villagers should receive greater consideration than they had under the Dutch. The new Forest Service's various conservative and liberal values were often contradictory and unresolved by forest policy makers. This was exemplified by the move to adapt the Dutch forestry laws to the goals of the new republic: Most laws were translated word-for-word.

Forest service leadership became disputed because of divergent management philosophies based on political affiliation and on differing interpretations of the Service's function. One major problem was that top Indonesian officials had been trained by the Dutch and had worked under the Dutch and Japanese. Adherents of the new nationalism and socialism saw the appointment of these men as inappropriate to the independent state. Similar ideological tensions affected all branches of the administration.

Notwithstanding the difficulties, during the first two years of the revolution most construction wood (87 percent in 1946 and 81 percent in 1947) was reportedly distributed to the local populace. Fifty-four centers for wood distribution were established in Central and East Java.[44] One wonders who bought it; few people could afford wood at any price. Teak timber cost six times as much as it had under the Dutch; even the price of nonteak saw timber had quadrupled. Teak and nonteak firewood prices had multiplied tenfold and fivefold, respectively.[45]

Despite the stated changes in philosophy, the "new" Indonesian Forest Service consistently reacted to forest-based conflict in almost predictable "old" ways. Six German and Australian foresters interned in prison camps for the duration of the revolution were released to aid the Indonesian Forest Service in restoring administration of forest lands to normal. Foreign (European) professors in agriculture and forestry were sought to teach in the newly established Gadjah Mada University in Yogyakarta. Old ties with large-scale Chinese teak wholesalers were reestablished.

The public image of forestry and foresters remained unfavorable, perhaps because the upsets of war prevented immediate implementation of new, liberal policies. In August 1948, during the Madiun rebellion, the Forest Service offices and forests of the primary teak regions were attacked and severely damaged by the Indonesian Communist Party and the People's Democratic Front. In one incident, a bridge over the Solo River in the heart of the teak forest was blown up. War brought restorative work in most of Java's forests to a standstill. Plans for reforestation of 7,400 hectares of teak and 4,450 hectares of nonteak forest were drawn up in 1947, but were never carried out.

The forests suffered extensive damage during the revolution. An estimated 220,000 hectares of state forest were destroyed or damaged during 1946. Of these, some 108,640 hectares were set aflame (compared with 10,900 hectares in 1938 under the Dutch Forest Service), presumably by clashing armies and individuals. Another 110,000 hectares were occupied by squatters or stripped of their timber by peasant households and the revolutionary armies for fuel. In some teak forests, whole "battalions" of armed villagers carried off the trees.[46]

Ironically, the notion of "criminal" uses of forest lands reemerged during the revolution and carried over into the period of independent state formation, when contemporary foresters noted that nearly 35,000 forest "crimes" recorded between 1945 and 1947 were still unsettled by the courts. By the end of the revolution in 1949, an estimated 500,000 hectares, or 17 percent, of Java's state forest lands had been either occupied by squatters or deforested by wood "thieves," i.e., peasants and the military.[47]

Why were people only now unleashing their pent-up feelings against the Forest Service and the forest access restrictions imposed for so many years? First, putting the stewardship of state forests in Indonesian hands meant little to the forest-based peasants when the structure of stewardship remained the same. Forest boundaries established by the Dutch were to be guarded. Teak and other forest species were to be extracted and sold by outsiders for use elsewhere; the surplus was hardly distributed more substantially to the local people. The language of the revolution was one of freedom and justice for all; yet many foresters were encouraging a return to Dutch exclusionary principles.

Second, political violence had been the means of change for nearly a decade. It was not simply that violence led to further violence; rather, conditions were such that collective action was inevitably expressed in collective violence: This was the "repertoire" of collective action in accordance with the broader repertoire of the time.[48] Men and women of the forest had gone off to join the fight for independence, and they were willing to fight for their claims to the forest.

When the Dutch withdrew from Indonesia in 1949, more battles over the "appropriate" state forestry ideology and structure shook the foundations of forest management in Java. The Forest Service remained part of the Ministry of Agriculture, as it had been under the Dutch. In 1957, a Directorate of Forestry was established. Provincial managers took over some responsibility for autonomous decisions concerning the marketing of forest products, forest management, forest exploitation (including labor practices), and forest protection. Policy, however, was still formulated at the center and all regional decisions had to concur with national policies. The provincial units' power further decreased when the Directorate of Forestry was reorganized later into a state corporation.

Political groups with conflicting ideologies struggled to control state forestry philosophy in the central offices and the field. For example, when the Indonesian government began returning occupied estate (plantation) lands to the prewar owners (most of whom were European) and the Forest Service began evicting the squatters from its lands, unions such as the Indonesian Forestry Workers Union (SARBUKSI) and the Indonesian Peasants Front (BTI) fought beside the peasants to prevent their eviction. Violent clashes between the foresters, the peasants, and their various supporters often took place. Hindley reported that "in some areas peasants were shot, and in many more the squatters' homes were destroyed, their crops plowed up."[49]

Such conflicts also constrained the Forest Service's ability to control forest theft and guard forest boundaries. The Darul Islam (DI) rebels hid in the wooded hills of the western half of Java. They fought against the Indonesian National Army (TNI) and hoped to establish an Islamic state. To be successful, guerrilla fighting requires cover, the thicker the better; thus, it was in the rebels' interest to maintain the forest cover. Their activities served to preserve the forest, but their relationships with forest villagers were less convivial. Forest villagers describe the period as one in which everyone was suspicious and suspected. Because everyone had to profess loyalty to both sides, one never knew where one's neighbors' or outsiders' real sympathies lay. Food and work were in short supply, agricultural cycles were disrupted.

Nationalist counterinsurgency strategies were more harmful to the forest. In the mid-1950s, the Indonesian army (TNI) burned corridors of forest to force the guerrillas out and prevent their return. Where nationalist forces pursued Darul Islam rebels through the forest, they were followed by villagers who sought wood to sell for a livelihood. During such operations, military personnel took advantage of opportunities to steal teak, driving truckloads of logs out of the forest. Many hired villagers or worked with other middlemen to acquire logs, lumber, or charcoal. Many foresters were afraid to take direct action.

Meanwhile, in the central and eastern parts of Java, the landless peasants who occupied the state forest and private estate lands were among the first to be organized by communist organizations. Without legal rights to the land they occupied and with generally few rights in their villages (as landless or land-poor villagers), the "squatters" were quick to realize the benefits of political organization. Until 1955, the Indonesian Peasants Front (BTI) was active only in villages adjacent to forest and estate lands. After the Darul Islam uprising ended in 1962, BTI factions entered forest villages in western Java where land distribution was severely skewed or the DI rebels had been harsh on local peasants. There, BTI coordinated peasant activities on forest lands as well as on the private lands of large landholders who had sympathized with DI.

The first Forestry Workers Union (SBK, later called SARBUKSI), was formed in November 1945 at the general meeting of foresters in Madiun. By the end of the war, the union leadership had adopted much of the philosophy of the left. Thousands of forest laborers were recruited and the union was further strengthened after affiliating with communist-led Indonesian Workers Central Organization (SOBSI), which claimed more than 60 percent of government employees as members in 1959. By 1962, SARBUKSI claimed 250,000 members including forest administrators, rangers, and laborers.[50] The less radical foresters formed another union, also called SBK. As the 1950s progressed, SARBUKSI influenced many policies affecting forestry workers in the bureaucracy and the field. SARBUKSI branches argued for squatters' rights to the land they occupied; they also supported promotions and salary raises for lower-level forestry officials. In 1956, squatters were permitted to appoint their own representatives to negotiate their claims with forestry officials.

SARBUKSI and BTI made the forestry issue a land issue, as the leaders felt this would draw the most peasant support. They also encouraged the counterappropriation of teak. BTI and SARBUKSI stated that farmers should exchange occupied forest land needed for hydrological purposes for land outside the forest, and on occasion offered to reforest barren land, but it is not known whether any action was taken.

In 1964, the Communist Party of Indonesia (PKI) and BTI encouraged peasants to engage in "unilateral actions." Peasants occupied lands belonging to large landowners, private estates, or the Forest Service, and cut down trees on forest lands and plantations. While a full description of this campaign is beyond the scope of this chapter, it is important to note the change in the tenor of resistance and the responses this evoked from non-PKI-affiliated officials.

In facing the growing strength of the Communist Party and its affiliates, Islamic and other political groups accelerated their activities among foresters. The nationalist party's alternative forestry union changed its name to SBK/BM and an Islamic Forestry Workers Union (SBKI) was formed as a branch of the Indonesian Islamic Workers Union (SARBUMUSI). To speed the processing of forest crimes through the courts, noncommunist foresters strengthened their ties with those regional legal and administrative authorities who were no longer sympathetic to the PKI. Until this time, the handling of these crimes was largely coordinated— and slowed down—by members of SARBUKSI. After anticommunist groups coordinated their efforts, mass public trials were held in "problem" villages, where the communists were strong, and convicted offenders were sent to jail for three months. Foresters tore down hundreds of allegedly illegal teak houses and sold the wood. In some districts, this faction of the Forest Service became strong enough to ensure that employees involved in tree theft or forest land occupation were severely reprimanded or fired.

SARBUKSI and others reacted by sending letters to other organizations and government bodies to discredit the opposing foresters. In response, the targeted foresters enlisted nationalist and Islamic party youth groups to help round up and bring peasants to trial. As soon as their short sentences were over, however, many of these peasants rejoined the agitative activities. Unorganized attacks on the forest lands of Java still occurred all over the island. Villagers converted small plots of forest land to agriculture, cut teak to sell or to use for construction, and collected branches and saplings for fuelwood.

THE POLICIES OF THE FORESTRY ESTABLISHMENT

Exactly how much forest land was lost or damaged during these turbulent years is not known. Exposed lands, particularly in the limestone hills where the island's best teak grew, were liable to be ruined by erosion and exposure to the harsh dry-season sun unless some vegetative cover was restored. Other reasons, however, behooved the Forest Service to rapidly reforest state lands in teak, mahogany, rosewood, pine, and other forest species. As under the Dutch, particular tree species indicated the legal classification of the land on which the trees were planted. Thus, not only political parties and organizations aiding forest laborers and peasants, but other government agencies such as the departments of Agrarian Affairs, Agriculture, Plantations, and the Interior, stood to gain from the Forest Service's loss of land and power.

In September 1951, the Committee for the Development of Forest and Agricultural Regions (*Panitia Pembangunan Wilayah Hutan dan Pertanian*) was established to handle the "squatter problem." This committee represented various government agencies, the military, and agricultural services. After two years, the head of the Forest Service reported that the committee constantly thwarted the Forest Service's interests in the land disputes, even though they had long been written into law. Even the guns that the forest police carried after 1962 were little help against the squatters. Many forest police were afraid that shooting a thief would lead to mass reprisals; injuring someone or threatening to do so had led to the deaths of colleagues.

The foresters also worked with Department of Information officials to convince people of "the meaning and functions of the forest" as the state defined it. Tree crops that could be grown in home gardens were promoted for use on marginal land. Informal leaders such as religious figures, youth groups, and women's organizations were mobilized to teach farmers the importance of tree crops for home gardens.

Two things are striking about the Forest Service's conceptualization of the forest problem and its solutions. First, foresters would not admit that part of the problem lay in the Service's methods of land, tree, and labor control. Second, foresters attributed deforestation to overpopulation and land hunger, without considering the contexts of these factors. The structural changes required to change the production relations in forestry and improve social relations between the Forest Service and forest villages, briefly recognized during the revolutionary period, were never made. In fact, postwar forestry in many ways polarized the relations between forest laborers and forest managers even further.

The urgency foresters felt to regain control of forest lands, to develop their industrial capacity, and to earn revenues even counteracted Becking's admonishment about restricting forest harvests over the upcoming thirty years. Production of construction wood in 1950 and 1951 nearly met the levels produced in 1940. Rather than sacrifice revenue earnings, according to one forester, it was better to postpone the demands of rural people on the forest.

Although "people's" wood auctions were held periodically in the forest district offices through the 1950s, local people actually purchased only 0.7 percent of construction wood, 0.3 percent of firewood, and 0.1 percent of charcoal. Discounted wood sales were also made to villages and accounted for slightly more of the wood sold by the Forest Service. Small businesses could also buy wood from the forest district office, but this was not an option for poor villagers.

Ten-year technical plans (called RPKH) for planting, harvesting, and maintaining forest districts were begun in those areas experiencing the least conflict. The boundaries of the most valuable forests were re-marked in the hope that this would deter squatters and the extension of adjacent private boundaries into the forest lands. Foresters allowed people to stay on land they were farming if they could prove ownership; the only legally binding form of proof, however, was a written certificate of title or the equivalent, a rarity even on long-established agricultural land.

In some Japanese-created villages, the peasants had already constructed irrigated rice terraces, fish ponds, housing compounds, and schools. Forest villages that had already erected such infrastructure, particularly irrigation systems, received some concessions. Often the provincial government became responsible for finding land to exchange for the occupied forest lands. Foresters generally recognized that the peasants who had been placed in the forest by the Japanese had somehow understandable claims, but they would not recognize the claims of those whose vision of life in the new republic included increased access to the forest for agriculture. The potential loss of Forest Service territory impelled foresters to resist changes in the standards for controlling forest land established under the Dutch.

Under "guided democracy," certain regulations strengthened the traditional forestry position, laying the base for its great power under the new order. Advocates for forest laborers began to lose power even before the unilateral actions. In 1960, a law (P.P. No. 51) was passed permitting eviction of squatters from state lands without court orders. Military authorities removed those who refused. The legislation was a coup for the traditional, authoritarian method of forestry; its enforcement foreshadowed the future of forest access control in the name of the state.

This legislation was followed by a reorganization of the Forest Service in 1961. A state enterprise, called P.N. Perhutani, was formed to produce foreign exchange to help finance reforestation and supply forest products to industry. This enterprise was generally inefficient and never succeeded in generating income as well as its New Order successor, the State Forest Corporation.

Ultimately, the ascending power of the left, including organizations backing poor forest peasants who challenged the forestry establishment, was halted by the events following September 1965. An alleged communist coup was attempted, provoking a counterrevolutionary movement by the right. The events that followed left a searing, permanent mark on the people whose lives and livelihoods were tied to the forest.

After the coup attempt, many people who had posed problems for the Forest Service—squatters, forest laborers in communist-affiliated organizations, and black market teak traders—were killed or interned as political prisoners. Surviving SARBUKSI members who were not exiled were fired permanently from the Forest Service; their children are still regarded with suspicion today. The attempts of forest communities to gain control of state forest lands through alignment with leftist political organizations in the 1950s and 1960s met with violent rejection by the government. The experience left many forest villages fearful of the state and reluctant to overtly demand extended access rights.

THE NEW ORDER AND FORESTRY

In 1969, the New Order's Ministry of Agriculture was established, subsuming the Directorate General of Forestry. In 1972, the P.N. Perhutanis of Central and East Java were combined to form Perum Perhutani (State Forestry Corporation [SFC]); West Java was added in 1978. Unlike its P.N. Perhutani predecessor, the SFC is an autonomous government corporation with its own budget mandated both to support itself and to provide 55 percent of its profits to the national development budget,[51] under the supervision of the Ministry of Forestry. The SFC controls the same territory on Java as the Dutch Forest Service.

Forest damage resulting from the political upsets of the past partially compelled the SFC to increase nonteak production. Management was intensified by making forest management districts smaller and targeting nonteak forests for industrial wood-pulp production. The SFC hoped pine plantations would generate more income and employment by providing resin tapping, logging, and transport opportunities. Plantation resin tappers, however, generally received lower incomes than local private and plantation agricultural labor.

By 1985, teak forest made up only one-third of Java's state forest land and one-half of Java's production forest, yet still provided 92 percent of the SFC's total income.[52] Java is one of the world's top three teak producers. While only 6.5 percent of Indonesia's timber comes from Java, this timber is primarily high-value teak, which alone provides 2 percent of the nation's foreign exchange earnings.

The Suharto government has a substantial ideological and financial commitment to development. The drop in oil prices in the mid-1980s forced the government to depend more on forest resources for development funds. Given that Indonesia is expected to import oil by the year 2000, the dependence on forest revenue can be expected to grow. These developments have forced the SFC to streamline its operations by restricting the number of civil servants, mechanizing some forest operations (even in labor surplus districts), and improving the quality of the processed teak it exports.

The 3,000,000 hectares of state forest land under SFC control, the agency's monopoly on domestic marketing and transport of raw teak, its controls on forest village development and forest labor, and its autonomous budget qualify the SFC as a "state within a state" as Robison calls the State Oil Corporation, Pertamina.[53] While revenue generation is a primary goal of the SFC, the agency is also mandated to promote development and provide for social welfare. Within its territory the SFC has sole responsibility for determining ecologically sound uses of forest lands, marketing its unfinished forest products, allocating forest labor, and sponsoring forest village development activities. Yet, the often competing goals of generating more state revenue and increasing village income are creating tension within the SFC.

The contradictions are exemplified by the organization of logging. Except for providing small-diameter branches from felled trees, logging benefits few forest villagers not employed in cutting or hauling timber. Logging in one teak production block generally proceeds for one or two years and is heaviest during dry months. The SFC retains no loggers on a permanent basis. Temporary labor is drawn from both adjacent and distant villages. Some men follow logging operations as they move to new blocks, migrating from their villages for a few weeks at a time, covering their own travel costs. The poorest forest-based families follow the logging trail to reforestation sites near new logging blocks. When possible, they construct dwellings of teak leaves and bark or apply to occupy tiny wooden houses constructed by the SFC as part of the forest village welfare program.

The costs of forest production are rising because of failed reforestation efforts, depletion of the older plantation trees without equal replacement, and unrecovered losses due to war damages.[54] The forest structure reflects these losses, raising questions about the sustainability of current plantation production systems, especially in the teak forests whose revenues support most SFC activities. Some 25 percent of Java's forest lands are effectively "empty land" and in Central Java, 31 percent of the teak forest is either unproductive entirely or does not produce teak. Nearly 70 percent of the productive teak forest is in the early, "noneconomic" stages of growth. The area of unproductive and non-teak-producing teak forest exceeds the area slated for clear-cutting over the next forty years, indicating the limited potential for maintaining current levels of forest production in the medium and long terms.

Two trends causing the unsustainability of the current system stand out. First, foresters are over-extracting teak, drawing from supplementary logging plans every year. They must do so because consistently high rates of tree theft, damage to standing stock, and reforestation failure prevent their meeting production quotas set in the ten- and two-year forest management plans. Second, three-quarters of the teak forests slated for clear cutting forty to eighty years from now are under twenty years of age and have been repeatedly replanted without success. Thus, much of the "unproductive" teak forest is the result of consistent reforestation failure due to theft, arson, grazing, and other human interference.

While the SFC has attempted to develop more conciliatory policies over the past decade, many rural people continue to believe the agency's primary interest is to reestablish strong central control over the forest, thereby threatening their own survival. Though the contemporary political climate precludes overt opposition to state forest policies, the tension is played out in clandestine actions of peasants in the forest.

New international and internal pressures to develop a more "social" approach to forest administration by involving local people in management decisions and allocation of benefits could constrain the corporation's ability to maximize state revenues. Consequently, the emerging social forestry strategy attempts to make state forest lands more productive—for everyone. Though not stated as such, a successful social forestry project could turn an unsustainable forest plantation system into a sustainable system. Some policy makers and development agencies are advocating that more benefits from teak production be filtered back to people living in teak-extractive regions. To meet these demands, the SFC would have to release some of the traditional controls they have claimed over Java's forest resources.

In the most recent attempts at social forestry, the SFC has relinquished some land and species control in order to expand villagers' use rights. Forest farmers may now plant horticultural crops and retain longer access to the forest lands for planting these and other crops in changing agroforestry regimes (see Chapter 12). Access to the forest is becoming a more valuable commodity, however, and structural changes may not take place rapidly enough to enable the poor to participate.

Perhaps the most serious threat to these forest development alternatives is that the basic nature of state forestry, in terms of established patterns of extraction and relations of production in logging, have not changed. This aspect of forestry will probably remain the most resistant to change, given the SFC's mandate to produce foreign exchange and to provide for its own budget.

If regulation, control, and extraction become too oppressive and are unable to respond to social needs through real transfers of benefits, unauthorized use of the forests may increase, further accelerating forest degradation. Local reactions to state exploitation of forest labor may take the form of active, violent resistance or clandestine extraction, both of which exacerbate the negative effects of state-sponsored extraction.

SUMMARY AND CONCLUSIONS

This chapter has traced the history of "scientific" forestry in Java and its effects on the forest, on people-forester relations, and on the nature of contemporary state forestry in Java. Several phases of access to and control over land, labor, and teak were discussed.

In the first period, the Dutch negotiated with Javanese kings and other nobles to gain access to a particular species—teak—and forest labor. Under the colonial state, Dutch foresters no longer needed to seek access, but sought only to better control access. By the end of Dutch rule, Dutch foresters controlled forest land, species, and labor, claiming legitimation based on an international ideology of conservation and state stewardship. The Japanese occupation caused a temporary breakdown in the traditional modes of forest control and the social power structures that supported colonial-style management systems. It also initiated a quarter-century of forest destruction for political or subsistence reasons. Indonesian foresters inherited the legacies of both Dutch and Japanese forestry.

Control of access to the forest lands became much more than a state ideology and legal configuration during the first decades of national independence; it was manifested in the political platforms and daily activities of individuals in all the major political parties and organizations throughout Java. Only by waging outright war on these opposing factions, within and outside of the Forestry structure itself, was the mainstream, traditional forestry philosophy of control reinstated. The state's authority over forest land has been further strengthened during the New Order government through the policies and practices of the SFC.

In Java today, the state is at once possessor, extractor, and access controller of forest products. Historical events, management systems, and rural population growth, however, have put the forestry agency in increasing competition with forest communities for access to these resources. The case of Java illustrates that, despite stringent state efforts to control access, the combination of excessive state extraction and continued rural dependence can lead to unsustainable levels of extraction and resource depletion. In this way, a theoretically sustainable management program is transformed into an unsustainable extractive enterprise.

This study illustrates the need for further empirical examination of the viability of resource management systems assumed to be sustainable. We need to understand the social processes generated by particular extractive or productive activities: relations of power, relations of production, and changing social landscapes on the peripheries of production. Plantation forestry is being extended through the tropics based on its assumed sustainability and potential for profitable connection with national wood-conversion industries. More careful research, combining macro and micro views of the social and environmental effects of plantation forestry, is likely to disprove the universality of these assumptions.

NOTES

1. See Peluso, Nancy Lee. 1988. "Rich Forests, Poor People, and Development: Forest Access Control and Resistance in Java." Ph.D. dissertation, Cornell University, Ithaca, N.Y., for a complete discussion of forest access control, the general historical circumstances leading to national state control, and some of the consequences of control. The history of the colonial forest service in Java is also described in a forthcoming edition of *Journal of Forest History*.

2. Blaikie, Piers. 1985. *The Political Economy of Soil Erosion in Developing Countries.* Longman Development Series, ed. D. J. Dwyer, London and New York: Longman.

3. Brascamp, E. H. B. 1921. "Houtleveranties onder de O.I. Compagnie IV. Houtleveranties te Japara onder den Resident B. Volsch in het jaar 1652." *Tijdschrijft voor Indische Taal-Land-Volkenkunde* 60:144–160.

4. Brascamp, E. H. B. 1923. "Het contract met den Soesoehoenan van 5 October 1705 en de Houtleverantie." *Tectona* 16:636–642.

5. Brascamp, E. H. B. 1924. "De eerste regeling van den houtaankap in de Preanger van 1684." *Tectona* 17:907–915.

6. Brascamp. 1923. 16:636–642.

7. Raffles, Thomas Stamford. 1817. *The History of Java*. Vol. I. London. (Reprinted 1965, Kuala Lumpur, London, New York: Oxford University Press.)

8. Selective figures cited in Peter Boomgaard, "The Dutch Colonial Forest Service in Java, 1677–1900," paper presented at the Conference on Environmental History in Australia and Asia, Canberra, Australia, 1987.

9. Apparently, however, enough forest remained in the coastal residency of Japara so that in the ensuing century and a half, much more could be depleted. Du Quesne van Bruchem (L. L. G. 1938a. "Debosschen der tegenwoordige houtvesterijen Kedoengdjati en Semarang in 1776 en in 1930." *Tectona* 31:865–75) made an interesting study comparing a 1776 report on the forests of Japara with the state of the forest in 1925. He calculated nearly 50,000 hectares had been converted to village territories, pasture, and agricultural land between 1776 and 1925. Thus, from an estimated area of 70,000 hectares, the forest had been reduced to 22,600 hectares, representing a 75 percent loss of forest area.

10. Lugt, Ch. S. 1933. *Het Boschbeheer in Nederlandsche Indie*. 3rd ed. Haarlem, The Netherlands: H. D. Tjeenk Willingk & Zoon N. V.

11. The use of this term in reference to loggers who work for the SFC persists in Java today, amongst both villagers and forestry personnel.

12. Lugt. *Het Boschbeheer in Nederlandsche Indie*.

13. Raffles. History of Java.

14. Schuitemaker, J. P. 1950. *Bos en Bosbeheer of Java*. Groningen, Jakarata: J. B. Wolters

15. Soepardi, R. 1974. *Hutan dan Kehutanan Dalam Tiga Jaman*. Vol. 1. Jakarta: Perum Perhutani.

16. Brascamp, E. H. B. 1922. "Regeling van het Indische boschbeheer in 1865 bij de wet." *Tectona* 15:1095–1110.

17. Raffles. *History of Java*.

18. The Cultivation System was introduced by Governor-General Van den Bosch and effected on Java from 1830 to 1870. The system was a means of organizing the production of agricultural crops for the state. The state profited greatly from the Cultivation System in the early years but its implementation had long and depressing consequences for the people's welfare and development in many regions.

19. Ordonnantie van 10 September 1865, Staatsblad no. 96: Reglement voor het beheer en de exploitatie der houtbosschen van de Lande op Java en Madura.

20. Onghokham. 1975. "The Residency of Madiun: Priyayi and Peasant in the Nineteenth Century." Ph.D. dissertation, Yale University; Moertono, Soemarsaid. 1981. *State and Statecraft in Old Java: A study of the Later Mataram Period, 16th to 19th Century*. Cornell Modern Indonesia Project Monograph Series (Publication No. 43). Second printing. Ithaca, NY: Cornell University.

21. Issued September 4, 1810, and February 5, 1811. To this day, a similar regulation for the taxation of privately marketed teak trees is enforced by the State Forestry Corporation.

22. The restrictions were irregularly imposed and easily misinterpreted. In forests from Cirebon residency eastward, which were not designated for large-scale exploitation, forest villagers and woodcutters were allowed to cut some wood for their own use, but were restricted to logs less than twenty feet long and six "thumbs" wide. Cutting wood for river craft, carts, and certain requirements of the regional government was also allowed. The cutting of wood for charcoal or wood that might go into future production for the government (an unpredictable variable) was forbidden. Waste wood, stumps, roots, and

underbrush were for the use of the forest people. If woodcutters used wood for restricted purposes, the wood was confiscated and the offender punished (Brascamp, 1924. pp. 917–918).

23. Soepardi. *Hutan dan Kehutanan Dalam Tiga Jaman*.

24. Lugt. *Het Boschbeheer in Nederlandsche Indie*.

25. The Dutch in Java were not the only ones turning to Germany for education in the relatively newly formulated "science" of forestry. Aspiring foresters from the other Dutch and English colonial services, and from free nations such as Sweden, Norway, Russia, and Japan, were sent to German forestry schools. German foresters migrated to other countries to develop principles of forest management and to cement these principles into the legal structures of their adopted states. See Fernow, Bernard. 1911. *The History of Forestry*. Toronto: University Press.

26. Teak forests were divided into those under regulated management and those that were not. See Peluso, "Rich Forests, Poor People, and Development: Forest Access Control and Resistance in Java," p. 59.

27. Koninklijk Besluit 7 July 1875. Indies Staatsblad no. 126.

28. Raffles. *History of Java*.

29. Small wage payments were given out in some forests. In other forests, small salt and rice allotments were paid to the workers in lieu of cash. See Brascamp, 1922, p. 1097. The percent of these wages that reached the forest laborers is unknown, for it is likely that they, too, were administered through either regents, village heads, or other intermediaries assigned by the Dutch to be "representatives" of the forest laborers. (Simon, Hasanu. 1983. "Peranan 'Interrelationship' antara masyarakat dengan hutan dalam pembangunan hutan di Jawa." Masters thesis, Gadjah Mada University.)

30. Giap, The Siauw. 1967. "The Samin and Samat movements in Java: Two examples of peasant resistance." Part I. *Journal of Southeast Asia and the Far East* 2:303–310; and Benda, Harry J., and Lance Castles. 1969. "The Samin Movement." *Bijdragen tot de Taal-, Land-en Volkenkunde* 125:207–240.

31. Simon, Hasanu. 1983. "Peranan 'Interrelationship' amtara masyarakat dengan hutan dalam pembangunan hutan di Jawa." Masters thesis, Gadjah Mada University.

32. Lugt, *Het Boschbeheer in Nederlandsche Indie*.

33. Meyier, J. E. de. 1903. "Het Boschwezen en de politie." *De Indische Gids* 25:1:709–715.

34. Beck, H. J. L. 1923. "De houtvoorziening uit de wildhoutbosschen op Java." *Tectona* 16:411–434; and Becking, J. H. 1926. "De houtvoorziening van de inlandsche bevolking." *Tectona* 19:904–913.

35. Westra, J. G. 1933. "Het djatibedrijf, de partikuliere handel en de consument van djatihout." *Tectona* 26:270–273.

36. Everts, F. E. C. 1933. "Het djatibedrijf en de partikuliere handel." *Tectona* 26:268–270.

37. Teak grows best where there are definite dry and wet seasons, in soils containing some calcium. In both its "natural" and plantation states on Java, it tends to become the dominant species in a forest, thus giving the impression that it was always planted. In some forests of India and Burma, teak does not dominate, but occurs as one of many species in a mixed forest environment.

38. Laan, E. van der. 1933. "Debat prae-advies, Het Boschwezen als werkgever." *Tectona* 26:317–320.

39. Benda, Harry J., and Lance Castles, "The Samin Movement." 207–240.

40. Soepardi. *Hutan dan Kehutanan Dalam Tiga Jaman.*

41. Forest History Team. 1987. pp. 17–20.

42. Ibid., pp. 25–26.

43. Soepardi. *Hutan dan Kehutanan Dalam Tiga Jaman.*

44. Forest History Team. 1987.

45. Soepardi. *Hutan dan Kehutanan Dalam Tiga Jaman.*

46. Ibid., pp. 60–62.

47. Forest History Team, 1987. p. 99.

48. Tilly, Charles, Louise Tilly, and Richard Tilly. 1975. *The Rebellious Century: 1830–1930.* Cambridge, Massachusetts: Harvard University Press.

49. Hindley, Donald. 1967. *The Communist Party of Indonesia.* Berkeley, Los Angeles: University of California Press.

50. Ibid.

51. Government of Indonesia and International Institute of Environment and Development. 1985. *A Review of Issues Affecting the Sustainable Development of Indonesia's Forest Lands.* Vol. II.

52. Perum Perhutani. 1985. "Materi Rapat." Proceeding Rapat Paripurna Perum Perhutani Tahun 1984 (Jakarta, 13–15 December 1984). Jakarta: Perum Perhutani, Publication No. 2.62.312.

53. Robison, Richard. 1986. *Indonesia: The Rise of Capital.* Sydney, London: Allen & Unwin.

54. Peluso. "Rich Forests, Poor People, and Development: Forest Access Control and Resistance in Java."

CHAPTER THREE

The Changing Upland Landscape
of the Northern Philippines

Percy E. Sajise and Elizabeth A. Omegan

PROBLEMS OF UPLAND degradation and social marginalization in the Philippines have received increased attention in recent years. Sporadic but catastrophic floods and drought, which are controversially associated with upland deforestation, are partly responsible for the concern. Upland deforestation is linked to poverty, social inequity, and political instability in the Philippines and throughout much of Southeast Asia. Although forest management has focused on timber extraction in the past, the social effects of forest-related problems are increasingly recognized. Deforestation in the Philippines has a long history, rooted in the evolving relationships between human society and the environment. This case study describes the evolution of land-use patterns in the Cordillera Mountains of northwestern Luzon and possible future trends.

HISTORICAL PERSPECTIVE

The Gran Cordillera is a series of parallel, narrow, high mountain ranges where many river systems feeding the agricultural areas of northern Luzon originate. Scattered human settlements are found between 500 and 2,000 meters elevation. The mountains are inhabited by seven major ethnic groups, including the Ibaloi, Bontok, Kalinga, Kakanaey, Tinggian, Ifugao, and Apaya, all of whom fall under the generic term Igorot. Politically, the region is represented by Abra, Benguet, Ifugao, Kalinga-Apayao, and Mountain Province (Figure 3.1). The Gran Cordillera uplands cover 24,000 square kilometers of northern Luzon.

To understand the impact of human activities on the Gran Cordillera, they must be considered historically and hierarchically. Five important periods have influenced the course of events in the Gran Cordillera in

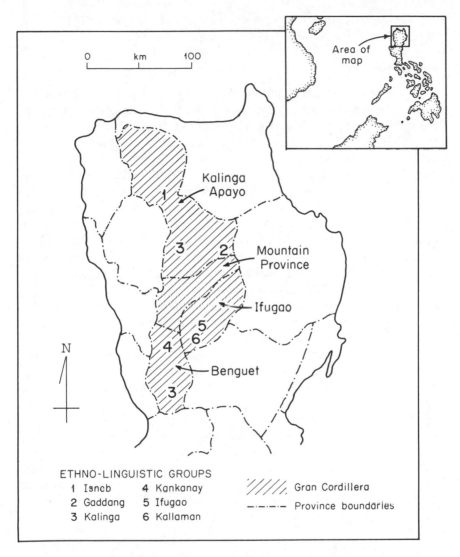

Figure 3.1. The Gran Cordillera region, northern Luzon, Philippines

Luzon and throughout the Philippine archipelago: pre-Spanish, Spanish, American, Japanese, and the Philippine Republic.

References on vegetation cover in the Cordillera region indicate that the area was only partially forested prior to human settlement. In the Cagayan Valley, the abundant fossils of large grazing mammals predating the appearance of humans indicate the area possessed extensive grasslands.[1] Wernstedt and Spencer postulated that, due to seasonal aridity, the plant cover of some of the western fringes of the Cordillera probably did not carry thick stands of trees.[2]

Pre-Colonial Era

The origin of settlement in the Gran Cordillera, which is related to the origin of the famous rice terraces, is still debated. Some scholars believe the Ifugaos started building rice terraces as early as 2,000 to 3,000 years ago.[3] Others see terrace construction as a recent development resulting from migration of lowland populations into the upper reaches of the Cordillera mountains due to Spanish expansion into northern Luzon in the sixteenth and seventeenth centuries.[4] Archaeological evidence indicates that the earliest settlement was founded as early as A.D. 560.[5] It is generally believed that during the pre-Spanish period there evolved in the Gran Cordillera small, autonomous villages based on swidden cultivation, hunting, and gathering. Their technologies, institutions, and social systems enabled them to use their resources on a sustainable basis.[6] Evidence suggests these upland communities were territorial, relied on village solidarity and cooperative work groups for agriculture and territorial protection. Labor and resource sharing is also reflected in elaborate rituals related to intermarriages and peace pacts.[7]

The prevailing social system, technologies and low population density resulted in sustainable land-use practices that had limited impact on the environment. Nevertheless, it is commonly assumed that, as upland population grew, the use of swidden cultivation began the gradual reduction of dense forest, creating open pine and grassland cover.[8] Although tree cutting predated the Spanish era, tree cutters selected wood of special quality for carving utensils and idols and probably only affected particular species. Hunting also affected forest regeneration. Fisher reported that "the deer is fond of feeding on young cogon grass in burnt-over areas and the hunter usually sets fire to extensive cogonales (*Imperata cylindrica* stand) adjoining forest lands to facilitate hunting."[9]

Spanish Colonial Era

Deforestation accelerated somewhat after the arrival of the Spanish in 1521, the beginning of a colonial period lasting for more than 300 years. Spain had three major interests in the Philippines, particularly in the Cordillera: gold, the spread of Christianity, and control of the Igorot tobacco contraband activities.[10] The "cross and the sword" were used to subdue the autonomous villages, allowing central authority to be gradually extended to the uplands. The colonial regime claimed all the land of the Philippine archipelago for the King of Spain under the Regalian Doctorine, and later established the tobacco monopoly, further controlling the people of the

Gran Cordillera. Missionaries came in contact with various ethnic groups and military expeditions were sent to search for gold and copper mines operated by the natives and to destroy contraband tobacco. To make the area more accessible for these campaigns, horse trails were constructed with corvee labor and revenues exacted from the natives. Lowland groups were also driven into the highlands of the Gran Cordillera during the Spanish subjugation of the lowlands.

Throughout the Spanish period, while shifting cultivation and terraced rice were the major cropping systems, new crops such as potatoes, coffee, and mint were introduced for trade with East India, China, and the Spanish American colonies.[11] Livestock established in the lowlands penetrated the Cordillera highlands and some Benguet families began raising cattle for a trade.[12] Forest areas were burned to create pasturage and allow the establishment of newly introduced fruit trees and crops. Shipbuilding required a substantial amount of timber. The tobacco industry used wood in the drying process. Mining, which took place on a small scale during the pre-Spanish and early Spanish periods, was later expanded to support industrial development in the 1950s, with growing timber requirements that accelerated the deforestation.

American Colonial Era

Succeeding the Spanish period in 1898, American colonization lasted over forty years, during which the major concern was the establishment of a Southeast Asian naval base and coaling station, as well as a base for trade with China. The United States was by then vying for position as a major world power. Two American policies affecting the Philippines as a whole were significant: the Public Land Act of 1905, which declared as public land all land not registered under the Land Registration Act of 1902, and the Mining Law of 1905, which declared all public lands in the Philippines to be free and open for exploration, occupation, and purchase by citizens of either the United States or the Philippines. The introduction of numerous temperate vegetable and fruit crops through the establishment of experimental stations and provincial fruit nurseries in the Cordillera stimulated the commercialization of upland agriculture. To make the areas accessible, roads were built. There was a change in the east-west orientation of the Spanish trails to the north-south vehicular road system of the Cordillera. This opened interior areas for timber extraction and accelerated the shift from swidden agriculture to temperate vegetable truck farming in logged-over areas. Mining, the establishment of government buildings and churches at town centers, urbanization, logging, and the conversion of farming systems to commercial vegetable production accelerated deforestation in the Cordillera during the American period.

Japanese Occupation

The Japanese period, although brief (1941–1945), added considerably to forest destruction. Upland people were driven into more remote areas and began cultivating steeper mountain slopes. As the resistance movement organized in the Gran Cordillera and other parts of the country, bombing of upland areas became more common.

Philippine Republic

In 1945, the new Philippine Republic was created. Numerous development programs were introduced in the Gran Cordillera, mostly involving logging and mining concessions and construction of hydroelectric dams. The result was further deforestation, alienation, and social conflict due to displacement of native populations and the erosion of indigenous land management systems. Conflicts over ancestral land versus public land became increasingly frequent. Armed resistence by communities in the Chico Dam and Cellophil Corporation development areas exemplified local community resistance to centralized government projects that undermined local ancestral claims to land and natural resources.

CORDILLERA FOREST RESOURCES

The three main types of forest vegetation in the Gran Cordillera are dipterocarp, pine, and mossy forests. Forest maps of 1911 and 1970 show there were extensive stands of dipterocarp forest in the northern section of the central Cordillera, in the foothills around the margins of the Cagayan Valley, in the Zambales Mountains, and along the east coast of Luzon.[13] Pine forests are located at elevations between 1,000 and 2,500 meters and are found mainly in the southern Cordillera and on the southwestern mountains of the Cordillera range. Just before World War II, pine forests were estimated to cover 18 percent of the Cordillera.[14] Mossy forests occur mostly above the pine belt and cap the headwaters of all the major river systems of northern Luzon.

Before the American occupation in the 1900s, there were no surveys of forests in the Gran Cordillera. A Spanish official estimated in 1876, however, that about 67 percent of the total Philippine land area was forested.[15] When the first forest census was conducted in 1900–1918, deforested areas were located along the river systems and in mining regions.

Of the three types of forests, the pine forest was the first to be subjected to industrial use. Pines were used primarily by the mining industry in Benguet. In the 1930s, pine forests covered 263,000 hectares, with a stand volume of sixty-three cubic meters per hectare. The average annual cut for pine timber was 126,000 cubic meters.[16] The mining industry used 85 percent of the timber cut and the rest was for local construction. To assure timber supplies for the mines, no pine timber was transported out of the region. The great demand by the mining industry far exceeded the recommended volume of cut pine timber.[17] By 1937 it was estimated that the annual volume of timber removed was 180,000 cubic meters.[18] By the mid-1950s, the number of sawmills and mining companies had increased and construction of the Ambuklao Dam intensified timber requirements. Widespread logging and commercial vegetable expansion wrought havoc to the forests of Philippine uplands. In 1918, over 56 percent of the country was under forest cover; by 1973, this figure had dropped to less than 30 percent. This process shifted the status of the Cordillera forest, particularly in Benguet, from a primary forest to a cultivated landscape.

CONTEMPORARY LAND-USE SYSTEMS
OF THE GRAND CORDILLERA

At present, there are at least three general types of landscapes in the Gran Cordillera, dominated, respectively, by paddy (terraced wet rice), paddy and swidden cultivation, and swidden fields (Figure 3.2). Type 1 land-use systems predominate among the Bontok, Kalinga, Kankaney, and Tinggian areas. In such areas deforestation is just beginning. The general environment is characterized as remote; the villages are compact, consisting of more than twenty houses, and accessible by one main road with outlying houses connected by rugged roads and trails. These communities are isolated and far from built-up areas. The council of elders remains the dominant socio-political body. The rice paddy system, which consists of terraces carved out from steep mountain slopes where water is available for wet rice cultivation, is dominant agriculturally and determines labor allocation to other land-use systems, including swidden fields.[19] Swidden fields are quite diverse, both in terms of crops planted and cropping patterns in time and space.

The Ifugao are the ethnic group generally using Type 2 systems. Their settlement pattern consists of groups of five to fifteen houses located near lowland areas and small mines. Ifugao society is mainly organized around a kinship system, as contrasted with the councils of elders which govern ethnic groups with Type 1 land use. In Type 2 areas the surrounding forest is still intact. The houses are surrounded with home gardens planted with both annual and perennial crops and fruit trees. Together with the wet rice terraces, these gardens are the main feature of the landscape.

Close examination of the steep mountain slopes shows that the breathtaking rice terraces are not cropped to rice alone but include several vegetable species. The communal grassland cultivation areas, locally known as *ponhabalan* and used primarily for sweet potatoes and occasion-

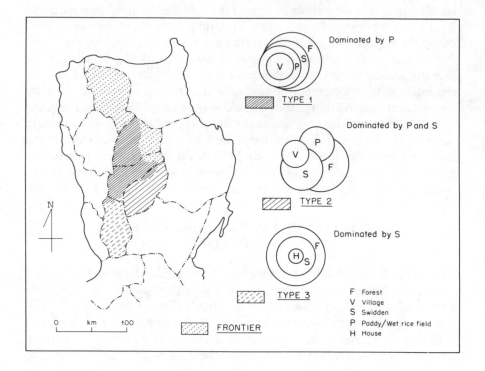

Figure 3.2. Land use types in the Gran Cordillera

ally corn, beans, mango, cassava, and bananas, are cropped depending on soil type and slope exposure. The sweet potatoes grown in shifting cultivation areas are important as a food source for households that do not own rice fields. Additional protein is obtained from wild game found in forests surrounding Type 2 communities.

Type 3 land-use systems are characterized by widely dispersed individual houses where shifting cultivation plots or household gardens are kept within one or two kilometers of the homestead. The clan is the dominant social organization in these communities. The nearest neighbor might be five kilometers away or more, in contrast to the two previously described landscapes where houses are located in settlement clusters. This pattern is shaped by the need for extensive tracks of land for raising livestock and for cultivation of crops for market in the lowlands and mining areas. The forest areas of Type 3 zones have frequently been denuded by the Ibaloi, the principal group in this landscape type, who have converted the forest to vegetable or grazing areas.

INDIGENOUS LAND MANAGEMENT SYSTEMS IN TRANSITION

Deforestation in the Gran Cordillera has been accelerated by mining, logging, the introduction of new crops (primarily temperate commercial vegetable species), the construction of access trails and roads, a lack of off-farm income, population growth, changes in cultural values, breakdown of traditional socio-political organizations, national policies encouraging agricultural expansion and exploitation of natural resources, and uncertainty and conflicts over land-tenure status. The combination of these forces over time has changed the nature of land management and stimulated rapid upland transformation.

Traditional cultures throughout the Gran Cordillera viewed land as a gift from above. High value was placed on group solidarity and reciprocity, communal labor and land-tenure agreements, and sustainable forest management. The indigenous land management systems and the cultural values and religious practices on which they are based have been eroded through interactions with external groups. The indigenous communities of the region have been influenced by Spanish and American colonizers and by the dominant lowland ethnic groups, whose values have been assimilated to varying extents. Some upland ethnic communities have substantially retained their cultural systems, while others have succumbed to outside cultural values introduced through political, economic, religious, and military channels. Cultural change among the ethnolinguistic groups of the Gran Cordillera is reflected in altered resource management practices and the social mechanisms used to control forest land use.

Traditional values promoted equity in exchange, communal sharing, and the right to subsistence. Existing religious practices, oral histories, and ethnographic research indicate that the indigenous populations developed social and technological strategies to cope with local mountain conditions, as well as with the climate, terrain, and water availability.[20] Upland communities living in landscapes of Types 1 or 2, where the terraced paddy rice system prevails, have developed a range of tools, labor sharing strategies, and an indigenous knowledge of the environment that allowed them to manage their land productively and sustainably. For people primarily engaged in wet rice production, group work is an important activity that must be synchronized. Coordination is necessary in various stages of the agricultural cycle, including the maintenance and repair of the communal irrigation systems. The *ub-ubbo* (group work), and *ubaya* or *teer* are Kankanaey and Bontok terms respectively for a community policy that prohibits residents from working on agricultural fields outside the settlement but allows them to work in the home gardens. It also prohibits visitors from entering the village. The religious rituals and the traditional institutions in these villages govern community and individual activities in a way that optimizes paddy rice production and distribution.[21]

Cultural values promoting community solidarity are also manifested in the *apa;* a local decree declaring a geographic area (such as a mini-watershed) off limits for cultivation, or in taboos locally known as *lawa* and *inayan.* These practices are instrumental in protecting resources in the long-term interest of various communities living in a diverse and rugged upland environment. In earlier times, headhunting forced Bontoc and Kalinga communities to develop only the resources within their territorial boundaries in order to ensure a locally sustainable food supply. This may have also led these communities to develop autonomous village structures with such sophisticated social institutions as the *ato* and *patpayan* among the Bontok and Kalinga, respectively. The *ato* is the Bontok council of elders, which is responsible for the religious, economic, and political affairs of the village. The *patpayan* is the meeting place of the Kalinga elders. Peace pacts or *budongs* on the other hand, govern intercommunity relationships, especially those involving the use of natural resources in a watershed. A strongly cultural concern for community equity is indicated by such prestige rituals as *canao* and *peshit* among the Ibaloi and *chono* among the Bontok, by which rich households distribute surplus resources to poorer households. These are also rituals of reciprocity, as the richer households are dependent on the poorer households for labor on their farms.

Traditional village layouts are also an important, but often overlooked factor in forest conservation. Traditionally, Bontoc rice granaries, for example, are located away from the houses because domestic fires could destroy the family food stock. Instead, they are located near the rice paddies and mostly along the forest and grassland fringes. The villagers protecting their granaries against fires thus also protected the forest and grassland. In Ifugao, there is an unwritten law that forbids cutting firewood in forests located above rice fields. These laws are so strongly held that transgressions of such communal regulations have led to murder in the past. In Apaya, the concentration of settlements along the big rivers, coupled with a fish diet, abated the clearing of forests for agricultural purposes.

It is clear from these examples that modes of production and community use of resources are not strictly economic matters but are tied to social, political, and religious customs.[22] Failure of the national government and the various colonial regimes to recognize this has created conflicts and rapid deterioration of upland forest cover in the Gran Cordillera. During the period before 1950, several national policies from colonial regimes promoted mining, logging, and commercial vegetable production, which required opening forest areas. This was hastened by the improvement of access trails and roads.

Although there is a lack of reliable data on forest cover before 1950 in the Gran Cordillera, the relationship between forest cover and agricultural land expansion can be seen in the Loo Valley in the northeastern portion of Benguet province.[23] The rapid decline of the forest area between 1950 and 1968 corresponds to the expansion of agricultural and built-up areas due to increased commercial vegetable production and logging, both of which were accelerated by improved access to these remote areas. During the same approximate period (1948–1970) the population in the Gran Cordillera grew from 365,000 to 730,000. Increased population pressure on resources, together with a national policy that generated conflict over land-tenure rights, promoted rapid and short-sighted exploitation of the uplands in the Loo Valley. Commercial vegetable production transformed the landscape, while traditional political structures and institutions broke down under the rapid and changing needs associated with commercial vegetable production technology. The new way of life embraced by some ethnic groups in the Gran Cordillera resulted in massive deforestation and pollution from agricultural chemicals. While the national government maintains that much of the Gran Cordillera is "public domain," ethnic groups continue to maintain their ancestral claims to the land. The perceived land rights of indigenous communities and the needs of government development projects for land have led to repeated conflict throughout the region. Since the rapid conversion of forest land to agricultural land in the 1950s and 1960s, forest clearing has slowed as the availability of that resource has been depleted. However, the population has doubled in the last twenty years, putting increasing pressure on the remaining forest lands.

CONCLUSION

The future of the Gran Cordillera should be evaluated within the context of past and present forces that have influenced upland landscape transformation. One of the most important recent governmental actions was the passage of Article 10, Section 15 of the 1986 Constitution of the Republic of the Philippines, creating autonomous regions in Muslim Mindanao and the Cordillera with legislative power over ancestral domains and natural resources. This legislation may help to remedy the problem of land-tenure insecurity in the Gran Cordillera by recognizing ancestral land claims of indigenous tribal communities and their land management systems. An integrated land management policy, however, is yet to be developed. Some government programs, such as the Highland Agricultural Development Project, continue to discourage sustainable forest management practices by encouraging vegetable growing. Policies and programs designed to increase agricultural production call for new and upgraded roads, improved market information systems to help farmers bargain for better prices, marketing facilities to channel transactions between producers and traders, and improved irrigation systems.

To promote establishment and protection of forest areas in the Gran Cordillera in the face of these impending changes, systematic attempts need to be made to reestablish local control over the natural resource base. Watershed land-use planning should be intensified at the local level by involving communities and interagency groups in establishing a land-use system to assure the long-term productivity and sustainability of resources in the Gran Cordillera. This land-use plan should utilize the existing socio-political systems of the Gran Cordillera. Wherever possible, indigenous management organizations, leadership, and traditional resource use systems should be incorporated into the plan. To reduce pressure on the uplands, opportunities and incentives must be created to draw labor into the off-farm sector. Incentives should be made available for intensifying and diversifying agricultural production systems in more ecologically stable areas in the Gran Cordillera. These are areas with fertile soil, available water for irrigation, and lower slope categories.

Because land-use patterns in a rural landscape are expressions of deep cultural, political, economic, and ecological conditions, reversing the trend of landscape transformation in the Gran Cordillera will not be immediate. An essential ingredient to progress is a good understanding of the past and present forces responsible for these transformations. This understanding will help at all levels—local, provincial, regional, and national—in facilitating upland regeneration in the Gran Cordillera and other places in the country.

NOTES

1. Vondra, C. F., M. E. Mathisen, D. R. Burgraff Jr., E. P. Kavale. 1981. "Plio-pleistocene Geology of Northern Luzon, Philippines," in Rap, G. Jr., and C. F. Vondra (eds.). 1981. *Hominid Sites: Their Geologic Settings.* AAAS Selected Symposium 63. Colorado: Westview Press, Inc., pp. 255–310.

2. Wernstedt, F. F., and J. E. Spencer. 1967. *The Philippine Island World: A Political, Cultural, and Regional Geography.* Berkeley: University of California Press, p. 742.

3. Barton, R. F. 1919. *Ifugao Law.* University of California Publications in American Archaeology and Ethnology 15(1):1–186; Beyer, N. O. 1955. "The Origin and History of the Philippine Rice Terraces," in *Proceedings 8th Pacific Science Congress,* 1953 1:387–397.

4. Keesing, F. M. 1962. *The Ethnohistory of Northern Luzon.* Palo Alto, Calif.: Stanford University Press; Lambrecht, F. 1967. "The Hudhud of Dinulawan and Bugan at Gonhadan." *Saint Louis Quarterly* 5:267–713.

5. Bodner, C. 1985. "Hoes and Pots from Before: Archaeological Investigations in Central Bontoc, Mountain Province." Paper read at Indo-Pacific Pre-History Association Conference. Pena Blanca, Cagayan, Philippines.

6. Scott, W. H. 1975. *History on the Cordillera.* Baguio, Philippines: Baguio Printing and Publishing Co., p. 213.

7. Prill-Brett, J. 1985. "Bontok land resource and management," in Sarise, P. E., and A. T. Rambo (eds.). *Agroecosystem Research in Rural Resource Management and Development.* University of the Philippines at Los Banos, College, Laguna. pp. 42–54; U.S. Bureau of Census. 1905. *Geography, History and Population.* Vol. 1. Washington. p. 619.

8. Kowal, N. E. 1966. "Shifting Cultivation, Fire and Pine Forests in the Cordillera, Luzon, Philippines." *Ecological Monographs* 36:389–419.

9. Fisher, A. F. 1926. *Annual Report of the Director of Forestry of the Philippine Islands for 1925.* Manila: Manila Bureau of Printing, p. 227.

10. Kowal. "Shifting Cultivation, Fire and Pine Forests in the Cordillera, Luzon, Philippines.

11. Mallat, J. 1946. *The Philippines: History, Geography, Customs, Agriculture, Industry and Commerce.* Manila: National Historic Institute, 1983. A translation from French; Merril, E. D. 1954. "The Botany of Cook's Voyages and Its Unexpected Significance in Relation to Anthropology, Biogeography and History." *Chronica Botanica* 14(5–6):244.

12. Bestre, P. 1981. "Buguias History." A project of the province of Benguet, Philippines. Unpublished manuscript.

13. Ahern, G. P. 1911. "Commercial Forests of the Philippine Islands—Exploration by Bureau of Forestry 1908–1910," in Whitfore, H. N. 1911. *The Forests of the Philippines Part I.* Bureau of Forestry Bulletin, no. 10. Manila: Manila Bureau of Printing. p. 94; Conklin, H. C. *Ethnographic Atlas of Ifugao: A Study of Environment, Culture, and Society in Northern Luzon.* New Haven: Yale University Press, p. 115.

14. Lansigan, N. P. 1941. "Relationship Between the Mining Industry and the Benguet Pine Forest in the Mountain Province." *Philippine Journal of Forestry* 4(1):37–55.

15. Mallat. *The Philippines: History, Geography, Customs, Agriculture, Industry and Commerce;* p. 75.

16. Prill-Brett. "The Bontok: Traditional Wet Rice and Swidden Cultivators of the Philippines". Lansigan, N.P. "Relationship Between the Mining Industry and the Benguet Pine Forest in the Mountain Province."

17. The 1923 Thompson report surveyed in detail the timber situation in the Baguio district and predicted a lumber shortage in twenty-five years. An annual cut of 18,000 cubic meters was judged ruinous to the forest. The demand went far beyond this estimate, and in 1937 it was ten times more (Lansigan, 1941, p. 48).

18. Prill-Brett. "The Bontok: Traditional Wet Rice and Swidden Cultivators of the Philippines". Lansigan, N.P. "Relationship Between the Mining Industry and the Benguet Pine Forest in the Mountain Province."

19. Dozier, E. P. 1966. *Mountain Arbiters: The Changing Life of a Philippine Hill People.* Tucson: University of Arizona Press. p. 299; Omegan, E. A. and P. E. Sajise. 1981. *Ecological Study of the Bontoc Rice Paddy System: A Case of Human-Environment Interaction.* Paper presented at the International Rice Research Institute. Los Banos, Laguna, Philippines; Fisher. Annual Report of the Director of Forestry of the Philippine Islands for 1925; Prill-Brett. "Bontok Land Resource and Management"; Conklin, H. C. *Ethnographic Atlas of Ifugao: A Study of Environment, Culture, and Society in Northern Luzon.*

20. Jenks, A. E. 1905. *The Bontoc.* Bureau of Science Ethnological Survey Publications, vol. 1. Manila; and Claerhoudt. 1967. *Songs of a People: Igarot Customs in Benquet.* Baguio City: Catholic School Press.

21. Omegan, E. A., and P. E. Sajise. 1981. *Ecological Study of the Bontoc Rice Paddy System: A Case of Human-Environment Interaction.* Paper presented at the International Rice Re-

search Institute. Lost Banos, Laguna, Philippines; Fisher, Annual Report of the Director of Forestry of the Philippine Islands for 1925; Prill-Brett, "Bontok Land Resource and Management."

22. Prill-Brett, J. 1986. "The Bontok: Traditional Wet Rice and Swidden Cultivators of the Philippines," in Marten, G. (ed.). 1986. *Traditional Agriculture in Southeast Asia*. Boulder, Colorado: Westview Press.

23. UPLB-PESAM-UPCB-CSC. 1986. *Dynamics of the Vegetable agroecosystem in the Cordillera, Philippines: The Case of Loo*. Unpublished manuscript, SUAN-EAPI Agroecosystem Study. EAPNI, Honolulu, Hawaii.

CHAPTER FOUR

Forces and Policy Issues Affecting Forest Use In Northeast Thailand 1900–1985

James A. Hafner

The flowing of the never-falling rivers, the fall of the periodical rains, the fervor of the tropical sun, the richness of the soil, all invite the cares of the cultivator, and would bring the recompense of abundant harvests.

—Sir John Bowring, 1857

SINCE THE EARLY Ayutthaya period, successive Thai monarchs faced the challenge of controlling a vast domain rich in resources but largely underpopulated. The country Bowring described a century ago still retained an essentially frontier character. Indeed, the last of these frontier areas, Northeast Thailand, did not come under central government control and settlement by lowland Thai until the latter half of the nineteenth century. At that time the region was still heavily forested and only sparsely settled. Since then, however, social, economic, and institutional changes have substantially altered the human-environmental balance. Among the many symptoms of this changing relationship, none illustrates it more clearly than the rapid dwindling of forest resources in the Northeast.

The postwar period has seen a rapidly accelerating depletion of Thai forest resources. Between 1945 and 1975, forest cover declined from 61 percent to 34 percent of the nation's land area and the rate of forest degradation over this period has been placed at 333,000 hectares per year.[1] Recent trends in Thailand's balance of trade in forest products indicate that Thailand, once a major world exporter of valuable timber and forest products, is now a net importer of forest products. Between 1981 and 1985, Thailand had the highest annual rate of deforestation in Southeast Asia and ranked third behind Indonesia and Malaysia in the area of tropical forest resources lost over this period.[2] The first symptoms of this problem were rising tenancy rates, shortages of arable land, and the conversion of marginal land to agriculture in the central region; the most alarming trends, however, develop in other regions, especially the Northeast.

Although awareness of contemporary forest management problems in the Northeast is growing, the process of deforestation is not new. Indeed, the situation has its foundations in conditions which began to develop at the turn of this century. This chapter explores the complex fabric of macro-level forces and policy issues that have affected the extent and use of forest resources in Northeast Thailand since 1900, particularly the relationships between population growth and the expansion of cultivated land, the postwar spread of field crops, the evolution of forest policy and law, changes in the land code, postwar investment in regional infrastructure, and the more tenuous links between internal political instability, national security policies, and new programs for forest land management. There is no intention here to rank these various factors in importance; indeed, the complexity of these relationships requires that, for the most part, they be examined separately. Our discussion spans the period from 1900 to 1980, beginning with a brief profile of Northeast Thailand and regional trends in deforestation in the postwar period.

THE PATTERN OF DEFORESTATION IN NORTHEAST THAILAND

Of Thailand's four major geographic regions, the Northeast is the largest, contains one-third of the nation's population, and by most measures is the poorest and least developed. This region encompasses 170,000 square kilometers in a large, gently sloping plateau of undulating mini-watersheds, flood plains, and a zone of hills and uplands that are most pronounced on the south and west. Regional per capita income is only 40 percent of the national average and just 60 percent of the average in the more developed central region.[3] The region's poverty is linked partly to its historical isolation from the capital in Bangkok, past neglect by the central government, and low agricultural production due to poor soils and erratic rainfall. A key problem throughout the Northeast is instability of rainfed farming, which varies in productivity and yields for paddy.[4] Floods and drought are common, rainfall occurs only occasionally during the dry months, and less than one-quarter of the farms are within reach of fixed-tank or reservoir irrigation. Consequently, the choice of cultivable crops is limited and much of the land is under a monoculture of rice, kenaf, or cassava. Postwar efforts at crop diversification have also been frustrated by declining external market demand for kenaf and an uncertain future for cassava.

The Thai government has long expressed a goal of maintaining at least half of the country under forest cover. Until the 1940s it appears this goal was never seriously threatened. At the end of World War II, 60 percent of Thailand's land area of 513,115 square kilometers was believed to be forested.[5] In the following decade the government revised forest laws, updated the land codes, and simplified reserved forest legislation to strengthen its ability to protect, preserve, and manage national forest resources.[6] A formal national policy was adopted of retaining at least 50 percent of the nation's land area in forests, a policy expressed in the first five-year development plan (1961–1966). In 1962, Royal Forestry Department surveys indicated that 57 percent of the country's land area remained in forest and, as recently as 1975, government officials stated publicly that adequate forest lands were available for new cooperative land settlements (nikhom), expansion of cultivated area, and population resettlement. In the fourth five-year plan (1977–1981), however, due to continued forest depletion, the target level for forest lands was revised to 37 percent.

Refined measurement techniques of the last two decades have dramatically altered the rather benign early estimates of Thailand's forest resources and their depletion rates. Estimated annual rates of decline in forest area vary from less than 3 percent for the period 1961–1975 to 10 percent for the period 1973–1977. Despite these discrepancies, it is generally acknowledged that deforestation has accelerated in some areas of the country. Comparative analysis of ERTS-1/LANDSAT imagery for 1974 and aerial photography for 1961 show that less than 37 percent of the nation was forested in 1974, a decline of 20 percent since the Royal Forestry Department's assessments in 1962.[7] In the Northeast, annual deforestation rates varied widely between 1961 and 1974 (Figure. 4.1). Among the Mekong provinces, Sakon Nakon and Ubon experienced rates of less than 1 percent annually, while Korat, Mahasarakham, Kalasin, and Udorn in the Korat Triangle exceeded 4 percent per year. There were similarly high rates of deforestation in provinces like Loei (3 percent) in the Western Hills and Nong Khai (3 percent) along the Mekong River in the north.

A more recent analysis by Wacharakitti and Chuntanaparb confirms three general trends.[8] Between 1973 and 1978, the average annual rate of deforestation in all watersheds was over 8 percent, although rates in Mun and Chi watersheds exceeded 10 percent per year during this period (Table 4.1). Between 1978 and 1982, the total deforestation rate for all watersheds had dropped 7 percent per year as the availability of forest land suited for conversion to agriculture diminished, leaving 15 percent of the region under forest. The largest conversion of forest land during this period has been to such field crops as kenaf, cassava, and sugar cane. While the deforestation process is generally slowing, in a few subwatershed areas in the Southern Hills and the upper Korat Triangle rates have actually accelerated. (See Chapter 10 for a discussion of the Lam Pao area of the Korat Triangle.) Projected trends suggest that forested area should have continued to decline to about 12 percent by 1986.

At current rates of population growth, the limits on arable land may be reached by the end of this decade. In fact, given present technological and ecological constraints on the rainfed farming systems of the Northeast, the recent declines in deforestation rates may indicate this has al-

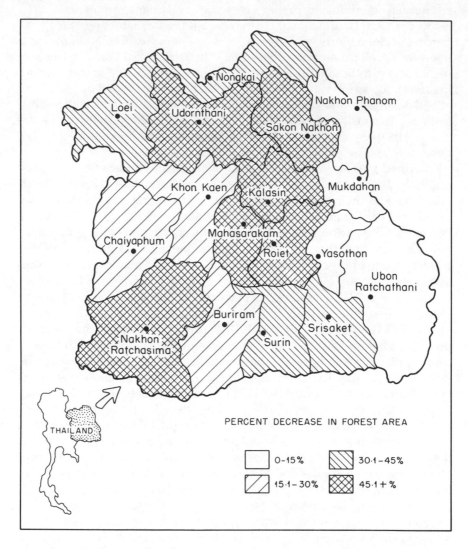

Figure 4.1. Percent decrease in forest area, 1961–1974

ready occurred and the better lands have been occupied. Demands for building materials, fuelwood, and cooking fuels, however, will persist. The region consumes an estimated 10 million cubic meters of firewood and charcoal yearly. The Northeast has the nation's highest regional consumption rate for fuelwood and many rural communities already face moderate to severe fuelwood shortages.[9] Despite expectations in the 1970s that off-shore natural gas could become an inexpensive replacement for fuelwood, this has not occurred. Under these conditions, conserving these

TABLE 4.1
Rates of forest depletion by watershed, 1973–1982

Watershed	Forest Area in km²		Annual Depletion Rate in %	Forest Area in km²		Annual Depletion Rate in %	Depletion Rate/Yr
	1973	1978		1978	1982		1973–1982
Mun	18,422	12,337	6.91	12,337	9,962	6.34	4.6
Phong	3,029	2,219	5.38	2,219	2,015	4.19	3.3
Chi	9,919	5,536	10.21	5,536	4,353	8.58	5.6
Khong	9,610	5,912	8.43	5,912	5,145	6.44	4.7
Phen	9,681	5,217	10.85	5,217	4,409	8.18	5.4
Total	50,671	31,221	8.40	31,221	25,886	6.95	4.9

Source: Department of Forest Management. 1985. *Land Use Resource Management in North-east Thailand*, Bangkok: Faculty of Forestry, Kasetsart University, p. 132.

resources while accelerating rural development in the Northeast is a major challenge for forest management.

THE CHANGING POPULATION–LAND BALANCE IN THE NORTHEAST

Historically, the Northeast has had a small population. Between the thirteenth and seventeenth centuries, the region was almost entirely "unpopulated." Lao and some lowland Thai populations filtered in slowly over the eighteenth century, particularly along the Mun and Chi rivers and around Nakorn Ratchasima in the southwest. In the early nineteenth century this situation was altered by political events and Siamese court policy, which encouraged Lao migration to the Northeast plateau. During the Third Reign (1824–1851), the thinly populated and densely forested region became increasingly occupied and controlled by the Siamese court in Bangkok. After the monarchy relinquished its claims to land east of the Mekong in 1893, this region was settled almost exclusively by lowland Thai. By contemporary standards, population density was still quite low in 1900; probably two-thirds of the region remained forested and suitable paddy land was being increasingly cleared and cultivated. Thailand's population has grown steadily since the beginning of this century, however, and except for a slowing of growth rates between 1939 and 1945, growth rates in the Northeast have consistently equaled or exceeded those for the entire country (Table 4.2). Constant population growth has accelerated settlement, substantially enlarged the area of land under cultivation, and placed increasing pressure on both land and forest resources, leading to their progressive decline.

Dixon has reconstructed the historical pattern of settlement based on

TABLE 4.2
Regional population growth rates in Thailand, 1920–1980

Region	1920–30	1930–40	1940–50	1950–60	1960–70	1970–80
Central	2.7	2.6	2.6	3.2	2.9	2.6
North	1.8	2.3	1.8	3.1	3.1	2.2
Northeast	2.4	2.8	2.5	2.7	3.3	3.8
South	1.9	3.2	2.2	3.0	3.1	2.7
Kingdom	2.3	2.6	2.4	3.0	3.1	2.7

Source: Cochrane, S. 1979. *The Population of Thailand: It's Growth and Welfare.* World Bank Staff Working Paper No. 337. Washington, D.C.: The World Bank; Goldstein, S., and A. Goldstein. 1986. *Migration in Thailand: A Twenty-Five Year Review.* Paper No. 100. Honolulu: East-West Population Institute.

the capabilities of the Northeast's four major ecological systems (flood plains, lower terraces, upper terraces, and the steeper ridges and ranges, here termed "uplands") as determined by soil fertility, water supply, susceptibility to drought and flood hazard, and land slope in each of these morphological types.[10] Throughout the nineteenth century, settlement expanded outward from the more fertile flood plains and reliable water supplies on lower terrace lands. By the early twentieth century, most lands suitable for homesteading were marginal or unsuitable for cultivation under existing farming methods. With continued population growth, village lands began to reach their maximum carrying capacities. In the Chi and Mun river valleys this produced overpopulation with respect to available land, declines in soil fertility, and emigration. Keyes reports that the population of Ban Nong Tun village in Mahasarakham province grew from 200 to 800 people between 1900 and 1940, and at least seventy-five families emigrated from the village between 1935 and 1963.[11] Many of those with insufficient land emigrated to Udon, Kalasin, and Khon Kaen provinces, where marginal land was still available. Similarly, in Amphoe Kaset Wisai, Roi Et province, where most villages were settled between 1883 and 1913, growing population pressures forced some families to establish newer villages. Pendleton has even provided first-hand evidence that, by the late 1930s, the "centrifugal diffusion" of population beyond these core areas was affecting forests as far north as Udorn.[12]

Thus, population growth in the first half of this century has contributed to increased settlement, expansion of cultivated land, and the penetration of agriculture into upland and forest areas. Also, the marginal quality of this terrain demands larger fields to compensate for lower production and greater variability in crop yields, thus increasing forest clearance and land development for agriculture.

The long-term decline in paddy yields per unit of land cultivated reflects these conditions. Between 1920 and 1960 paddy yields in the

Northeast dropped from approximately 260 kilograms per hectare to less than 150 kilograms per hectare. Only when new agricultural technologies were introduced in the 1960s did productivity begin to recover to levels close to those of forty years earlier. Thus, while other rice-growing areas of Southeast Asia intensified land use to meet rising population, the response in the Northeast was to expand area under cultivation and convert more marginal uplands and forest lands to agricultural use. The acceleration of this process in the last quarter-century is reflected in two corollary phenomena, rising population densities and intraregional population mobility.

The Northeast is still the least urbanized region of the country; only 4 percent of the population lived in urban areas in 1980. Yet, between 1947 and 1970, population density more than doubled to seventy people per square kilometer, a level second only to the central region. Most of this increase has come in rural areas, especially those provinces which had relatively large areas of undeveloped uplands and forest land. The highest percentage gains in population density have taken place in provinces like Loei (58 percent), Nong Khai (69 percent), Udornthani (49 percent) and Sakon Nakhon (40 percent), which have recently had high rates of deforestation. Intraregional population mobility in the last thirty years also indicates the diminishing availability of cultivable land and the effects of population growth on forest land. Throughout the postwar period, the Northeast has had net losses of population through emigration, mainly to the central region.

Within the Northeast, however, there has been a persistent pattern of intraregional, interprovincial migration, dominated by movements from the older, more densely settled areas of the Mun and Chi river flood plains to the less densely settled uplands and more mountainous landscapes in the Western Hills and northern Mekong provinces (Figure 4.2).[13] This pattern can be seen as part of a long-term trend in settlement growth and the use of a land-extensive system of agricultural production, a trend involving movements from densely populated areas with unstable rice production to increasingly accessible uplands and forests where sandy and low-fertility soils are better suited to field crop production. One cost of this adaptive response has been the accelerated conversion of forest land to agricultural uses.

Throughout the first half of this century, forest clearance took place at a socially optimal rate. Excess rural population was absorbed through an expansion of settlement and land under cultivation. Rather than intensifying land use, farmers sought to maintain traditional land-extensive cultivation systems by forming new settlements and expanding cultivated areas. Due to the instability of paddy production and variability in rainfall, extensive cultivation also minimized risk. For much of this century, the existing natural resource base has sustained this expansion, even

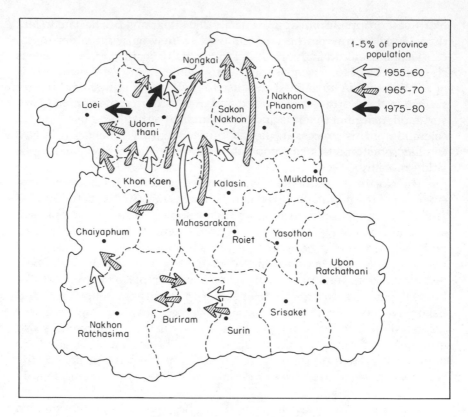

**Figure 4.2. Interprovincial migration flows in
Northeast Thailand, 1955–1980**

though it involved increased conversion of forest lands to agricultural uses.
However, high postwar population growth and the prevailing system of
rainfed farming have accelerated the process of clearance and conversion.
Paddy cultivation has spread into more marginal uplands and forest areas
where farming techniques cannot sustain production levels. This has encouraged intraregional migration and continued depletion of forests and
has led rapidly toward the limits of arable land. The process was further
accelerated in the last three decades by the rapid expansion of field crop
production in the Northeast.

THE GROWTH OF UPLAND CASH CROPPING

The rapid commercialization of the Thai economy is generally attributed
to expanded rice production after the Bowring Treaty of 1855. In the Northeast, increases in production and shipments of paddy to Bangkok, especially after the improvement of rail services early in this century, reflected

this change. Since 1950, however, when almost 96 percent of the area under cultivation was still planted to paddy, there has been an even more remarkable agricultural revolution in upland or field crops in the Northeast.

Between 1950 and 1984, the share of cultivated land under paddy in the Northeast declined from 96 percent to 73 percent, the number of total holdings increased by over 36 percent, and the total area in holdings rose by 53 percent. These shifts were due primarily to the dramatic growth in upland cash crops over this period. Beginning in the 1950s, three crops began to dominate the area being planted to upland crops in the Northeast: corn, kenaf, and cassava. Corn production, which first grew in response to export market demand (although since 1975 the local animal feed industry has absorbed a growing share of total production), expanded rapidly in the postwar decades. Most of the early production was concentrated in the Northeast, but by 1960 this share had dropped to less than 15 percent and the focus of production had shifted to the upper central region. Behrman attributes this to the Northeast's somewhat less favorable soil conditions and the increased profitability of kenaf due to rising prices between 1959 and 1961. Kenaf rapidly began to replace corn in upland areas and by 1965 it accounted for two-thirds of the land in field crops in the Northeast (Figure 4.3).

Between 1957 and 1965, when kenaf was concentrated in the southwestern half of the Northeast, production expanded at 35 percent a year. While kenaf drew somewhat on the same labor supplies as rice, it was grown primarily on uplands and did not displace paddy from lowland soils. Despite official views (especially after 1966 when yields began to decline) that farmers had begun to cultivate more virgin upland and forest soils, some studies have tended to contradict this.[14] Nevertheless, in 1969, 38 percent of the farmers in Huey Sithon, Kalasin, were either clearing forest for kenaf or had assumed land-use rights over kenaf fields newly cleared from forest.[15] By the early 1970s, cassava was replacing kenaf on upland soils and newly cleared forest land, primarily due to the decline in kenaf prices and problems with labor supplies and access to water needed for retting the crop, factors which made cassava easier to produce. In 1983, cassava accounted for almost half of the area under field crops in the Northeast and production represented 62 percent of the nation's total output.

The spread of field crop production in the Northeast has significantly affected the depletion of forest resources. Field crops are better suited to the marginal drought conditions and poorer soils of uplands and forested areas, where production and yields of paddy have been highly unstable. Also, field crop expansion has coincided with increased cultivation, especially after the mid-1960s; that is, paddy and field crops are not directly competing for land, but rather field crop production has increased through

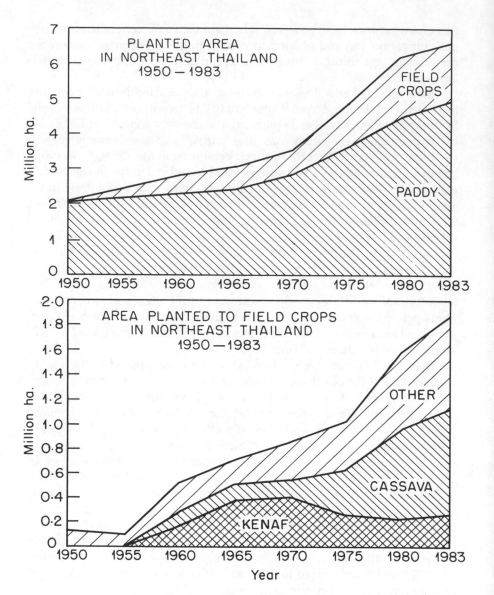

Figure 4.3. Paddy crop and field crop area in
Northeast Thailand, 1950–1983

expanded conversion of newly cleared land and forest that is less suitable
for paddy. This process can be briefly illustrated with an example from
Kalasin province.

Between 1963 and 1968, a dam and storage reservoir were constructed in the lower Lam Pao watershed to irrigate some 52,000 hectares of land. The original vegetation in this area was dry deciduous dipterocarp forest, but most of this savanna forest had already been destroyed by heavy logging, fires, and illegal charcoal making. Migrants from the more crowded provinces of Roi-Et and Mahasarakham had traditionally preferred this area but, "as population densities rose in the more congested lower terrace areas, [migrants moved] to the forest margins to maintain the extensive land-use system."[16] The resulting expansion of cultivated land, especially during the 1960s when kenaf cultivation grew rapidly, had been almost entirely in field crops. Almost two-thirds of the farmers in the irrigated project area acquired upland holdings for cultivating kenaf and, later, cassava. Throughout this process, the scrub and forest margin has gradually receded to accommodate the production of these cash crops.

Private entrepreneurs contributed significantly to the extension of field crop production by meeting farmers' financial needs and providing as much credit as state agricultural institutions towards the production, marketing, and processing of these crops. Thus, the rapid clearance of land for field crops was substantially underwritten by small merchants, middlemen, and traders.[17]

Some observers also contend that the government's rice premium policy has altered relative crop profitability, thereby encouraging farmers to diversify their crops and adopt land extensive kenaf and cassava.[18] This policy was intended to lower domestic rice prices and generate income, but its depressant effect on the farm price of paddy may have made field crops a more profitable source of cash income, thus providing farmers an incentive to diversify crops and extend field crop production by clearing forest land. The fact that the expansion of these crops has not occurred on land under paddy emphasizes the effects of the increased cash cropping on forest lands. In short, expanded cash cropping in the Northeast is at once a result of market and price incentives and a cause of increasing degradation and deforestation of forest lands.

FOREST POLICY AND FOREST LAND MANAGEMENT

The modern Thai economy is partly founded on an abundance of natural resources. Rice, rubber, tin, and teak accounted for over 80 percent of total annual Thai exports from the last half of the nineteenth century through 1951. Although the contributions of teak to total exports peaked early in this century, the commercialization of timber harvesting significantly influenced the creation of the Royal Forestry Department and subsequent forest policy and legislation. Despite substantial legislation covering forest use, logging permit procedures, replanting procedures, penalties for violations, and the settlement of public lands, forest land degradation has accelerated in the past quarter-century. Indeed, this body of legislation, its interpretation, and enforcement have partially caused this problem.[19]

Until the late nineteenth century, the cutting and collection of timber or harvesting of forest resources was, except for teak, unregulated. The Royal Forestry Department (RFD), the basis for modern institutions for forest management and forest policy, was created in 1896 in response to concerns over the commercialization of teak production and weak administrative and tax controls on teak harvesting in northern Thailand. The policy embodied in the Forest Preservation Act of 1897 emphasized protection and management to increase production, supervision and administration of forest resources by the RFD, definition of forest rights, and the collection of revenues and control of timber in transit.[20] The RFD had no control over the exploitation of nonteak forests, however, until the Forest Conservation Law of 1913 was enacted, dividing forest species into reserved and unreserved categories. The latter types of forest species were unregulated and could be cut by anyone. Reserved species, including teak and *yang* could be legally harvested only through licensing and payment of stump fees. This legislation extended over most of the country, but was not enforced in areas where no forest products trade existed, as was generally the case in the Northeast. In 1925, the RFD estimated that 44,000 square kilometers, two-thirds of the forest area in the Northeast, was in dry deciduous forest, mostly unexplored or undeveloped. In 1937 this figure had been revised only slightly downward to 60 percent, suggesting that the annual deforestation rate over this period was less than 1 percent.

The harvesting of forest products has always been an important element of village economy in the Northeast. Rural households use fuelwood, charcoal, timber for house construction, and a variety of edible and inedible forest products. Loopholes in the original Forest Conservation Law have allowed collection of these products and harvesting of timber for domestic use to continue. Households residing near public forest lands, for example, were allowed to cut up to 26 cubic meters for house construction. The level of forest product harvesting by rural farm households reflects the failure of the 1949 Forest Act to close these loopholes. The 1953 farm survey indicated that 90 percent of farm families cut wood for home use, almost 4 percent earned income through wood sales, and the value of fuelwood for home use represented 8 percent of total farm production.[21] Although timber harvesting for domestic use was subsequently prohibited in the 1960 Forest Act, other loopholes in the 1941 and 1960 acts still allowed households legally to possess up to 0.2 cubic meters of lumber for domestic use, and to circumvent even this limit. Houses constructed from timber cut for domestic use may be sold after a two-year waiting period and illegally cut timber, including teak, is often used to construct rough house frames which, after remaining unoccupied for two years, are dismantled and the timber sold at rather high prices.[22] In Ban Non Amnuay, a new village in the Dong Mun National Reserved Forest in Kalasin province, sixty of these "houses built for sale" were constructed between 1983 and 1985 with timber cut from the reserved forest. Similar practices were observed in at least three other villages in reserved forest areas in Chaiyaphum and Nakhorn Ratchasima provinces. Although the 1949 Forest Act further restricted cutting of nonteak species by setting quotas for different categories of trees, "common trees" could be cut without restrictions. Banubatana, former director general of the Royal Forestry Department, noted that these methods of forest management and imprecise quotas had disastrous effects and encouraged the repeated cutting of timber near villages and transport routes.[23]

Forest conservation issues were officially acknowledged early in this century, but forest policy continued to emphasize exploitation until the 1930s, when the Protection and Reservation of Forests Act was passed, allowing for the designation of reserve and protected forests. Almost ten years passed, however, before the details of this legislation were clarified. In 1949, the United Nations Food and Agricultural Organization (FAO) recommended that an area of approximately 70,000 square kilometers in the Northeast be set aside as reserved forest. Yet, despite new revisions of the Protection and Reservation of Forest Acts in 1953 and 1954, the process of creating reserved forests made only modest progress. In apparent conjunction with this legislation, the Thanarat administration amended lenient forest laws, increased penalties for violations of these statutes, authorized courts to confiscate equipment used in violation of the Forest Act, and created the Forest Police and Forest Protection Units within the Royal Forestry Department. By 1957, only 12.5 percent of the areas proposed for reservation had actually been established, although by 1980 a program of accelerated mapping and registration had raised this to 64 percent. Nevertheless, protection of these reserved forests continues to be problematic. Few reserved forests have formally marked boundaries, and the rural population often does not recognize areas that have been identified as reserved forests. Inadequate budget allocations have hindered recruitment and training of forestry officials and the development of an effective public information and education program.[24]

Throughout this period, little thought was given to rates of population increase, existing population-land conditions, or the pressures they would create on newly designated reserved forests, especially in the Northeast. Under the 1954 Land Code, a National Land Classification Program was created to assess and reallocate land within Thailand. Budgetary and staff problems delayed this program until the first five-year plan (1962–1966). The National Land Allocation Committee was charged with designating areas for both reserved forest and the proposed conversion of nearly 5,000,000 hectares of forest land to agriculture use. (This figure was based on 1950 estimates of 30.7 million hectares of land in forest and a target level of 50 percent for forest lands.)[25] This program, according to Chuntanaparb and Wood, "opened the gates for a massive influx into forest areas, causing its destruction and conversion to agriculture, before much of it could be declared as forest reserve."[26] Efforts to curtail mounting illegal encroachment and deforestation in the 1960s were increasingly influenced by the threat of a leftist insurgency movement in the Northeast. In response, the government made several policy and program decisions that inadvertently accelerated forest degradation.

In 1975, the Thai Cabinet granted amnesty to all illegal residents of reserved forests, with the intention of (1) supporting national security policy concerned with suppressing community insurgency and influence, especially in areas of reserved forest, (2) consolidating the forest resident population in villages where they could be better insulated from communist subversion, (3) addressing the problems of illegal forest encroachment and degradation, and (4) pursuing development and forest management programs consistent with these conditions. In the Northeast, this decision resulted in increased migration to reserved forests and further degradation of these forest resource systems. This apparently occurred because the general population misunderstood the amnesty conditions and many people believed that occupying forest land would qualify them for titles to this land.

A second Thai Cabinet decision in 1975 authorized the Royal Forestry Department to develop programs for improving the management of illegally occupied and degraded forest lands. The National Forest Land Management Division (NFLMD) was established within the RFD to design and implement these programs, one of which, the Forest Village Program, has used the forest village concept to stabilize degradation and implement improved forest management policies.[27] Key elements of the forest village strategy include granting use rights rather than titles to forest land, limiting these rights to land allocations of 2.4 hectares per household, providing village infrastructure and services, and developing cooperative, credit, and agricultural extension programs. Between 1975 and 1981, a total of 64 villages in reserved forests in the Northeast were established under this program, and over 10,500 hectares of forest land allocated for houselot areas and farming.[28] Preliminary evaluations of this program at three sites in the Northeast show that (1) increased immigration and settlement in reserved forests accompanied the announcement of new projects, (2) the supply of land alienated for allotment has not met demand, which has encouraged continued degradation and deforestation, (3) land allotments have been insufficient in area and quality to meet basic household needs, and (4) frequent land conflicts based on traditional tenure claims have fostered further forest encroachment.[29]

Over the last two decades, many observers have agreed that some of the most urgent problems in managing Thai forest lands lie with the forest codes themselves. Tongyai has suggested that Thai forest policy has four major weaknesses: (1) arbitrary choice of "competent officials" and their spheres of authority, (2) the leniency of prescribed punishments in both extent and judgment, (3) conflicts with the Land Code about the definition and legal uses of public versus private land, and (4) the general lack of emphasis on participatory corrective measures.[30] Furthermore, a major policy paper issued by the National Land Allocation Committee in 1984 stated that farmers would not receive full land titles in new land allotment projects until the Land Code was revised. This tends to strengthen the argument that both land codes and inadequate forest legislation and enforcement have contributed to the depletion of forests. They have allowed generally open access to these resources, which has been reinforced by traditional views of rights toward land and forests and has done little to discourage forest clearance as the agricultural frontier expanded. Certainly these conditions prevailed until the postwar period, when more restrictive policies and legislation were enacted. Yet, in some respects these changes reflect the continued failure of officials and planners to appreciate both the nature of the country's forest problems and the forces underlying them. Until these more fundamental problems are addressed and the social and natural dimensions of forest systems are acknowledged, the nation's approach to forest management will remain at the center of the problem.

LAND CODES AND TENURE SYSTEMS

The foundations of land occupance and ownership in Thailand are based on the principle of eminent domain. Full rights to land have traditionally been held by the crown or state, which in turn grants private ownership to individual citizens. Since 1901 a series of land codes have sought to refine the terms and conditions under which land may be owned and the steps required to obtain legal title to land. However, conflicts have persisted within the Land Code and between various civil codes and more traditional and informal land-tenure systems with respect to individual rights of possession and ownership of land. This situation has been further confused by differing interpretations of successive pieces of legislation, delays in implementing the 1954 Land Code, inadequate funding for land management agencies, and the persistence of traditional land-tenure systems in areas where modern institutions of the Thai state have been slow to be established. Although these conditions are not unique to the Northeast, they have facilitated illegal occupation of land, encroachment on reserved forests, and depletion of forest resources.

Until the twentieth century, the Northeast's low population density and slow rates of natural increase probably imposed few constraints on access to land. Thailand's first modern land legislation, approved in 1901, extended legal protection of land rights only to those with proper ownership. Keyes has noted that this legislation probably slowed encroachment on public lands in the Northeast as people came to recognize the legal restrictions on occupying land without proper title documents.[31] This process was also slowed by the increasingly marginal quality of most public and unclaimed land for paddy cultivation. It was probably only in the first quarter of this century, as land suitable for paddy became scarce, that emigration in search of new land and legal rights to land assumed somewhat greater importance. The 1954 Land Code, adhering to ideas established in earlier legislation, is the most important piece of contemporary land legislation.

The code recognized three different stages in land acquisition: occupancy, use, and legal possession. Each category had a corresponding form of documentation, abbreviated as N.S.2, N.S.3, and N.S.4 certificates respectively. The enabling legislation for the 1954 Land Code also established certain provisions for recognizing legal rights to land occupied prior to the implementation of the Code. The S.K.1 certificate, or form for reporting land occupation, was established by this legislation, but accords no ownership rights, prohibits the sale or mortgage of land, and allows for land transfers only through inheritance. Nevertheless, many farmers continue to recognize the S.K.1 as evidence of legal ownership of land.[32] It is perhaps this provision which has created the most problems regarding illegal land claims and encroachment on forest lands in the past quarter-century.

There is evidence that the 1954 Land Code actually encouraged clearance of forest lands, particularly in allowing S.K.1 certificates to be issued for previously occupied public land. In effect, this allowed people who had been using land without any formal land documents to register those holdings with district officials pending implementation of the new Land Code. In the Thap Lan National Reserved Forest in Nakhorn Ratchasima province, Subhadhira reports that many people obtained unoccupied and reserved forest land by making false claims of occupancy to obtain S.K.1 certificates.[33] Once these documents had been received, the new certificate holders moved to clear land that had been claimed. Limitations on household labor and technology, however, made it rare for a single household to clear more than four hectares. In 1985, some of these original land claims had been given to relatives or sold to new immigrants. Local and district officials were also found to have claimed large tracts of forest land in a similar manner in order to sell it. Both actions were direct violations of the conditions of the S.K.1 certificate.

Questionable sales of land also enabled upland crop production to be expanded in the Lam Pao irrigation area of Kalasin province. "In contrast to lowland areas, about half of the upland area had been acquired [through purchase and self clearance]. . . . as a form of compensation for the effort devoted by those who cleared the land originally. Most of the recently developed upland cropping areas and some of the paddy areas come under this form [S.K.1] of ownership."[34] In retrospect, this appears to have encouraged continued or renewed land claims without the obligation to register those claims or secure more formal certification. Significantly, the 1954 Land Code provision that claims not registered within 180 days after the Code was implemented would be declared unoccupied was abolished in 1971.

In many parts of the Northeast, local tenure systems incorporate conditions of legal codes that preceeded the 1954 Land Act, interpretative responses to this act, and traditional modes of tenure. This situation results from delays in implementing the Code, the lack of land surveys, and the fact that provincial land offices only began to be established in the Northeast in the 1960s. It is not surprising that villagers persist in claiming and clearing previously unused land. Numerous examples of farmers claiming, clearing, buying, selling, and renting out unoccupied land or land in reserved forests have been documented. For example, a 1983 study of 125 households in six areas of reserved forests in Loei province has shown that over 40 percent of all land was held without any form of documentation, 45 percent carried S.K.1 certificates, and only the remaining land in houselot areas was registered with N.S.2 and N.S.3 documents.[35] Most of these farmers expressed the belief that occupancy of the land or possession of S.K.1 certificates demonstrated ownership. Similar cases have been documented for areas of reserved forest in Kalasin, Udornthani, Chaiyaphum, and Nakhorn Ratchasima.[36] Consequently, recently designated areas of reserved forest represent both the final margins of the land frontier and those areas in which both formal and informal land tenure systems remain ambiguous.

Although our evidence is far from conclusive, it suggests that land rights and legislation controls over land ownership have been a significant factor in the accelerated depletion of forest resources in the Northeast. For the first half of this century these issues may have been less important, given the rather low population-land ratio and slow commercial growth in the region. In the postwar period, however, the more aggressive policy of legislative control over land has itself contributed to illegal occupation and use of land, particularly forest lands. The events following the promulgation of the 1954 Land Code and the rather ambiguous provisions for its implementation have encouraged the taking of undeveloped or unoccupied land. In the contemporary situation of rapid population growth, an expanding cash economy, and a growing scarcity of land, there is an urgent need to clarify land legislation. Unless many of the problems surrounding land rights are resolved in an equitable and efficient manner, solutions to Thailand's problems of forest depletion will remain elusive.

INFRASTRUCTURE, REGIONAL DEVELOPMENT, AND SECURITY

Development planning and investment in Thailand since 1950 has been largely directed toward increasing production. An important element of this strategy has been the priority given to expanding infrastructure, especially transportation and multi-purpose dam and irrigation facilities. These investments in the Northeast have contributed to changes in agricultural land use as well as the depletion of forest resources. However, evidence of the relationships between an expanding infrastructure and regional changes in land use can be identified as early as 1900.

At the turn of this century, the Northeast was still isolated from Thailand's expanding commercial economy. Only 6 percent of the country's provinces, all in the immediate hinterland of the capital, were linked by rail to Bangkok. The extension of this rail network to Korat in 1900 resulted in some immediate changes in interregional trade, rice production, and clearing of forest in the Northeast. Rice shipments to Bangkok rose from 200,000 piculs (one picul equals 60 kilograms) in 1905 to 1.25 million piculs in 1925, reaching 4.6 million piculs by the mid-1930s, a level equal to almost 20 percent of total Thai exports.[37] As we have noted earlier, this growth in paddy production and interregional trade from the Northeast resulted from an expansion of land under cultivation and the enhanced accessibility produced by new rail service. Over the next 20 years, the rail line was extended further, reaching Ubonratchathani in 1929, Khon Kaen in 1933, and Udornthani in 1941. As the rail line expanded, railheads became terminals for rice and paddy shipments resulting from increased production, especially on forest land converted to agricultural uses. In 1940, Pendleton observed "a marked increase in paddi [paddy] growing since the opening of the rail line to Ubon and expansion of padi growing into the forest. . . of thousands of hectares."[38]

The construction of new rail lines also created a demand for timber and wood for fuel, carriages, bridge timbers, and general construction that was initially met by clearing forests adjacent to the rail right-of-way. This was accompanied by increased local timber trade, the sawing of dipterocarps into planking for housing, and the extraction of minor forest products for local domestic use. More recently, the depletion of forest resources has also been reflected in changes in commodity shipments by rail from the Northeast. Charcoal shipments to Bangkok, for instance, declined between 1958 and 1968 and metropolitan supplies of logs and poles from the Northeast have also diminished with "depletion of accessible forests (largely *mai pradu, teng,* and *rang*).[39] It is hard to escape the conclusion that the expanding rail network was a leading cause of forest land clearance before 1950, especially in the southern subregion of the Northeast where prewar rail development took place, and that proportional declines of forest products in rail commodity flows indicate the continued depletion of these resources as the limits of accessible cultivable land have been approached.

Until the immediate postwar period, the government's transportation investment policy considered roads only as feeder services to the rail system. The monarchy supported this policy as a means of keeping the state railway solvent and ensuring that foreign loans were serviced. There is little record of state-supported road construction in the Northeast except in municipal areas. Although few all-weather roads were constructed in the Northeast before 1950, Pendleton has reported for the period between 1935 and 1940 that, where new routes were developed, rapid forest clearing followed. After 1950, the government policy changed, and in the Northeast road building was given a high priority. The government's development strategy emphasized investment in infrastructure as a way to encourage agricultural production, crop diversification, and trade, and in industrial development to increase economic growth (a strategy favored by the United States and international credit organizations such as the International Monetary Fund). A fundamental effect of the shift from rail to road development was to extend the area under subsistence cultivation through improved accessibility to more isolated areas containing lower poulations and unoccupied uplands and forests. Between 1956 and 1960, when the first all-weather highway was built linking Bangkok to Korat, the road network increased to 4,505 kilometers, although only a third of this network was serviceable all year. Before the end of the decade, however, most districts in the Northeast were linked by road to provincial capitals and the interprovincial highway network. Only Buriram, Sirsaket, and Surin had no direct highway connections to Bangkok.

During the 1960s, infrastructure investment in the Northeast was about $325 million (U.S.), of which over half was used for road construction and improvement and a quarter for multipurpose dam and irrigation projects. The government's emphasis on highway development was also consistent with its use of economic programs to strengthen national security.[40] Road construction was seen as a way of countering subversion and promoting loyalty to the government by stimulating economic growth (an argument also used to support the Forest Villages developed in the past decade).

In addition to improvements in communications, postwar development strategies have strongly emphasized investment in multipurpose dam and irrigation facilities. As these facilities were developed, settlements were created in reserved forests, poor resettlement planning led to forest degradation by resettled populations, and other groups of the displaced rural population migrated to areas where they claimed and cleared land in reserved forests. Several large and small-scale multipurpose dam and irrigation projects were developed in the Northeast in the 1960s. Between 1964 and 1969, over 15,000 rural households were displaced by six projects in Khon Kaen, Kalasin, Ubolratchathani, Udornthani, and Nakhon Ratch-asima provinces. The vast majority of those displaced resettled on their own in eighteen different provinces, mainly in the rural Northeast, rather than to government-designated resettlement areas. A study of over 4,300 of the displaced households shows that they migrated twice as often after being displaced as those moving to planned resettlement areas; they cultivated almost 20 percent more land, and 65 percent more area in uplands, than before being displaced, much of which was obtained by clearing forest; and they rarely held title documents to the new land.[41] The development of the Nam Pong dam and reservoir provides one of several examples that illustrate this point.

When the Nam Pong dam was completed in Khon Kaen province in 1964, 60,000 hectares of reserved forest land were set aside as the Ubolratana Resettlement Area. Over half of this land was already occupied; the resident households were compensated for their land and each given 2.4 hectares of land in the resettlement area at no cost. By 1973, however, only 13 percent of the 5,012 households displaced by the project were living in the new resettlement area.[42] Between 1965 and 1975, the amount of forest in the resettlement area declined by almost half due to clearance for agriculture by the resettled population, encroachment by landless farmers, and illegal timber cutting for poles, posts, lumber, and charcoal production.[43]

Farming opportunities differed sharply for households in the resettlement area, those in the reservoir draw-down zone, and those in areas served by irrigation. Net household income in the areas of irrigated agricultural land was almost four times larger than in the resettlement areas. Furthermore, most of the land allotted to resettled households was unsuitable for rice cultivation, land allotments were too small to meet household needs, soils were poor, and no irrigation was available for dry season cropping. Consequently, farmers found it difficult to change from rice to upland crops and were confronted with major economic problems. Johnson has observed in this context that most families "tended to intrude into the government forest areas to obtain wood and wood products for charcoal making [and many] were forced to look for alternative sources of income, of which illegal activities such as cutting firewood and making charcoal in the reserved forests are attractive alternatives."[44]

The development of infrastructure, especially improved communications and irrigation facilities, has featured prominently in Thai development strategies in the Northeast since 1960. The relationship between improvements in the road network and the depletion of forest resources cannot be determined precisely, but road systems have clearly been necessary for developing upland cash cropping, which has in turn accelerated the conversion of marginal uplands and forests to agricultural use. New roads have improved accessibility, widened marketing networks, and accelerated the process of forest clearance as logging has become increasingly mechanized. This has also made forest lands more accessible for settlement and farming by the poor and landless segments of the population. Infrastructure, including projects to expand irrigation, have contributed directly and indirectly to forest depletion. The removal of reserved status from forest lands to allow population resettlement and creation of new land settlements has had a direct impact on these resources. Displaced populations who have sought new land in the open market have also contributed to the problem by purchasing or claiming undeveloped or reserved forest land under existing land tenure conditions. While infrastructure investment had slowed significantly by 1980, its effects are already apparent in accelerated clearance of forest land and the closing of the land frontier in the Northeast.

POLICY, PEOPLE, AND FORESTS

Forest clearance for agriculture, authorized and illegal timber harvesting, and the collection of forest products by the rural population have all contributed substantially to the depletion of forest resources in Northeast Thailand. Throughout the first half of this century, land-use practices and forest clearance were determined by their profitability. As populations grew, returns from land clearance for both subsistence and slowly expanding commercial agricultural production, as well as extraction of forest products, encouraged expansion of cultivation, which increasingly took place at the expense of forest resources. In addition, existing forest policy allowed rather open access to forest resources. These conditions also allowed the population to maintain a more land-extensive system of agriculture production. In the first half of this century, the Northeast was being converted from forest to a variety of more profitable uses, primarily agricultural production, with forest clearance occurring at a socially optimal rate of exploitation under existing social and economic conditions.

In the last quarter-century, depletion of forest resources has exceeded this socially optimal rate. Population-land pressures have fostered migration between and within regions, deforestation rates have accelerated, fuelwood shortages have developed, and negative effects of forest land clearing are increasingly manifest in erosion, silting, and flooding. This situation is partly the result of long-term social, economic, and institutional forces. Yet, over the short term, new pressures have emerged with increased population growth rates, improved accessibility, construction of dams and irrigation facilities, which have forced rural populations to seek new land in the open market. Market price incentives for cash crops have also encouraged the spread of cash cropping into previously unoccupied forest lands. These pressures have been further strengthened by lax enforcement of existing forest and land legislation, failure to revise legislative provisions that allow continued exploitation of forests, and economic and personnel inefficiencies in the administration of forest lands. In the last two decades, policy and program decisions aimed at resolving regional security issues, often at the short-term expense of improved forest land management, have further compounded the problem.

Despite recent attention to deforestation in Thailand, there have been few initiatives of the type necessary to resolve the situation. In 1987, the Thai army launched the "Green Northeast" project, which aims to rehabilitate environmental resources, raise incomes, and improve the standard of living throughout the region by allowing the army to facilitate and integrate programs that other government agencies have pursued for decades. Initial efforts have been directed at developing water resources, strengthening the forty-six Forest Protection Units responsible for guarding the remaining 2.4 million hectares of forest, and reducing the rate of forest destruction from 48,000 to 14,000 hectares per year. (In April 1988, responsibility for this project was transferred to the National Rural Development Committee.) Nevertheless, critics have questioned the over-protective nature of the government's forest policy, its lack of a clear consensus on appropriate forest management strategies, and the continued lack of coordination among government agencies responsible for development in the Northeast. Other long-term schemes involve tapping the Mekong River for irrigation water, promoting crops more suited to the region's climatic conditions, and creating more cooperatives to enable producers to influence market prices. It is uncertain whether proposals of this type will ultimately resolve the complex issues contributing to deforestation; clearly, however, institutional changes in the property rights system, incentives to encourage more intensive agriculture and industrial employment opportunities, and more effective and equitable forest management policies will be essential. Without a broad-based effort to overcome the varied social, institutional, and economic barriers to a stable and productive forest resource system, the once-rich forest resources of the Northeast will survive only in the memories and folklore of the people of Isan.

NOTES

1. Smitinand, T. 1984. "Review of Literature," in *The Village Woodlot: Its Implementation in Thailand*, ed. Kamon Pragtong. Bangkok: National Forest Land Management Division, Royal Forestry Department, Ministry of Agriculture and Cooperatives.

2. World Resources Institute. 1985. *Tropical Forests: A Call for Action*. Washington, D.C. The annual rate of deforestation has been calculated at 2.4 percent, the thirteenth highest rate among all developing nations in the humid and subhumid tropics. The area of forest lost to encroachment by farmers, degradation by illegal logging, and harvesting of

timber for fuelwood, charcoal production, and building materials has been estimated at 260,000 hectares per year, the ninth highest rank among this group of countries.

3. Meesook, O. 1979. *Income, Consumption, and Poverty in Thailand: 1962/63 to 1975/76.* World Bank Staff Paper No. 364. Washington, D.C.: The World Bank.

4. KKY-FORD 1982. *An Agroecosystems Analysis of Northeast Thailand.* Khon Kaen: Faculty of Agriculture, Khon Kaen University. Recent research designed to develop cropping systems for rainfed areas of the Northeast has identified four major systems: the Korat Triangle, the Mekong Provinces, the Southern Hills, and the Western Hills. These systems have been differentiated with respect to levels of annual rainfall, stability of paddy cultivation and production; percentage of acreage in field crops; soils; and elevation and topography, among other variables.

5. Smitinand. "Review of Literature," in *The Village Woodlot: Its Implementation in Thailand.*

6. Forest resources are by law publicly owned and their exploitation is regulated by permits and licenses issued by the Royal Forestry Department. However, in practice there is a considerable gap between the traditional views of rural people and official government policy.

7. Thailand. 1975. "Comparisons of Forest Area From Air Photos and LANDSAT Data," mimeograph. Bangkok: Royal Forestry Department and Department of Land Development.

8. Wacharakitti, S. and L. Chuntanaparb. 1984. *Land Use and Resource Management in Northeast Thailand.* Bangkok: Department of Forest Management, Faculty of Forestry, Kasetsart University.

9. Panya, O. et al. 1988. *Charcoal Making in Rural Thailand.* Research Report, KKU-Ford Rural Systems Research Project: Khon Kaen: Khon Kaen University; Smitinand, T. 1984. "Review of Literature," in *The Village Woodlot: Its Implementation in Thailand*; Subhadhira, S. et al. 1987b. "Fuelwood Situation and Farmer's Adjustment in Northeastern Thai Villages," in *Proceedings of the 1985 International Conference on Rapid Rural Appraisal.* Khon Kaen (Thailand): Rural Systems Research and Farming Systems Research Projects, Khon Kaen University, pp. 229–326; The Fifth National Economic and Social Development Plan focused on developing alternative energy sources as one priority. The initial efforts to develop a sustained source of fuelwood production for villagers through the planting of village woodlots in the northeast are discussed in Kamon Pragtong, ed. 1984. *The Village Woodlot: Its Implementation in Thailand.* Bangkok: National Forest Land Management Division, Royal Forestry Department, Ministry of Agriculture and Cooperatives.

10. Dixon, C. J. 1978. "Settlement and Environment in Northeast Thailand." *Journal of Tropical Geography* 46:1–10.

11. Keyes, C. 1976. "In Search of Land: Village Formation in the Central Chi Valley, Northeastern Thailand," in *Population Land and Structural Change in Sri Lanka and Thailand*, ed. James Brow. Contributions to Asian Studies, vol. 9, pp. 45–63.

12. Pendleton, R. L. 1940. "Soils of Thailand." *Journal, Thailand Research Society*, Natural History Supplement 12, no. 2, pp. 235–260 (reprinted in Montrakun, S. 1964. *Agriculture and Soils of Thailand.* Bangkok: Technical Division, Department of Rice, Ministry of Agriculture, pp. 245–278).

13. Pejaranonda, C., S. Goldstein and A. Goldstein. 1984. *Migration.* Subject Report No. 2. Bangkok: National Statistical Office. Although the 1980 Population Census shows that Nong Khai, Khon Kaen, Udon Thani, and Nakhon Ratchasima were destinations for the four largest interchangwat migration streams in the Northeast between 1975 and 1980, the volume of these flows has slowed relative to the period 1965–1970.

14. Chuchart, C., N. L. Wake, and S. Suthasathein. 1967. *An Economic Study of the Production and Marketing of Thai Kenaf.* Report No. 1. Research Project No. 1/10—Economic Studies on Kenaf, mimeograph. Bangkok: Applied Scientific Research Corporation of Thailand.

15. United Nations. 1970. "Report on a Socio-Economic Survey of Farmers in Huey Sithon (Kalasin), 1969–1970." Bangkok: Economic Commission for Asia and the Far East, Committee for Coordination of Investigations of the Lower Mekong Basin. WRD/MKG/INF. L.412 (October).

16. School of Oriental and African Studies. 1978. *Land-Use and Socio-Economic Changes Under the Impact of Irrigation in the Lam Pao Project Area, Thailand.* London: University of London.

17. Subhadhira et al. have reported that merchants from the provincial market in Nakhorn Ratchasima province have been directly linked to problems of forest land encroachment and illegal cultivation of cassava on reserved forest lands. Landless farmers were encouraged to migrate to forest areas and provided with capital and tools to clear the land for cultivation in exchange for a share of the harvest. Hafner and Chantrasuwan have noted a similar situation with respect to the spread of *luk duai* (Job's Tears) among illegal residents of some reserved forest areas in Loei.
    Subhadhira, S. et al. 1987a. *Case Studies of Human-Forest Interactions in Northeast Thailand.* Final Report 2. Northeast Thailand Upland Social Forestry Project. Bangkok: Kasetsart University; Hafner, J. A., and S. Chantrasuwan. 1985. *Rural-Rural Migration and Land Use Change in the Uplands of Loei Province.* Khon Kaen: Research and Development Institute.

18. Silcock, T. H. 1967. "The Rice Premium and Agricultural Diversification," in *Thailand: Social and Economic Studies in Development,* ed. T. H. Silcock. Canberra: Australian National University Press, pp. 231–57; Rigg, J. 1987. "Forces and Influences Behind the Development of Upland Cash Cropping in North-East Thailand." *The Geographical Journal* 153 3:370–382.

19. A recent summary of the major features of this legislation can be found in *Thailand National Man and the Biosphere (MAB) Committee Report.* M. L. Prachaksilp Tongyai (ed.).

20. Banubatana, D. 1962. "The Management of Forest in Thailand," no. R. 49. Bangkok: Royal Forestry Department, Ministry of Agriculture.

21. Pendleton, R. L. 1962. *Thailand, Aspects of Landscape and Life.* New York: Duell, Sloan and Pearce.

22. Banijbatana, D. 1978. "Forest Policy in Northern Thailand," *Farmers in the Forest.* eds. Peter Kunstadter, E. C. Chapman, and Sanga Sabhasri. Honolulu: East-West Center, The University of Hawaii Press, pp. 54–60.

23. Banubatana. "The Management of Forest in Thailand."

24. Pinyosorosak, P. 1984. "Strategies Adopted in the Development of Diversified Forest Rehabilitation Project, North-East Thailand," in *Strategies and Designs for Afforestation, Reforestation, and Tree Planting,* ed. K. F. Wiersum. Netherlands: PUDOC Wageningen, pp. 180–192.

25. 1961 aerial surveys by the Royal Forestry Department indicated that only 171 million rai (27.4 million hectares) of land was actually in forest.

26. Chuntanaparb, L., and H. I. Wood. 1986. *Management of Degraded Forest Land in Thailand.* Bangkok: Northeast Thailand Upland Social Forestry Project, Kasetsart University.

27. There are indications that this program was originally conceived under the National Forest Development program, but proposed by the Internal Security Operations Com-

mand (ISOC) as a strategy to combat the growing influence of leftist guerrillas, especially in reserved forest areas. While overall responsibility for this program was held by the National Office of Readiness under the Development Projects for National Security, project design and implementation responsibility was given to the Royal Forestry Department.

28. Chuntanaparb, L., and H. I. Wood. 1986. *Management of Degraded Forest Land in Thailand*. Bangkok: Northeast Thailand Upland Social Forestry Project, Kasetsart University.

29. Subhadhira, S. et al. 1987a. *Case Studies of Human-Forest Interactions in Northeast Thailand*. Final Report 2. Bangkok: Northeast Thailand Upland Social Forestry Project, Kasetsart University.

30. Tongyai, P. 1980. *The Sakaert Environmental Research Station, Its Role as a Knowledge Base for the Determination of Forest Lands Conservation Policies for Establishing Maximum Sustained Yields on Forest Resources*. Bangkok: National Research Council, Kasetsart University, and Thailand Institute and Technological Research.

31. A general outline of Thai land law and the implementation of the 1954 Land Act can be found in Kemp, 1981; Ratanakhon, S. 1978. "Legal Aspects of Land Occupation and Development," in *Farmers in the Forest*, eds. Kunstadter, P., E. C. Chapman, and S. Sabhasri. Honolulu: The University Press of Hawaii, pp. 45–53; Yano, T. 1968. "Land Tenure in Thailand." *Asian Survey* 8 10:853–863.

32. Ingram, J. C. 1971. *Economic Change in Thailand, 1950–1970*. Stanford: Stanford University Press.

33. Pendleton, R. L. 1940. "Soils of Thailand." *Journal, Thailand Research Society*, Natural History Supplement 12:2:235–260 (reprinted in Montrakun, S. 1964. *Agriculture and Soils of Thailand*. Bangkok: Technical Division, Department of Rice, Ministry of Agriculture, pp. 245–278).

34. Rimmer, P. J. 1971. *Transport in Thailand*. Research School of Pacific Studies, Department of Geography Publication HG/6. Canberra: Australian National University.

35. Ibid.

36. Pa Mong Resettlement Research Project. 1976. *Rural Resettlement Alternatives*. Working Paper No. 5. Ann Arbor, Mich.: Department of Geography, The University of Michigan.

37. Lightfoot, P. R. 1979. "Alternative Resettlement Strategies in Thailand: Lessons from Experience," in *Population Resettlement in the Mekong River Basin*, Studies in Geography No. 10, ed. L. A. P. Gosling. Chapel Hill, N.C.: Department of Geography, University of North Carolina, pp. 28–38.

38. Johnson, S. H. III. 1979. "The Effects of a Major Dam Construction: The Nam Pong Project in Thailand," in *Too Rapid Rural Development: Perceptions and Perspectives from Southeast Asia*, eds. C. MacAndrews and C. L. Sien. Athens, Ohio: Ohio University Press, pp. 172–207.

39. Ibid., p. 199.

40. Ibid.

41. Pa Mong Resettlement Research Project. 1976. *Rural Resettlement Alternatives*. Working Paper No. 5. Ann Arbor, Mich.: Department of Geography, The University of Michigan.

42. Lightfoot. "Alternative Resettlement Strategies in Thailand: Lessons from Experience," in *Population Resettlement in the Mekong Basin*.

43. Johnson, S. H. III. 1979. "The effects of a Major Dam Construction: The Nam Pong Project in Thailand," in *Too Rapid Rural Development: Perceptions and Perspectives from Southeast Asia*, eds. C. MacAndrews and C. L. Sien. Athens, Ohio: Ohio University Press, pp. 172–207.

44. Ibid., p. 199.

Part II

Tools and Techniques for Participatory Management

Introduction

Mark Poffenberger

PART I REVIEWED the evolution of indigenous and state forest management systems in Southeast Asia, and the growth of conflicts between forest communities and government forest bureaucracies over forest usufructs. These jurisdictional conflicts have limited the ability of both the state and the community to effectively control forest use, and have contributed to uncontrolled exploitation and mismanagement. Part II explores processes and methods which may help to resolve conflicts over use rights through the development of collaborative forest management systems responsive to both state and forest communities needs.

These chapters focus on five elements in the development of effective community forestry which include: establishing an environment that supports experimentation and learning within forestry agencies; helping communities develop local forest management organizations; collecting information and creating dialogues to improve mutual understanding and generate joint management priorities; enhancing the authority and tenure security of forest communities; and developing agroforestry technologies that are sustainable, productive, and responsive to the needs of community managers and the nation.

In Chapter 5, Poffenberger notes that while forestry bureaucracies, like other large organizations, often resist change, these agencies are under increasing pressure from a variety of international, national and local groups to improve management practices. The proliferation of community-oriented forestry projects over the past decade also reflects a growing openess among planners and foresters to experiment with alternative management systems which consider rural peoples' needs. However, despite growing social responsiveness among some foresters and the emergence of policies more supportive of forest dwellers' needs, these agencies still have limited experience working with forest villagers. Forest departments have few staff trained to work collaboratively with community groups, and most field foresters continue to view forest users as part of the problem, rather than as part of the solution. This section explores how forestry organizations might develop the capacity to work effectively with forest communities.

In Chapter 5 Poffenberger reviews Southeast Asian experiences in creating problem-solving environments within state agencies and opportunities to experiment with participatory management. These include the use of agency based, informal working groups as forums for discussion, internal and external organizational change agents who facilitate the formulation of new policies and procedural options, and university and non-government resource persons who provide additional perspectives on management problems and solutions. The chapter examines methods of improving information flows between the center and the field to inform senior forestry officials of the problems and issues emerging in jointly managed forest areas.

In Chapter 6, Fox describes ways to increase communication between foresters and forest users. Starting with the premise that much of the conflict between governments and forest communities results from misunderstandings, he suggests that dialogues can resolve conflicts and produce a consensus about compromise forest use systems. Citing field trials in Indonesia, the author presents tools foresters and villagers have used to illuminate local forest use practices, problems and opportunities. These included the use of large format aerial photographs and simple sketch maps to initiate discussions between farmers and foresters. Dialogues stimulated by the use of these diagnostic tools have helped to facilitate the establishment of collaborative management systems.

Throughout Southeast Asia, use rights and tenure questions are often at the heart of disputes over forest access. In Part I we saw the problems of viewing tenure simply as a distinction between state versus private land. Indigenous tenure systems allowed for a variety of arrangements determined by the needs of the users and their production system. Grazing, hunting, and fishing grounds were often held in common. Burial grounds, palm groves, and swidden gardens were sometimes controlled by residential or kin groups. Private ownership designations were primarily used for improved land under intensive agriculture. Discrepancies between traditional tenurial and land-use systems and national land law classifications have confused usufruct rights and hindered the establishment of more viable resource use systems.

In Thailand and Indonesia, for example, while many forest communities continue to allocate land on the basis of customary tenure laws under the jurisdiction of the community, no operational procedures exist to allow community groups to gain formal government recognition of their communal rights. While individual arrangements may be appropriate for family house and farm plots, they do not fit the needs of production systems based on common or group access. In Chapter 7, Cornista and Escueta review the Philippines' experience with communal forest lease contracts, one of the few countries in the region with the tenurial tools to recognize community authority. These twenty-five year roll-over leases are used to enhance the tenure security and management rights of entire communities through a formal land-use agreement with the Forest Management Bureau. To better understand how communal forest lease management systems are arranged and implemented, the authors present the case of the Ikalahan tribe, who received their certificate in 1974. They discuss the tribe's procedures for resolving problems and formulating internal land-use policy. The chapter concludes with a review of the intracommunity tenurial arrangements, including land allocation and production systems. They find the communal forest lease was an effective means of protecting the environment and responding to community needs. The authors stress the utility of indigenous institutions and conservation strategies in helping communities develop sustainably productive agroforestry systems.

One approach to maintaining forest cover in areas where people are highly dependent on forest land is to develop or intensify agroforestry production systems which absorb labor and generate greater incomes, thereby taking pressure off other forest land. Where population densities are sparse, natural forests admirably meet the needs of hunting and gathering communities; however, migrants entering these areas in search of land and commercial forest products may upset the balance, resulting in mismanagement and forest destruction. In more densely settled areas like Java, secondary forests are under intense pressure from rural people in need of fuelwood and farmland. Government efforts to guard degraded secondary forests or maintain monoculture timber stands may be unrealistic and socially unacceptable, especially when forest agencies can no longer effectively protect these lands against pressing local needs.

In Chapter 8, Stoney and Mulyadi discuss the experiences of the State Forest Corporation of Java, which has pioneered a range of agroforestry technologies to respond to community needs for employment, land, and income generation. The agency began mixing timber species and food crops in the 1870s as a means to reforest logged areas. During the last ten years, forest farmers have experimented with a wide range of timber, fuelwood, fruit trees, and food crops grown in a variety of forest ecosystems. Some valuable medicinal herbs were shown to grow well in the shade of established production forests, which brought substantial income to caretaking families and encouraged communities to protect the forest. By providing subsidized seed and fertilizer, the State Forest Corporation helped farmers to increase food crop productivity, while gaining their support in replanting deforested tracts with timber and fruit tree species.

This chapter discusses issues which need consideration in the design and implementation of collaborative agroforestry systems. The experience in Java indicates that the success of forest production systems depends on the degree to which they fit village labor availability, local ecological conditions, and the level and stability of income flows generated by them.

Chapter 8 concludes that many agroforestry production systems can generate more revenue and create more employment than monoculture timber stands grown on the same land. Agroforestry systems that rely on fruit trees and other "farmer species" were also shown to increase community commitment to forest protection, thereby reducing agency costs for policing and replanting.

The authors note, however, that polyculture systems acceptable to both state and community require more time and information to develop, and have higher initial costs than traditional forestry techniques. Foresters' attitudes and procedures may be biased against the integration of "farmer species" into management systems. Low income families are often too poor to invest labor in trees whose fruits and products will need five to ten years to mature, thus creating equity problems. In the future researchers will need to work more closely with forest farmers to develop agroforestry systems that meet both ecological requirements, and household needs for food, income, and employment.

The chapters in Part II introduced some of the approaches being used in the region to formally devolve forest management responsibilities to communities. The authors reviewed ongoing efforts to create learning opportunities within government forestry agencies, develop dialogues between foresters and farmers, resolve tenurial conflicts, and formulate ecologically and economically viable production systems. In Part III we will examine the experiences of forestry agencies in developing collaborative management systems, discussing both national programs and specific social forestry projects.

CHAPTER FIVE

Facilitating Change in Forestry Bureaucracies

Mark Poffenberger

THERE IS GROWING concern over the inability of Asia's national forestry agencies to sustainably manage vast areas of state-controlled forest lands. Given existing staff constraints, forest agencies need to create the capacity to work with forest communities if sustainable forest management systems are to be developed. In Indonesia, it is estimated that 30 to 40 million people live on or near 143 million hectares of state forest land. With a staff of 50,000, of which only one-third are full-time field staff, the Ministry of Forestry attempts to regulate human use of national forest lands representing nearly three-fourth of the country's total land area.[1] To adequately monitor activities of logging concessionaires alone, a recent review estimated the Ministry would need ten times as many field staff; a twenty-two-fold increase would be required to protect national parks and reserve forest areas.[2] In fiscal year 1983–1984, the government of Indonesia was already allocating 36 percent of the routine budget to civil servant salaries and an additional 20 percent to interest payments on the national debt.[3] In fiscal year 1987–1988, the debt service costs surpassed 40 percent of the budget. Given this debt burden and the existing costs of government, a massive increase of agency staff to protect and monitor the nation's forest lands is not realistic.

Thailand faces a similar problem. In 1988, with a staff of only 7,000, many of whom are office-based administrators, the Royal Forestry Department (RFD) attempts to manage approximately one-third of the country. RFD forest lands are currently occupied by millions of migrant farmers and tribal communities, most of whom have no or little formal tenure status under the law. The RFD maintains a dual policy: mandatory resettling of some "illegal squatters" in unforested areas while formally giving use rights to other forest settlers. Thus far, neither strategy appears to have slowed deforestation, as evidenced by the continued clearing of forest lands and the tenurial uncertainty of many Thai forest communities.

The lack of agency staff and the financial constraints to increasing their number are common problems throughout Asia. The Forest Management Bureau of the Philippines, with a limited staff of foresters, holds government jurisdiction over 62 percent of the total land mass.[4] Much of this land is located in upland watersheds inhabited by an estimated 7.5 million people divided among indigenous tribal communities, Islamic groups, and Christian migrants from lowland areas. The forest agency's attempts to protect forest lands against occupancy by upland and migrant groups have led to widespread conflict and poor land management.

One of the few solutions to the agencies' severe staff and financial constraints is the transfer of local management responsibilities to community groups. Such measures have sweeping implications for forest policies and procedures that have been in place, in many cases, for over 100 years. Empowering local groups requires agencies to give up some of their authority; this demands a strong political commitment to the devolution of power on the part of the bureaucracy.

Over the past thirty years forest agencies began to experiment with ways to respond to the needs of forest communities through woodlot programs, activities to generate minor forest-product income and employment, and resettlement schemes. Each organization has had its share of problems and frustrations with past attempts to meet community needs, partly due to centralized planning procedures that were too rigid to respond to localized needs and opportunities, and due to a lack of political commitment and policy support for more substantial delegation of management authority to forest communities. As David C. Korten has observed, frequently efforts of such government agencies failed to "give more than lip service to relating in a meaningful way to locally identified needs or to examining the management systems which dominate the agency's programs to see whether they are consistent with a participative approach."[5] Conciliatory agency projects were often compartmentalized as special activities, while traditional state forest management systems proceeded unchanged. Mainstream forest policies, laws, procedures, and attitudes remained basically untouched by the socially responsive rhetoric that characterised community forestry projects. In the words of Robert Chambers, effective community participation required "reversals in management," and these were not taking place.[6] Over the past decade, however, a new generation of social forestry programs has evolved. While agency capacity is still limited, a growing number of young foresters are gaining insights into the changes they will need to make in their organizations to effectively involve rural groups in collaborative forest management activities.

These new activities are based on the premise that improved communication between the field and the center is necessary to help agency staff better understand community needs and problems. The joint planning groups that direct these efforts assume they need new policies and procedures to enable forest communities to collaborate with forestry agencies. While the process of organizational change has been slow, these programs provide insights and encouragement regarding the prospects for bureaucratic response to changing societal needs.

The experience presented here is drawn from the social forestry programs of the State Forest Corporation on the island of Java, the Indonesian Ministry of Forestry Outer Island Working Group, the Royal Forestry Department of Thailand, and the Forest Management Bureau of the Philippines. The following pages describe some of the ways in which forestry agencies have sought to learn new operating styles that could lead to more efficient forest management and better public service.

THE PROCESS OF AGENCY CHANGE

To make major shifts in institutional policies, procedures, and attitudes takes time, even when societal and organizational conditions are conducive to change. Some organizational change specialists have tried to divide the process into successive stages and strategies. Hage and Aiken's study of American corporations observed change occurring in four phases: an initial period of study or assessment, *i.e., evaluation;* second and third stages in which new programs are *initiated* and *implemented;* and a fourth period of *routinization* in which the organization attempts to stabilize the effects of the new program.[7] The authors noted that most studies of organizational change have examined the causes and consequences, rather than the pattern or process through which change occurs.

David Korten's article is of particular interest as he bases his analysis of organizational change processes on the experiences of government and nongovernment organizations in developing countries.[8] He proposes a paradigm in which organizational capacity is developed in three phases through a learning process. During Phase 1, the organization learns to be more effective through action research. The organization learns to accept its past errors and learn from them; it learns how to involve people in the planning process and how to link learning with action. Staff members work with a small number of communities to better understand village needs and local issues. In these field laboratories, the staff works with communities to create new approaches to planning and implementing programs that use local knowledge responding to the unique socio-economic and environmental characteristics of each area. During Phase 1 of the social forestry programs, field staff seek to learn what issues are behind conflicts between the agency and forest communities. They try new approaches to gathering information about appropriate agroforestry systems and land-use patterns, and new methods for generating group discussions.

In Phase 2, the organization learns to efficiently use and integrate the new methods of project planning and implementation developed during the first phase. Phase 2 also attempts to integrate the new procedures into the broader structure and operations of the organization. Strategies developed during the first phase to enable communities to establish sustainably productive management systems for forest lands are adjusted to correspond to available human and budgetary resources.

According to Korten, once "acceptable levels of effectiveness and efficiency have been obtained," Phase 3 expansion can begin. Successful expansion depends on introducing regional and local staff to the new concepts and procedures on which the participatory management systems are based. Coordinating expansion temporally and spatially is critical to the success of management transition. Expansion that proceeds too slowly will leave the agency little changed, while too rapid expansion could outpace the organization's ability to train staff and adjust local procedures to facilitate implementation. Particular attention needs to be given to creating a learning mechanism within an agency and facilitating transitions to successive phases.[9]

THE ROLE OF CHANGE AGENTS

Systematic organizational change is usually driven by individuals within the agency who perceive problems and solutions, and then act. In many cases change primarily occurs through policy decisions by senior members of management. "Pen-stroke" decisions can be effective in changing such policies as hiring and salary practices, pricing and marketing procedures, and so forth. However, these types of policy decisions may do little to change staff attitudes or develop better management procedures. Learning-based change is more likely to occur through discussions and experimentation by a working group representing different perspectives of organizational problems and needs.

The Facilitator

If an organization is open to changes, the process can be accelerated and made more systematic through the work of a "facilitator." In the case of the Southeast Asian social forestry programs, facilitators have played a catalytic role in the establishment of problem-solving working groups. The facilitator, whether from a forestry organization, university, nongovernment agency, or donor organization, needs to be sympathetic both to the agency's objectives and the problems experienced by forest communities. The facilitator should know the policy and procedural issues facing the agency, ideally from extensive discussions with both a cross-section of agency staff and the communities whom forest policies and procedures affect.

Before Phase 1, the facilitator's role is to learn the perceptions of agency staff regarding their organization's goals, procedures, and problems. Through these discussions, a facilitator can identify key staff who are concerned about procedural inefficiencies and agency-community conflicts and who are interested in seeing them changed. Often such individuals have been lobbying on their own for some time but have met with limited success because there is no forum to discuss management issues and alternatives. Once such advocates of internal change have been identified, the facilitator can help them organize such forums and formulate problem-solving strategies.

The Southeast Asian experience suggests that concerned agency staff and outside resource persons, once found, can be brought together with the facilitator's help to exchange ideas directly. Small working groups allow for informal and substantive interactions. Before each meeting it is helpful for the facilitator to meet group members individually to discuss issues on the agenda. This process of "groundworking" is useful because it allows meeting participants to arrive with similar expectations regarding issues to be addressed. The agenda should be structured to help the group reach a consensus about the nature and sources of management problems and outline the action strategy they might use. The structure of the meeting should encourage informal discussions and allow participants to speak from their own knowledge and experience rather than as representatives of institutional policies or ideological views.

Key Insiders

Key insiders are the members of the organization who formally represent the change process to the outside world, and it is they who must build a coalition for change among their agency colleagues. They are the ones who best understand their agency, its problems, and how ideas for improvements can be effectively integrated into existing procedures and policies. They must be risk-takers, but also respected as knowledgeable, loyal members of their agency. Senior officials can play an important role by creating an environment conducive to open discussion of policies and procedures; however, it is the mid-level managers with more detailed knowledge of operational problems who carry the responsibility for developing new management strategies. In the case of the Southeast Asian social forestry working groups, the key figures lobbying for and creating participatory management systems were mid-level administrators. Many had, for some time, advocated greater flexibility in responding to the needs of forest communities. They had personal experience with past agency-community forestry projects and knew of the weaknesses of such efforts. They therefore viewed the working group as a way to accelerate the change process and provide it with more informed direction.

Outside Resource Persons

While committed agency professionals are essential in initiating change within an organization, outside perspectives are also important in illuminating problems and developing solutions. Forestry agencies can seek the views of university-based researchers, private-sector professionals, and nongovernment development practitioners from a range of backgrounds, but they may have difficulty involving such individuals if they have never had a prolonged association with them or if they distrust them for past criticism. Facilitators can be helpful in bringing together outside advisors and concerned agency staff. Single meetings are usually insufficient to improve understanding on either side; experience with social forestry programs suggests that it is close collaboration on long-term field programs that establishes trust among working group members.

The Southeast Asian social forestry programs indicated that outside resource persons often need time to understand the organizational problems and constraints faced by the agency. To assist in formulating micropolicies and procedures conducive to community-oriented activities, university-based scientists need to understand the inner workings of forestry organizations, their actors, rules, goals, and operating systems. A sympathetic, constructive approach to the agency is often effective: it enables the agency, just as the agency must enable the community, to develop new management capabilities.

Nongovernment organizations (NGOs) can also contribute to building new participatory management systems in forest organizations, yet few are able to respond effectively when social forestry activities begin. Many environmental NGOs are suspicious of the objectives of forest bureaucracies, while community development NGOs usually have little understanding of the agency context or how it can be improved. Further, few NGOs have experience in combining community organizing, agroforestry technologies, and land-use planning methods to develop processes to help villages create effective forest management systems.

Consequently, there is a need to improve problem solving both in forestry organizations and among university researchers and NGO groups. Individuals from these groups usually need to meet repeatedly with foresters and forest communities to achieve some common understanding of the issues and possible strategies. In Southeast Asia, some early working group members left in frustration, but others continued to try to find some common ground for collaboration, and became more effective as their knowledge of the issues and alternatives grew. University participants in diagnostic research programs were able to gain a new understanding of agency-village conflicts and insights into their resolution, while contributing to the programs by devising appropriate community profiling methods and documenting conditions in a range of forest communities.

Some NGOs with experience in training community development workers were able to help agency project staff improve social forestry training by introducing new ways to create a more open learning environment in the classroom and the field. Confidence in working group collaboration grew among the members as individuals found ways to contribute to the program. These groups learned that while there were no "experts" with prepackaged solutions to forest management problems in either the agency, the university, or the NGO community, working groups can build capacity to respond to management problems.

ESTABLISHING WORKING GROUPS

Bureaucratic change is inhibited by a number of factors: Staff who advocate change are often scattered in different parts of the organization; hierarchy restricts procedural and policy change to only the most senior officials; organization staff with the authority to initiate change are usually so busy with routine matters that they have little time to reflect or take action on deep-seated management problems. As a result, a way is needed to bring concerned members of an organization together in an open atmosphere to discuss problems in an unhurried manner. The working group can provide such an atmosphere.[10]

When the Java Social Forestry Working Group first gathered in 1984, agency staff, in their opening remarks, let the participants know that the organization's problems could be discussed frankly. The meeting was structured to allow participants to break up into discussion groups, each focusing on a particular forest management context. Senior Indonesian ecologists and sociologists were interspersed among the groups to provide the foresters with additional perspectives and information and to raise policy questions and encourage greater candor. As a result, early in the program an atmosphere conducive to frank discussion and cooperative problem solving emerged. This meeting marked the beginning of a process of change initiated by a coalition of mid-level managers. The action plan that was produced recommended diagnostic research to examine forest land conflicts and was forwarded to the Minister of Forestry, who ratified it. This official approval gave the working group further authority to pursue their program.

The formation of the Java Social Forestry Working Group is not unlike what occurred in the Philippines. In the mid-1970s, the Bureau of Forest Development (BFD; recently renamed the Forest Management Bureau) was concerned over the rapid deforestation of upland forest areas due to growing numbers of lowland migrants moving into the upper watersheds. To improve forest land-use management and reduce conflicts between upland communities and lowland migrants, the BFD established a policy of recognizing the rights of occupants of state lands and involving forest communities in managing upland areas.[11] The problem was how to effectively institute the new policy. Because the BFD had limited staff and experience to develop participatory forest management systems with communities, a facilitator from the Ford Foundation initiated discussions with universities and NGOs to support experimentation and research in this area. In 1981, the BFD Upland Development Working Group was created, drawing in these outside resource persons from local universities and non-government rural development organizations. Over the next five years, the working group directed the development of a number of innovative approaches to community forest management through a series of pilot activities. By 1986, the group realized the need to develop working groups at the regional level that could direct the expansion of social forestry activities in local provinces.

The philosophy of both the Indonesian and Philippine groups is to encourage members to participate openly as concerned individuals, rather than as representatives of institutions. Experience suggests that the working groups whose members are appointed and which operate in a more conventional bureaucratic fashion are less successful in stimulating an open dialogue and a commitment from their members.

In some working groups, membership changed as new participants entered and old members left because of their available time and interest. In Indonesia, the membership of the Java Social Forestry Working Group went through a series of changes as the program moved from diagnostic research to pilot projects to expansion. During the research phase there was a heavy representation of university program directors from institutions supplying masters and doctoral researchers. Some of these individuals left the group and were replaced by NGO rural development practitioners as the program moved into the implementation period. As the program expanded, new members were added from the agency itself. While this contributed specialized expertise for the succeeding phase, the group also partially lost touch with what it had learned during the diagnostic research period.

Generally, social forestry working groups in Southeast Asia found that sharing common expectations and objectives helped working groups to function effectively. Over time, most of these groups established an increasingly open, relaxed approach to problem solving, but they are also encountering problems along the way. The Jakarta-based Indonesian Outer Islands Working Group, which is responsible for pilot projects scattered in the remote islands of Kalimantan, Sulawesi, and Irian Jaya, found it difficult to maintain close contact with distant field programs. Because high air transportation costs prohibited frequent visits to meet with provincial working groups and field staff, pilot projects developed slowly and misunderstandings between national and local forestry offices occurred. In

Irian Jaya, nearly 2,500 miles from Jakarta, it was only after a local NGO took an active leadership role in the local pilot project (almost two years after its initiation) that the provincial working group became more involved in running the field program. The logistical problems confronted by the Outer Island Working Group greatly constrained both the progress of the pilots and the ability of agency and nonagency participants to learn from the field activities. This contrasts sharply with the experience of the Java group, which dealt with a single island with a well-developed communication and transportation infrastructure.

In Thailand, the Royal Forestry Department seems to be responding effectively to the need for both a national working group to monitor the overall program and local working groups to supervise regionally based projects. This is facilitated by capable social science and agricultural research groups, based at Khon Kaen University in the northeast and Chiang Mai University in the north, which have strengthened the local working groups' ability to plan and analyze their program needs.

In summary, all of the region's working groups have had their successes and problems and their experiences offer many lessons. Meetings need to be regularly scheduled with clear agendas. Membership should be based on the interest of individuals and their ability to contribute relevant skills and knowledge to learning and problem solving. While there is a need to maintain a national working group, local working groups are also important in facilitating learning and in implementing pilot and expansion projects. To the extent permitted by the host agency, programmatic decisions should reflect a group consensus after thorough discussion. Whereas agencies generally follow rigid time schedules, working groups need to revise the timing of programs continually to respond to opportunities and problems as they arise while adapting new planning and implementation processes to agency routines. Flexibility allows pilot project planners to synchronize field activities with the agency site-selection procedures, budgeting process, and reforestation planting schedule. By attempting to anticipate the scheduling requirements of evolving diagnostic, planning, and implementation procedures, the groups are more likely to integrate these new processes into the mainstream of agency activities.

LEARNING FROM THE FIELD

The learning process paradigm uses the working group as a center of learning during the agency's transformation. The group must develop new paradigms and processes that allow government organizations to work with communities as partners in forest management. How does the working group learn? Although group members bring with them a great deal of relevant experience and may have considerable understanding of broader management problems, they tend to come from urban middle-class backgrounds and consequently may have had little first-hand knowledge of conditions in rural forest communities. The group must establish communication with the field and find ways to learn from villagers and field staff.

Most of the region's social forestry working groups began by fielding diagnostic research teams that examined the interaction of the agency and communities in forest areas and the sources of conflict between them. The working groups, whose members may lack the time for extended fieldwork, could then meet with and learn from the field study teams. In Thailand, Java, and the Philippines, case studies provided systematic documentation of management problems. The research both deepened the working group's understanding of the weaknesses of existing management practices and bolstered the agency's commitment to management reorientation and organizational change. The Southeast Asian social forestry working groups developed three major methods for learning from their pilot projects. The first involved the routine review of field reports. In the case of the Philippines, special process documenters were placed in pilot project villages to keep daily accounts of the activities of the community organizers and foresters, and records of their interactions, problems, and needs. These documents, forwarded to the working group for monthly review, offer some of the most thorough reporting to date of any social forestry project's implementation. Analyzing the vast quantity of information generated, however, required a large amount of time from experienced staff members.

In Indonesia, the community organizers simplified the monitoring process by preparing their own reports that were presented by their field supervisors to the working group. These reports, however, tended to focus on the achievement of planting targets and tree survival rates and provided little information on the implementation process and the roles of the community and forestry field staff. Consequently, the working group learned little about procedural and attitudinal constraints to better community participation. Far more useful data was collected by a volunteer attached to the working group who periodically visited project locations for a few days or a week to document community reactions to the program, local agency support for the activity, and procedural problems. To get better information, the working group is attempting to establish a special documentation team to acquire more detailed information on the agency intervention process and the agroeconomic aspects of new forest management systems. In particular, the group needs to determine whether the new agroforestry systems are providing community participants with sufficient income to meet their economic needs and maintain their long-term commitment to the management of the state forest lands.

Process-focused field reports are important in informing the working group of progress and problems in pilot areas, but not all group members have the time to study the reports before meetings. Group leaders therefore need to highlight key issues for discussion and decision making. Further, project documentation and analysis must focus not only on what is happening in the field, but on issues and problems confronted by forest agency administrators in implementing new participatory strategies.

A second way for working group members to better understand field problems is to involve field staff in meetings. This helps to establish an upward flow of information and focuses discussions on field-level problems. However, junior staff may fear they will be branded as disloyal complainers and that their careers may suffer if they frankly discuss field and organizational problems. Incentives need to be created to encourage younger staff to help identify problems and solutions. Once the precedent has been set, frank discussions between junior and senior members can be easier, improving problem identification and communications with the field.

A third learning technique used by some working groups involves bringing senior members into the field to talk with local staff and the communities. Many senior foresters make regular field visits, but they tend to focus on technical problems related to forest management. Field visits conducted by the working groups encouraged the discussion of the social, economic, political, and organizational issues that arise in collaborating with communities in formulating new joint management systems. There is always the danger, however, that field visits will result in little more than what Chambers describes as "rural tourism."[12] To learn from field visits, visitors must have opportunities and time to listen to community members and local field staff. It is also useful to identify key issues or problems requiring clarification before the visit. Staying several days and nights in the community affords further learning opportunities. If experienced individuals are available to help coordinate the efforts, visitors may attempt to conduct systematic data collection using the growing body of methodologies covered under rapid rural appraisal research techniques.[13]

Field visits for community group leaders and field staff can also be an effective way to transmit learning between field sites and forest districts. Solutions to problems encountered in one pilot project site are often apparent in other locations. Aside from gaining information that could help solve implementation problems, visitors to neighboring areas may be encouraged to find that they are not alone in struggling with management problems.

MANAGING EXPANSION

Diffusing learning throughout the organization becomes increasingly important as programs move through the pilot stage into routine implementation of new policies and practices. Working groups may find themselves under pressure to educate additional agency staff when social forestry activities are rapidly expanded. In Java and the Philippines, pressure to expand was felt early in the program. While the working groups were successfully completing Phase I diagnostic research and were still struggling with Phase II pilot projects to learn how to implement new participatory strategies effectively, senior officials were pushing programs into Phase III expansion. As a result, important procedural changes and attitudinal shifts among staff had not yet occurred and many questions remained concerning the capacity of the forestry agencies to effectively work with communities in organizing management systems and developing appropriate agroforestry technologies on a national scale. Field staff implementing the expanding social forestry activities often find local administrators poorly informed about the program's objectives and the new procedures they entail. This unconducive environment often results in misunderstanding and limits community participation, a key ingredient for the success of the new strategy.

In Indonesia, both the Outer Island and Java working groups are trying to reorient internal staff by holding meetings for senior officials to update them on the new micro-policies and procedures being implemented in the pilot projects and the expansion areas. While these meetings are helpful, there are thousands of individuals at various levels of the organizations, even excluding those not directly involved in the program, who need to be informed. One-day meetings are usually insufficient to clarify the complexities of the new program or change staff attitudes. As a result, such information campaigns may largely fail to overcome the confusion and suspicion these programs incur. Despite pressures to keep these programs moving, time must be given to developing systematic in-service training programs.

Mid-level staff also need to be supportive and well informed regarding the program's objectives. In Java, the working group's agency coordinator arranged workshops in each province to discuss the pilot project and, later, to explain expansion strategies to regional staff confused about the new initiative. In some cases, regional staff were skeptical because the concept of collaborating with rural communities on a equal basis had no foundation or precedent in forest management traditions. They were also sometimes suspicious and alienated by centrally initiated efforts to change procedures.

When the Java program began, there was a close collaboration between central office staff and field workers that by-passed the intermediary levels of the organization. This allowed senior officials to be linked directly with the problems in the rural community, but it also threatened the positions and roles of mid-level officials. It was therefore crucial to integrate staff at these levels into the learning process during the pilot project phase. Once new management systems are adopted as routine procedures, it is the mid-level managers who will supervise them. To do this effectively, they need not only to understand the new operating style, but to support its adoption. Meetings with regionally based staff made it clear that if the new approach to community involvement in forest land management were to succeed, the organization would need to provide both training in new skills and operating methods and incentives and an environment that motivated staff to support the effort.

The largest group of agency staff work at the field level and generally they have the least formal education. Yet this is the group that most directly influences the way rural communities view the agency. Diagnostic studies conducted throughout the region indicate that for decades local foresters have made their own informal agreements with villagers to respond to each group's distinctive needs for fuelwood, fodder, and labor. While such arrangements represent a useful response to local needs on both sides, they also present opportunities for corruption. Alliances between forest rangers and local elites are not uncommon and work to the disadvantage of poor members of the community. Social forestry programs stressing equity and responsiveness to the needs of rural poor can often threaten such informal local arrangements. It is therefore important that forestry field staff who help communities develop forest management systems should not be subject to such conflicts of interest. In part this problem can be overcome through careful staff selection and training.

Although forestry agencies will always require field staff specialists in technical fields and forest protection, it is apparent in each program that a large cadre of community organizers will be needed to transfer management authority to communities on a national scale. To facilitate the reorientation of a sizable proportion of forestry field staff, the curriculum of field staff training centers should be revised. Some working groups are currently developing new course materials using some of the teaching strategies developed by NGO community development specialists for the early pilot project staff training programs. In some cases NGO trainers are beginning to work with agency teaching staff to compile new curricula.

As expansion continues, individuals whose interests and personalities make them suitable community organizers (COs) must be carefully selected from existing field staff. Staff selection for social forestry programs often seems to occur randomly; in other cases district foresters select individuals who are not otherwise occupied or, where training opportunities are attractive, individuals with greater seniority. To involve the most appropriate individuals in social forestry activities, the characteristics, skills, and personality types associated with successful community organizing need to be identified. For example, pilot project documentation reveals that field workers are more effective if they have knowledge of local language, an ability to empathize with community needs, and a capacity to enjoy rural life and appreciate traditional knowledge of agriculture and the environment. The key lesson learned to date is that not everyone is well suited to be a CO, and while many forestry agency members are, there are many who are not. Careful selection and training of COs could make a national program much more successful.

While most agencies are not financially able to hire new staff to implement social forestry programs, additional staff can be added on a limited basis as new positions open up through retirement. Unfortunately, many of the agencies in Southeast Asia have restrictions that make it difficult to hire men without backgrounds in forestry or women from any discipline. In Java, women COs with social work backgrounds proved to be some of the most effective staff in forming forest land management groups and involving them in the planning and implementation of new agroforestry management systems. Yet, while their contributions were well recognized and appreciated by agency project staff, their sex and disciplinary background prohibit any professional career in the State Forest Corporation and they are gradually leaving the program. Given the interdisciplinary nature of social forestry programming and the mixed gender of rural communities, agency barriers to hiring women and individuals with alternative perspectives, experiences, and skills need to be removed in order to broaden the ability of forestry organizations to relate to forest communities.

Aside from in-service training and hiring, a range of other staff-related decisions must be made as social forestry programs expand. New staffing roles will need to be formalized through new job descriptions. The organization must also consider new criteria and incentives to evaluate and motivate foresters who play new roles within the agency. Forestry staff who work as community organizers cannot have their performance assessed on the same basis as forest production managers. Staff carrying out new tasks should have their own support and incentive system within the organization. Consequently, as the agency expands the community forest management systems, it must begin standardizing the processes, procedures, job descriptions, and schedules affecting program staff.

At some point the elite of an organization must decide whether or not a new program is meeting the organizational need for which it was designed. Because there are few studies of the reasons some programs are retained and others are allowed to die, it is hard to generalize regarding the correlates of successful expansion. There are many cases of successful rural development pilot projects, but few pilots ever evolve into successful national programs. One reason for this may be the artificial environments in which they are developed. Pilot projects are frequently directed and encouraged by highly motivated individuals with considerable administrative flexibility, greater staffing intensity, and financial resources. They are not subject to the leadership, financial, and organizational constraints that characterize implementing institutions. Those constraints can make it difficult to fit the strategies and processes developed in the action research communities into the routine workings of the national agency. Further, policies and practices that may be politically acceptable in a pilot project may not be acceptable to policy makers as strategies for national implementation. Therefore, it is important for early experimentation with alternative management systems to be carried out under normal field conditions and operating procedures, with consideration given to methods of phasing in more liberal components as the policy environment permits.

Aside from financial and staffing problems, political factors may also influence the expansion of social forestry strategies. Program administrators need to be aware of the political arena in which their program is being implemented and the forces that may attempt to manipulate it at the national and local levels. While future political pressures or events cannot always be anticipated, it is helpful for working groups to consider options for program development that could be used in a changing political environment. For example, after the Aquino government came to power in the Philippines, members of the Uplands Working Group were able to channel much of their experience into a reformulation of land-tenure and uplands management policies. This also accelerated the formal adoption of policies more supportive of participatory management of forest resources.

In planning the expansion of pilot activities, it is important to coordinate the rate of policy change with the capacity to implement. If, for example, a new policy to transfer local forest land management authority to communities does not receive local government support, rural people and local staff may become frustrated and the agency may lose credibility. The Irian Jaya social forestry project is such a case. When community organizers and tribal leaders began discussing the establishment of a community-managed buffer area between neighboring ancestral land and a national park, tribal leaders were generally supportive. However, after the provincial working group failed to meet for over a year and the provincial governor delayed signing the letter of decision supporting the program, community and field staff commitment to the project diminished rapidly. After the policy decision to support the activity was made, staff enthusiasm began to return.

Senior officials may even stop an agency's field program if it begins to experiment with strategies that are inconsistent with policy. This occurred during the Java social forestry project when field staff and farmers began planting more fruit trees on state forest land than senior agency officials felt appropriate. The COs were instructed to reduce fruit tree planting for a time, until the policy was reversed. The challenge for working groups is to assess the rate and direction of policy change and adjust new micro-policies, procedures, and staff capacity for each phase of the program, while preparing for the successive stage.

The appropriate speed for program expansion and transitions from one phase of organizational reorientation to the next depends on the agency's capacity to change its procedures and orientation and the complexity of the reforms intended. If a program moves very quickly, the quality of participatory management systems may fall far short of expectations, which may lead planners to lose interest in the strategy and even the program. If the change process moves too slowly, however, the program will lose momentum, and in some cases collapse or become marginalized and unable to influence mainstream management practices. Experience in Southeast Asia indicates that, because forest management problems had often reached a state of national crisis by the time alternative management systems were being developed, policy makers often found themselves under pressure to expand social forestry programs rapidly at the first sign of success.

In the case of the Java social forestry program, the working group suggested focusing initial expansion in a few forest districts where population pressures, unemployment, and vast areas of deforested land indicated participatory management systems had the greatest potential. By concentrating the projects in a few districts rather than scattering them throughout the island's provinces, project staff hoped to concentrate their limited supervisory and training resources. Later the proposed plan of clustered expansion was not accepted due to perceived internal political needs to provide all forest districts equal access to the new program. In the Philippines and Thailand, similar concepts of regional, sequential expansion are being explored.

CONSTRAINTS TO ORGANIZATIONAL CHANGE

The reorientation of any organization is a long-term process requiring continuity and stability within the agency. Such programs are vulnerable to the withdrawal of political support by senior officials, the cutting of budgets by the agency, termination of a project by a donor, and the loss of critical staff and working group members through rotation, retirement, or death. In a large government bureaucracy, significant procedural and attitudinal changes resulting from a learning process will often take four to five years to gain momentum, and possibly a decade or more to have a broad impact on the organization. Although it is impossible to ensure a program's security in any organizational environment, certain actions may help to sustain change strategies. A facilitator may be able to broaden the program's financial support base by acquiring funding from a number of sources, including donor agencies or other divisions within the organization. Keeping support costs low and field implementation expenses in line with an agency's routine operating budget minimizes the need for project subsidies. Even if subsidies are slashed, routine budgets can keep such programs going.

The working group can also help prevent a program from losing key personnel by diversifying the leadership and increasing the number of informed resource persons involved in the program. The working group, once a program is in progress or during its planning, can urge the host organization to lift staff rotation policies on key participants without damage to their careers. The problems of staff rotation and the erosion of personnel need careful attention at all program levels. Learning takes time and stability, and much time can be lost by the repeated orientation of new staff to a program. As Frances F. Korten notes, there are strong centrifugal forces pulling a working group apart, including the different disciplinary perspectives of its members and the agendas of their respective institutions.[14] It may largely be the membership's belief in the endeavor and their shared vision that rural communities have an important role in forest land management that holds a working group together. Rotation may not always undermine a program, however; experience with some working groups shows that senior agency officials who were indifferent or only mildly supportive of organizational change may be replaced through rotation or retirement by more supportive, dynamic individuals. Further, as experienced social foresters grow in number and gain seniority within their organization, they will be increasingly able to move into more influential positions through rotation.

SUMMARY OF THE CHANGE PROCESS

Assisting government bureaucracies to make systematic transitions from being resource managers to helping communities develop resource management capabilities is a complex process. Little systematic work has been done in this area either in Western countries or in the developing world. In recent years, however, our understanding of ways natural resource management agencies in Southeast Asia can learn to change has increased. Experience suggests that establishing working groups as forums for learning is an important step. Working groups can be a nexus of open discussions and experimentation to create new methods for sharing resource management responsibilities with rural people. Working groups linked to field-level action research programs have effectively channeled information about rural conditions, needs, and opportunities into the heart of conservative, centralized agencies, giving them new perspectives on problems and possible solutions. In the rest of Part II, tools and techniques used by working groups to develop community management systems for forest areas will be discussed.

NOTES

1. Ministry of Forestry. 1986. *Forestry Indonesia: 1985/86.* Jakarta, p. 17.

2. IIED. 1985. *A Review of Policies Affecting the Sustainable Development of Forest Lands in Indonesia,* vol. 2, Jakarta, p. 86.

3. Republic of Indonesia. 1983. *Nota Keuangan dan Rancangan Anggaran Pendapatan dan Belanja Negara Tahun 1983/84.* Jakarta, p. 230.

4. Castro, Charles P., ed. 1984. *Uplands and Uplanders: In Search for New Perspectives.* Proceedings of the First National Conference on Research in the Uplands: April 11–13, 1983. Quezon City, Philippines: Bureau of Forest Development, p. 168.

5. Korten, David C. 1980. "Community Organization and Rural Development: A Learning Process Approach." *Public Administration Review* (September/October), pp. 480–511.

6. Chambers, Robert. 1983. *Rural Development: Putting the Last First.* London: Longman, pp. 210–211.

7. Hage, Jerald, and Michael Aiken. 1970. *Social Change in Complex Organizations.* New York: Random House, pp. 92–93.

8. Korten, David C. "Community Organization and Rural Development: A Learning Process Approach," pp. 19–21.

9. Frances F. Korten provides an insightful descriptive analysis of the process through which the National Irrigation Administration of the Philippines began to transform its organization from being a primary implementor of projects to one enabling communities to acheive development goals. Korten, Frances F. 1988. "The Working Group as a Catalyst for Organizational Change," in Korten and Siy (ed.) *Transforming a Bureaucracy.* West Hartford, Conn.: Kumarian Press.

10. Ibid., pp. 3–4.

11. Chion-Javier, Elena Ma. 1987. *Building People into Forestry: Field Experiences in Bureaucratic Reorientation.* Manila: Research Center De La Salle University.

12. Chambers. *Rural Development: Putting the Last First,* p. 18.

13. A recent publication by Khon Kaen University provides a wealth of information on the conceptual basis for RRA, a range of methodologies and tools, and case studies. Khon Kaen University. 1987. *Proceedings of the 1985 International Conference on Rapid Rural Appraisal.* Khon Kaen, Thailand: Rural Systems Research and Farming Systems Research Projects. For copies of this volume please contact: Dr. Terd Charoenwatana, FSR and RSR Projects, Faculty of Agriculture, Khon Kaen University, Khon Kaen 40002, Thailand.

14. Korten, Frances F. "The Working Group as a Catalyst for Organizational Change," p. 78.

CHAPTER SIX

Diagnostic Tools for Social Forestry

Jefferson Fox

THIS CHAPTER DESCRIBES ways to facilitate the exchange of information between forest users and forest managers. The methods discussed are semistructured interviewing, aerial photographs, and sketch maps. These tools provide a basis for communicating with users and for soliciting community participation in forest management. The use of these tools is illustrated with examples from social forestry programs in Indonesia.

Conflicts over state forests are frequently caused by misunderstandings between the farm families who use forest lands and the foresters responsible for forest management. The farmers and foresters are little prepared by their experience to understand the problems, goals, and perspectives of the other side. The first step in any successful social forestry program is to establish communication between the people who use state forests and the people who manage them.

If foresters and farmers are to communicate, the onus is on the forester to start the process by understanding farming practices. This includes knowing the crops grown, the place, time, and methods for planting and harvesting, how the products are disposed of, and how income and other benefits are shared. In addition, understanding how forest management plans affect different members of the community requires some knowledge of village tenure systems. Understanding patterns of conflict and cooperation within and among villages requires some knowledge of historical land-use practices, while sensitivity to local priorities requires some knowledge of farmers' perception of environmental problems. To increase farmers' involvement in managing degraded lands, social forestry programs often give local inhabitants access to, and some control over, public lands. This requires that farmers and foresters agree which lands are public. Without an awareness of these factors, foresters may fail to appreciate the roles played by different elements in highly specialized production systems, and thus be forced to proceed by guesswork and arbitrary assumptions.

As a consequence, foresters need to know how private and public lands are used and need to view land-use practices in their spatial context. Knowing which practices are found where, and how location affects these practices, is as vital as knowing what the practices are and who owns the land. Because social forestry programs have a practical rather than theoretical goal, it is important to see this process not as an "academic" exercise but as a process whereby farmers and foresters learn about each other, develop a foundation for cooperation, and begin negotiating on the design and implementation of forest management plans. Currently, foresters generally lack training in skills and techniques for understanding farming practices and for establishing dialogues with rural people. Diagnostic tools are methods for meeting these objectives. Semistructured interviewing techniques help foresters obtain information on existing farming systems, and aerial photographs and sketch maps are useful for placing these systems in a spatial context. Together, these tools provide a basis for establishing a dialogue with farmers and increasing community participation in the management process.

THE TOOLS: SEMISTRUCTURED INTERVIEWS, AERIAL PHOTOGRAPHS, AND SKETCH MAPS

Semistructured Interviews

The best way to learn about local conditions is to ask local people. In a semistructured interview, an interviewer seeks to learn from a farmer or key informant about village life and land-use practices and why these practices have been adopted. A good interview appears to be nothing more than a friendly conversation, but in reality it is carefully structured by the interviewer. The "art" of semistructured interviewing lies in establishing rapport with the interviewee and in sensing the proper balance between open-ended questions and directed inquiry. Semistructured interviewing is a cyclical process planned to gain and assess information as quickly as possible and is based on the assumption that questions and hypotheses can be progressively revised as new information is generated. The major difference between a semistructured interview and a formal survey is the use of a list of topics rather than a carefully prepared questionnaire. Identification of the initial list of topics relies on the researchers' experience—their ability to cast a wide net in the early rounds of questioning.

Social forestry programs in Indonesia have used semistructured interviewing to gain information on the physical and socio-economic environments, agricultural and horticultural practices, livestock management, and the use of forest land. Once an interviewee is chosen and is placed at ease, questions are asked in a conversational format with the understanding that the interviewer is interested in learning about the village and villager at hand. Questions are geared to probe the subject at hand and to lead to an increased understanding of this subject. A set of questions based on who, what, where, when, why, and how helps to establish the basic situation. The interviewer must listen closely to what is said, challenge answers, ask for back-up details, seek increased depth and specification, and refer forward and backward in time.[1] Quick notes can usually be taken on names, quantities, varieties, for example, but notes should not be allowed to slow the interview and should not be taken at all if they appear to disturb the farmer. A well-conducted semistructured interview is an intense and tiring experience.

Interviewers often begin with key informants who can provide information about the broader system beyond their own experience. Key informants in the village include local leaders, school teachers, and local merchants who know the problems at hand and are willing to speak out. Protocol usually requires that these people be contacted first; but it is also generally easier to interview these people as they tend to be the wealthier, better educated, and more powerful members of a village. To offset status and gender biases introduced by key informants, it is important to do follow-up interviews with small farmers, landless laborers, and women representing different views and experiences. In talks with individual respondents, interviewers seek to learn about a person's knowledge and behavior, and not about what he or she thinks of the knowledge and behavior of others. Individual respondents are chosen to represent a cross-section of the village population. These respondents may be chosen through chance encounters, but an effort must be made to obtain all views by seeking out at least three different perspectives (triangulation).[2]

Group interviews have several advantages. They are useful for learning about natural resource patterns, the spatial distribution of land-use practices, and the history of land use. They are also instructive about issues that are common knowledge within a village but which a single respondent may not want to discuss with outsiders. Groups need to be kept small; usually no more than six to eight people can be included productively. Group interviews are not useful for acquiring information that group members want to keep secret from one another.

Another important aspect of a semistructured interview is direct observation. Chambers states that one of the dangers of rapid assessments is being misled by myth.[3] People often have beliefs about their activities and environment that do not correspond with reality. Consequently, direct observation is extremely important for supporting interview findings and for generating on-the-spot questions. This means, of course, that the interviewer must allow time for walking to the farmers' fields or the forest, and it may be necessary to time the interview according to the activity of interest.

Other conceptual tools are also useful for soliciting, recording, and correlating information. These include crop calendars, labor calendars, activity-sequence calendars, and animal-feed calendars.[4] Aerial photographs and sketch maps, treated more thoroughly in the next section, have traditionally been used for mapping land cover or earth surface patterns but can also be used to facilitate interviews with villagers and farmers about the land-use practices reflected in the mapped patterns.

After the interviews are finished, the interviewers compile the results to form a description of farm and forest practices. It is important to remember, however, that in conducting individual and group interviews the interviewer establishes a relationship with the local community that becomes the basis for incorporating the community into the design and implementation of forest management programs.

Aerial Photographs

Aerial photographs provide a fast and efficient way to collect information about topographic patterns such as settlements, land cover, and deforestation. Delineating and understanding the land-use practices that lie behind these patterns, however, can be difficult. What factors cause some settlements to be nucleated and others to be dispersed? Why are some forests degraded and others in pristine condition? Such questions must be answered if the photographic data are to be useful for social forestry projects. To answer these questions, the photointerpreter needs either a first-hand understanding of the area under study or the close cooperation of local informants. Because it is impossible for photointerpreters to have an intimate understanding of all areas in which they work, it has become increasingly clear that involving local informants in the photointerpretation process is important.

The ability of uneducated farmers to interpret aerial photographs has been documented by a number of researchers, but aerial photographs differ in many respects.[5] Among other factors, they can be distinguished by scale, film type, and angle of photography. For aerial photographs to play a role in social forestry programs, it is important to know how these factors affect their interpretation by local informants. Scale refers to the relationship between one unit of distance on a photograph and the number of units on the ground. Scale is usually described as small (greater than 1:50,000), medium (1:10,000 to 1:50,000), or large (less than 1:10,000). Larger-scale photographs provide greater detail, an important factor in many social forestry programs. Smaller-scale photographs make it easier to understand the site's relation to the broader landscape.

Film type refers to the sensitivity of film to incoming energy. Aerial photographs are normally made with black-and-white panchromatic film, color film, black-and-white infrared film, or false-color infrared film. Black-and-white panchromatic film, long the standard film for aerial photographs, is sensitive to energy from the ultraviolet and visible portions of the spectrum. Color film is sensitive to the visible spectrum, and infrared film is sensitive to both visible energy and reflected infrared energy. The advantage of color over black-and-white film is that the human eye can discriminate many more shades of color than it can tones of gray. Infrared film is usually used when it is important to discriminate healthy green vegetation from sick or stressed plants.[6]

Angle of photography refers to the angle between the ground surface and the camera axis. Vertical photographs are taken with the camera axis vertical to the surface of the earth. This positioning minimizes spatial distortions; hence, vertical photographs are valuable for making high-quality maps. When viewed with a stereoscope, aerial photographs with a 50 to 60 percent overlap can be seen in three dimensions, making it possible to plot contour lines accurately. Professional aerial photographers are required to make vertical photographs; consequently, these products tend to be quite expensive. Oblique photographs result when the angle between the camera axis and the ground surface is not vertical. This angle distorts the spatial positioning of objects located off the center of the photographs and seriously limits the use of oblique photographs for mapping purposes. However, since the position of the camera is not important, oblique photographs can be taken with hand-held cameras from the windows of a small aircraft. They are therefore relatively easy and inexpensive to acquire and thus ideal for monitoring purposes.

Aerial photographs can be used as interviewing tools for soliciting and recording spatial information. An interviewer begins by placing the farmer at ease and explaining the photographs. The interviewer then proceeds to locate a few well-known objects on the photographs and asks the farmer to do likewise. Once the farmer demonstrates familiarity with the photographs, the interviewer proceeds to inquire about land-use practices on both private and public lands. Responses are recorded on clear plastic sheets covering the photographs. Before the interview, the interviewer prepares a list of topics to be covered but, as in all informal interviews, formal questionnaires are avoided.

Sketch Maps

Although aerial photographs are an excellent source of information about land cover and spatial relationships, they are generally unavailable or not available at a scale useful to social forestry programs. Sketch mapping is an alternative way to approximate the spatial aspects of land-use practices.[7] On the largest-scale topographic maps available, project sites are located from identifiable physical features such as road intersections or major river bends, or from compass readings on recognizable peaks. The area of interest is then enlarged to a working scale (1:5,000–1:10,000). The enlargement may be done on a copying machine or by overlaying the original map with a system of grid-cells. Enlarged grid-cells are drawn on a separate piece of paper, and the map is redrawn cell-by-cell at the enlarged scale. Local assistants help the social forester to identify and draw physical objects (roads, rivers, schools) and land cover on the enlarged map. This base map is then copied, and the copies used in interviews to record information about the land-use practices of local farmers.

CASE STUDIES: SOCIAL FORESTRY PROGRAMS IN INDONESIA

The Indonesian State Forest Corporation (SFC) and the Indonesian Ministry of Forestry are sponsoring, in collaboration with the Ford Foundation, a series of social forestry projects on the islands of Java, Sulawesi, Kalimantan, and Irian Jaya. These projects train social foresters and community organizers to work with villagers to identify land-use problems and to cooperate with local extension and forestry officials in solving these problems. The community organizers aim to acquire an understanding of land-use practices to help villagers identify appropriate production systems for forest lands and to help villagers design collaborative management plans acceptable to the forestry department. To achieve these objectives, community organizers use semistructured interviewing techniques, aerial photographs (both vertical and oblique), and sketch maps.

Case Study I: Sukatani

This study explored the usefulness of vertical photographs as interviewing tools. Community organizers interviewed farmers about their land-use practices and recorded the responses on clear plastic sheets attached to the top of the photographs. The photographs, which are available for all of Java with government approval, were useful for mapping precise locations, measuring areas, and determining the location and extent of land degradation problems. Sukatani, a village in the Puncak area of West Java, lies on the border of a newly established national park. Farmers in Sukatani traditionally collected wood and other forest products from land within the park. In the past several years, serious conflicts have developed between farmers in Sukatani and the SFC, the agency responsible for managing public forest lands on Java. In fact, farmers and foresters developed such hostile relations over problems with stolen firewood that foresters started carrying guns and making house-to-house searches. In response, the SFC established a social forestry program in Sukatani to seek a mutually acceptable solution to this conflict.

The community organizer in Sukatani began by acquiring recent (1981) medium-scale (1:30,000) false-color infrared photographs of the area. These photographs provided an excellent basis for mapping land cover and for interviewing villagers about their forest-use practices. Villagers had little difficulty in understanding these photographs despite their false color (vegetation appears red on false-color infrared film). From these interviews, the community organizer learned a great deal about the history of these forests, the places in the forest where most people collect firewood, why villagers do not use other forest lands, and the location of forest lands used by other villages. From this information, the community organizer identified the sites and causes of the most severe conflicts between the villagers and the foresters. Negotiations were then initiated between the villagers and the SFC for a mutually acceptable piece of land for development as a communal woodlot.

That vertical photographs are ideal for mapping purposes is well known. Locations can be mapped precisely, the area covered by any crop or village can be measured, and changes in land cover through time can be evaluated from photographs of different dates. Only recently, however, has it been recognized that if scale and film type are chosen correctly, farmers have little difficulty in understanding vertical photographs and can provide an interpreter with a wealth of information about the land-use practices that lie behind the land cover recorded on the photographs. For interviewing purposes, color photographs appear to be more useful than black-and-white, and large scales appear to be better than small scales. When vertical photographs are available from government mapping agencies or previous projects, their cost is relatively inexpensive; but if it is necessary to hire an agency to make these photographs, their cost can be prohibitive. Unfortunately, vertical photographs are often unavailable and, if available, permission from government agencies to purchase or borrow them may be difficult to obtain.

Case Study II: The Cyclops

The use of small-format oblique photographs for natural resource management has been well documented.[8] In the Cyclops project, an aircraft was rented and small-format oblique photographs were taken with a hand-held single-lens reflex camera to evaluate their usefulness in understanding land-use practices. Community organizers used these photographs to build a photomosaic of the study site and to interview farmers about the acceptability of alternative land management plans.

The Cyclops, a small and heavily forested mountain range, lies on the north coast of Irian Jaya (the Indonesian half of Papua New Guinea; see Figure 6.1). Isolated from the next mountain range by a broad expanse of swamp, the Cyclops hosts several endemic plant and animal species.

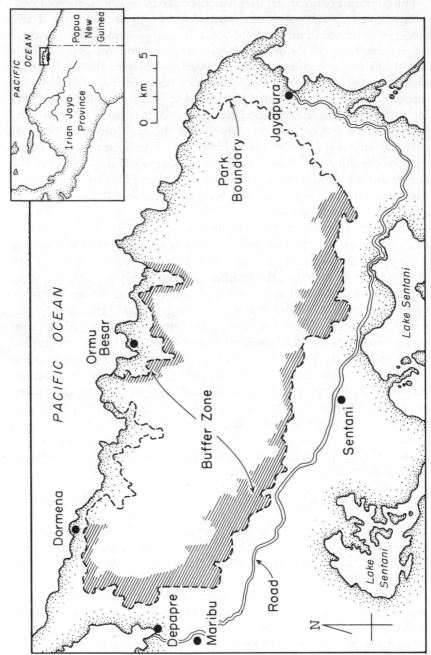

Figure 6.1. Cyclops Mountains Nature Preserve, Irian Jaya

At the eastern foot of the Cyclops lies Jayapura, the provincial capital of Irian Jaya. In the past decade, subsistence farmers moving closer to off-farm job opportunities in Jayapura and land speculators hoping to benefit from a building boom in the city have begun to deforest and degrade these mountains. In light of the potential value of the endemic species and because the Cyclops is the major watershed for Jayapura, the Indonesian government recently declared the Cyclops a nature preserve. The World Wildlife Fund (WWF) prepared a management plan for the preserve, and the Ford Foundation has been working in cooperation with the WWF and the Indonesian Forestry Department to implement this plan and to establish a community-managed buffer zone around the preserve.

Community organizers hoped to use existing medium-scale (1:20,000) black-and-white photographs of the area to determine a border acceptable to farmers and forestry officials. Photographs taken in 1959 show an area that until recently had been densely forested. Age, cloud cover, and a lack of recognizable features made it difficult for villagers to understand these photographs without considerable help. Given the poor quality of these vertical photographs, staff members chose to make oblique photographs of the nature preserve. The project rented a small plane at minimal cost from a local university and obtained permission from the authorities to fly over the preserve. The staff acquired locally available color-print film and developed the photographs in Jayapura. The resulting photographs ranged in scale from approximately 1:8,000 to 1:15,000. A forester prepared a photomosaic of the preserve providing the first up-to-date view of land-use practices around the preserve. This information helped community organizers to recognize key problem areas. A local photography studio enlarged (4x) the photographs of the study villages, and the community organizers used these enlargements in interviews with local farmers. In one village, community organizers used these photographs to discuss land-use practices with villagers and located swidden fields, sago palms, and fruit trees, as well as a rock quarry from which villagers historically obtained their rock axes. [Today, young men still use rock axes from this quarry as a bride price (mas kawin). Management plans will need to incorporate access to important cultural features such as the quarry if the nature preserve is to win acceptance among the local people.] Community organizers are currently using these photographs to collect information from farmers around the entire preserve. This information will help foresters establish the borders of the preserve and identify a zone on the periphery of the preserve for low-intensity use. A sketch map of land use and proposed use zones was made using the photographs in discussions with villagers (see Figure 6.2).

The value of oblique photographs for monitoring changes in land cover and for interviewing purposes is just beginning to be appreciated. Oblique photographs are relatively quick, inexpensive, and easy to make and are

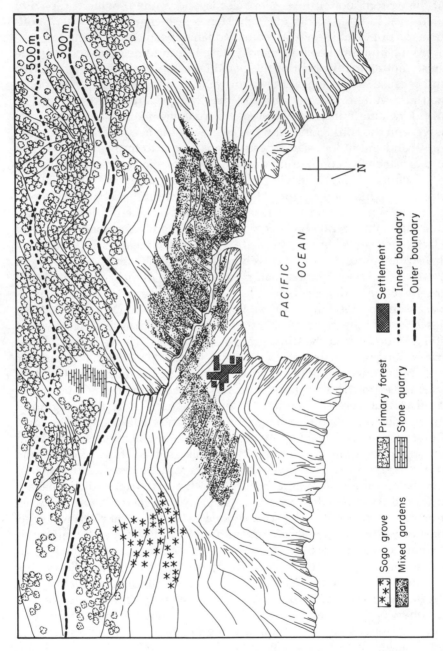

Figure 6.2. Sketch map of land use and proposed boundaries in Ormu Besar

very useful for collecting baseline data and monitoring changes in land-use practices. Once an airplane has been rented and the photographs acquired, the negatives can be developed and enlarged locally. Photomosaics can be made that provide an overview of a project area, or enlargements can be used in interviews with farmers about their farming practices. The major disadvantage of oblique photographs is the spatial distortion caused by the angle between the ground surface and the camera axis. This distortion limits the usefulness of oblique photographs for mapping purposes. In some cases it may be difficult to rent an airplane or to acquire permission to fly over a project site; in such circumstances, sketch mapping is a useful alternative method.

Case Study III: Ciramaeuwah Girang

This study used sketch-mapping techniques to learn about land-use practices and to identify sites of possible conflict and cooperation between farmers and foresters. The community organizers designed a micro-management plan for the forest lands near this village based on these sketch maps.

Ciramaeuwah Girang lies on the border of a state-owned forest in West Java. Many farmers in this village are landless or possess extremely small landholdings and have traditionally relied on the state forest to make up shortfalls in agricultural production. Because of the difficulty of managing this land, the local forestry department asked for assistance in developing a social forestry program in Ciramaeuwah Girang.

The community organizers could not acquire aerial photographs of Ciramaeuwah Girang, but were able to obtain a 1:25,000 map of the village showing its boundaries and the state forest lands. The community organizers used the grid-cell method to enlarge this map to 1:10,000 and conducted interviews to determine the location of well-known physical objects on this map. The community organizers then field-checked the map and made numerous photocopies of the corrected base map, which they used in interviews with villagers to learn about land-use practices. Maps were produced showing footpaths, schools, and mosques, the spatial distribution of privately owned land, and forest use practices. Interviews with forestry officials produced a map of officially sanctioned forest uses. After comparing the map of actual uses of forest lands with the map of sanctioned uses, community organizers produced a map of conflict areas (Figure 6.3). This map was used in negotiations with the forestry department and local farmers to identify an acceptable site (without conflicts) for an agroforestry project. In the first year (1987), a group of farmers planted teak and mahogany trees on this twenty-hectare site in exchange for the right to interplant food crops (*e.g.*, corn, pepper, banana) between the trees.

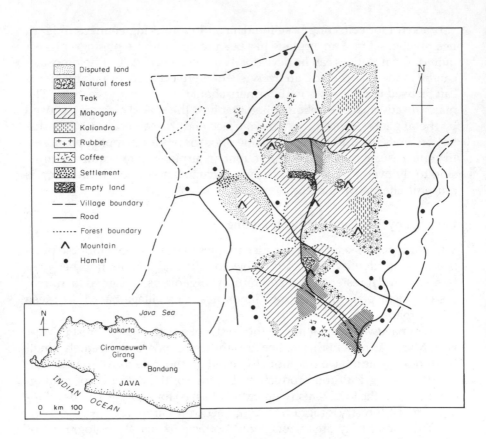

Figure 6.3. Ciramaeuwah Girang, showing areas of
forest–farmer conflict

In the second year, the community organizers conducted a more broad-based micromanagement exercise in which villagers and forestry officials used sketch maps to identify areas in which they agreed to cooperate on forest management (Figure 6.4). This produced a management plan specifying three sites for pilot projects and the farmer groups that will be developed to manage these lands. Still, a number of disputed sites remain where farmers are actively farming state forest land. Although sketch mapping has not solved the problems, it has helped farmers and foresters to delineate the problem sites and to talk about how these lands can be managed for the benefit of all.

For social forestry, sketch mapping is perhaps the most appropriate but least appreciated technology. As this example demonstrates, sketch mapping is a powerful tool for understanding and resolving land-use conflicts. Sketch maps are relatively easy and inexpensive to make and do not require aerial photographs. It is also easy to teach sketch mapping

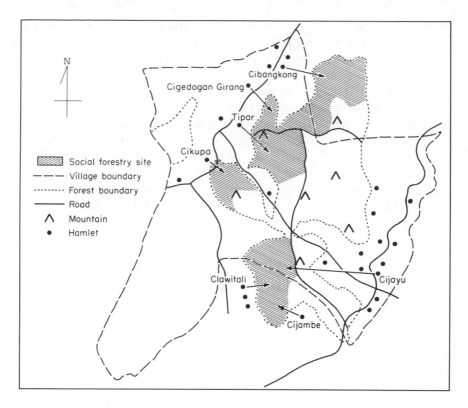

Figure 6.4. Proposed community-forest agency territorial agreements in Ciramaeuwah Girang

to community organizers. The major disadvantage of sketch mapping is the inaccuracies and distortions introduced in the mapping process.

TRAINING FORESTERS TO USE DIAGNOSTIC TOOLS

Successful social forestry programs require forestry departments to train lower and mid-level personnel in ways to learn from and communicate with rural people. Experience has shown that with the social forestry project in Indonesia the most difficult skills to teach are interviewing techniques. Interviewing is difficult for several reasons. Because it is similar to conversation, many people assume they need no training. Because land-use practices and problems can be observed and read about, many people assume they will learn nothing new from farmers. With careful explanation and with role playing, these problems can often be overcome. Another difficulty is the tendency to ask questions that confirm the interviewer's opinion or call for a "yes" or "no" answer (*e.g.*, "Do you collect firewood in the forest?"). Responses to leading questions are not necessarily wrong, but they are difficult to confirm once the expected affirmative or negative answer is given. Far stronger answers are obtained from questions that ask the interviewee to make a statement (*e.g.*, "Where do you collect firewood?"). Although even experienced interviewers can have trouble avoiding leading questions, role playing is essential for teaching foresters to identify and minimize their use of leading questions.

Because foresters traditionally receive training in aerial photointerpretation and mapping, they have little difficulty applying these skills to aerial photographs and sketch maps once they have learned interviewing techniques. These social forestry programs in Indonesia indicate that if the forestry bureaucracy is supportive, materials can be developed for successfully training foresters to communicate with farmers who use forest lands. Although some people communicate better than others, all can benefit from a training program.

CONCLUSIONS

Geographers, foresters, watershed managers, and other land-use specialists have long valued aerial photographs and topographic maps for the information they provide on the spatial distribution and extent of earth's resources. The full value of these tools for social forestry programs, however, is just beginning to be realized. Aerial photographs and sketch maps are useful tools for learning about spatial relationships among land-use systems and for interviewing farmers about these practices. Results from interviews based on aerial photographs or sketch maps, however, are only as good as the interviewer. It is important to make the farmer feel at ease, to have a good understanding of the area, and to be able to ask probing questions without suggesting answers. In the hands of a skilled interviewer, these tools are useful for gaining information about land-use practices and for promoting the goals of social forestry programs.

NOTES

Author's Note: I gratefully acknowledge the assistance of many people. At the Indonesian State Forest Corporation, I am indebted to Ir. Mulyadi Bratamihardja, Ir. Poedjorahardjo, Ir. Teguh Purwanto, Ir. Zulfi Pohan, Ir. Dadan, and Ir. Ellan. At the Indonesian Department of Forestry, I would like to thank Dr. Beni Nasendi. In Irian Jaya, I am grateful to Mr. Arthur Mitchell and the staff of the social forestry project. Finally, I would like to thank Dr. Mark Poffenberger and the Ford Foundation, Jakarta. The opinions reflected in this chapter are my own, and I assume responsibility for all mistakes. This paper is reprinted from: Fox, J. M. 1989. "Diagnostic Tools for Social Forestry," *Journal of World Forest Resource Management* 4(1).

1. Grandstaff, S., and T. Grandstaff. 1987. "Semi-structured Interviewing by Multidisciplinary Teams in RRA," in *Proceedings of the 1985 International Conference on Rapid Rural Appraisal*. Khon Kaen, Thailand: Rural Systems Research and Farming System Research Projects.

2. Ibid.

3. Chambers, R. 1985. "Shortcut Methods of Gathering Social Information for Rural Development Projects," in Michael M. Cernea (ed.). *Putting People First: Sociological Variables in Rural Development*. Oxford University Press, World Bank.

4. Limpinuntana, V. 1957. "Conceptual Tools for RRA in Agrarian Society," in *Proceedings of the 1985 International Conference on Rapid Rural Appraisal*. Khon Kaen, Thailand: Rural Systems Research and Farming System Research Projects.

5. Fox, J. M. 1986. "Aerial Photographs and Thematic Maps for Social Forestry." ODI Social Forestry Newsletter, Network Paper 2C, London; Carson, B. 1985. "Aerial Photography as a Base for Village Level Planning in Nepal," in *Proceedings: Regional Symposium on Remote Sensing Applications of Socioeconomic Aspects of the Environment*, ESCAP and the Ford Foundation, Bangkok, Thailand; Vogt, E. Z. (ed.) 1974. *Aerial Photography in Anthropological Field Research*, Cambridge: Harvard University Press; Conklin, H. C. 1980. *Ethnographic Atlas of Ifugao: A Study of Environment, Culture and Society in Northern Luzon*. New Haven: Yale University Press.

6. Lillesand, T. M., and R. Kiefer. 1979. *Remote Sensing and Image Interpretation*. New York: John Wiley and Sons.

7. Fox. "Aerial Photographs and Thematic Maps for Social Forestry."

8. Evans, B. M., and L. Mata. 1984. "Acquisition of 35-mm Oblique Photographs for Stereoscopic Analysis and Measurement." *Photogrammetric Engineering and Remote Sensing* 50(11):1581–1590; Killmayer, A., and H. Epp. 1983. "Use of Small-Format Aerial Photography for Land Mapping and Resource Monitoring." *ITC Journal* 4; Needham, T. D., and J. L. Smith. 1984. "Consequences of Enlarging 35-mm Aerial Photography." *Photogrammetric Engineering and Remote Sensing* 50(8):1143–1144; Graham, R. W., R. E. Read and J. Kure. 1985. "Small Format Microlight Surveys." *ITC Journal* 1.; Hofstee, P. 1985. "An Introduction to Small Format Aerial Photography for Human Settlement Analysis." *ITC Journal* 2; Shafer, R. V., and S. A. Degler. 1986. "35-mm Photography: An Inexpensive Remote Sensing Tool." *Photogrammetic Engineering and Remote Sensing* 52(6):833–837.

CHAPTER SEVEN

Communal Forest Leases as a Tenurial Option in the Philippine Uplands

Luzviminda B. Cornista and Eva F. Escueta

DURING THE 1970s and 1980s, growing human dependence on public forests put political pressures on some Asian forestry agencies to begin formally recognizing the presence of forest communities. As part of this process and in varying degrees, management authority for blocks of state land is being transferred to individuals and communities. Empowerment often takes the form of long-term, renewable leases to the individuals using the land. The primary tenurial agreements in the Philippines (certificate of stewardship contract, CSC), Thailand (STK certificate), and Java (Surat Perjanjian/Kontrak) provide use rights to farmers for small plots of land. In Southeast Asia, agreements between communities and forestry agencies for managing larger tracts of forest land and small watersheds are far less common.

To date, little systematic study has been done on the relative merits of different tenurial agreements and the extent to which they enhance the lessees' land security, create incentives for sustainable forest management, and protect the holder from exploitation by private-sector elites and corrupt officials. While individual agreements may provide greater security for a household farmlot, community-level agreements are likely more effective methods to establish management authority for common pastures, watersheds, and forests used for hunting and gathering. Communal agreements may also be a more efficient way to establish local control, given the larger size of the lease area covered under each contract.

To better understand how group leases can be used to empower community management systems, it is useful to review the experiences of the Philippines Integrated Social Forestry (ISF) program with communal agreements. The ISF program is based on granting twenty-five-year stewardship contracts, renewable for another twenty-five years, to individuals, communities, or associations. Communal forest leases are issued by the Forest Management Bureau [(FMB); formerly called the Bureau of Forest

Development (BFD)] to indigenous ethnic groups, known in the Philippines as cultural communities. The leases confer formal government recognition of upland communities' rights to large tracts of forest land, provided such areas are not excluded from occupancy and their continued use will not damage the forest resource. To receive stewardship agreements, communities must have formal organizations registered with the Securities and Exchange Commission (SEC).

By early 1988, nine communal leases had been issued to a variety of groups, including Ikalahan, Igorot, and Mangyan communities in northern Luzon, and Islamic and migrant groups in Mindanao. The lease areas ranged from 50 to over 15,000 hectares in size, but averaged from 1,000 to 4,000 hectares per lease. This chapter examines the experience of the Ikalahan, an upland Luzon tribal community of 5,000 people. In 1974, the Ikalahan received the first communal lease in the Philippines. Kalahan provides important insights into the organizational, legal, and technical aspects of communal land management.

THE KALAHAN COMMUNAL FOREST LEASE

In the early 1970s the Ikalahans organized a producers cooperative and tried, with the help of a Protestant missionary, to register it with the proper government agency to gain legal recognition. To meet bureaucratic requirements, they changed their organization into the Kalahan Educational Foundation (KEF), which was registered with the Securities and Exchange Commission (SEC) on November 26, 1973. The Ikalahans then sought government assistance in surveying their lands for land title proceedings. The Presidential Assistance on Claims and Land Conflicts of the Philippines discussed the problem at two high-level conferences and proposed that the Ikalahans have a communal forest lease area to protect their ancestral lands from land-grabbers.

The BFD director advised the Ikalahan elders to draft a contract embodying their idea of a self-governed communal forest lease area. The elders met and consulted the people on the proposed provisions of the lease agreement. Finally, on May 13, 1974, the contract was signed by all parties concerned and duly registered as Memorandum of Agreement No. 1. Among the conditions specified in the contract are:

(1) The KEF has the right to manage and use the area to the exclusion of all other parties not "subsisting" within the area at the time of signing.

(2) The KEF is required to protect the forest from incursions from outsiders, prevent forest fires and grass fires, and protect adjacent forest stands.

(3) The KEF is disallowed from subleasing any portion of the area for any

reason, and is required to provide funding for projects designed to implement the agreement.

(4) Because the KEF is a non-profit corporation, taxes and fees normally collected for forest use are waived.

The area leased to the KEF covers 14,730 hectares of public forest land located in the western part of Nueva Vizcaya and the northeastern part of San Nicolas, Pangasinan (see Figure 7.1). It includes six villages or *barangays*: Imugan, Baracbac, Bacneng, Maliko, Onib, and Santa Rosa. Its center is Imugan, which is about six kilometers from Santa Fe town proper.

ORGANIZATIONAL STRATEGIES

Tungtungan and the Structure of the KEF

Throughout the Philippines, upland cultural communities possess a variety of conflict-resolution mechanisms. Some rely more heavily on the decisions of the elder members of the community, while others are based on the consensual decision of all members. In both cases the community members or their representatives meet to resolve problems, plan activities, and manage group affairs through an open dialogue, which usually results in mutually acceptable agreements. In the case of the Ikalahan, this process was called *tungtungan*, which literally means "coming together for a meeting." The KEF adopted the *tungtungan* as its primary planning and decision-making process. In practice, the *tungtungan* serves as the forum through which community problems and conflicts are raised and resolved. Anyone can call for a *tungtungan* to settle a problem, whether personal or communal. Anybody can participate in the discussion, cross-examine the litigants, and give counsel to the conflicting parties; final settlement of the issue, however, rests on the council of elders, which also presides over the *tungtungan*.

Among the Ikalahans, all *tungtungan* decisions of the council of elders are final and followed without question, which indicates the social role of elders inherent in Ikalahan culture. To be recognized as a community elder, one has to possess wisdom and character beyond reproach.

Using the *tungtungan* and the council of elders as a framework, the KEF is governed by a board of trustees that approximates the council of elders, forming policy and making decisions on all KEF matters. It is currently composed of ten elected representatives of the *barangays* within the communal forest lease area. Representation on the board is based on the number of families in each *barangay*. Imugan, the most thickly populated, has more representatives.

The trustees representing the *barangays* are usually the recognized

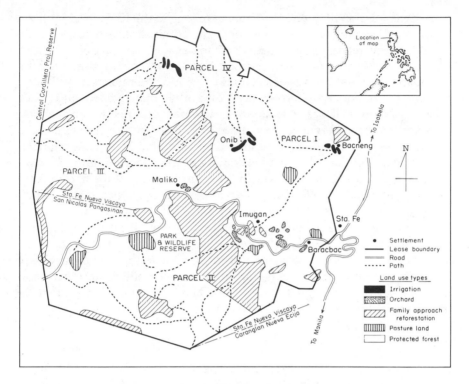

**Figure 7.1. Land use patterns in the
Kalahan Educational Foundation lease area**

elders in the village, but not necessarily those who compose the village government, known as the barangay council. Because the board of trustees acts like the traditional council of elders, its decisions on matters relevant to the KEF are respected by the constituents within the communal forest lease area. This factor largely contributes to the apparent effectiveness of the communal forest lease granted to the foundation.

The concept of popular participation inherent in the *tungtungan* is manifested in the KEF in that villagers elect their own representatives to the board and directly participate in deciding critical matters pertaining to the foundation. For instance, a community assembly was held to discuss whether or not to adopt communal titling. Board meetings are also open to the villagers to ensure that interested parties can participate and react in the board's deliberations.

Day-to-day KEF operations are performed by an administrative team composed of the principal of the Kalahan Academy and the coordinators in charge of the different foundation programs: food processing, agroforestry, clinic, services, and office. In the past, an executive officer, in the person of the missionary mentioned above, managed the KEF alone. At present, this missionary is only a member of the administrative team, formally acting as a secretary but informally serving as a liaison between the KEF and the "outside world," whose main task is to generate funds for the foundation's projects and establish marketing and other linkages. Although he remains an important force in the KEF, both in management and policy making, potential Ikalahan leaders are now being trained to replace him.

Among the different groups in the KEF, the agroforestry team is the most visible in terms of implementing the communal forest lease contract. It is in charge of parcellary map sketching of the allocated farmlots, issuance of individual land claim certificates, supervision of the agroforestry development plan, and issuance of various permits, including tree-cutting and pasture lease permits. It manages the KEF orchard farms and provides raw materials to the food processing plant. It also sees that the boundaries of the communal forest lease area are protected from encroachers, illegal loggers, and forest fires. At present, the agroforestry team has five regular staff members, although occasionally, if necessary and if funds permit, forest guards are hired. These forest guards are usually residents of the area where they are assigned.

Organizational Problems

KEF has two major internal problems. The first is financial. The KEF needs a continuing source of funds to pay the salaries of regular staff who implement the communal forest lease. The food-processing project was established to generate funds, but the income from this project was insufficient to meet management costs. The missionary has played a critical fund-raising and leadership role in the KEF in the past. Consequently, his retirement threatens the economic viability of the organization. Although the educational arm of the KEF has developed a number of potential leaders, it is still uncertain whether these leaders can duplicate the networking of the missionary, whose dominant role has also created a psychological dependency on him.

The KEF also has jurisdictional problems with local civil authorities within the *barangay*, the smallest administrative unit. Due to the KEF's encompassing authority, some members of the *barangay* councils feel their leadership is undermined. This tension is aggravated by the fact that the *barangay* council concept is based on lowland social organizations alien to the upland villagers; the people of Kalahan prefer to consult the KEF board of trustees, which is patterned after the indigenous *tungtungan*. Some of the *barangay* leaders are consequently demanding to become automatic members of the board of trustees to strengthen their political positions. To meet these problems, the KEF has attempted to delineate its jurisdiction vis-a-vis the village political unit.

Jurisdictional problems also arise between the KEF and the local district office of the BFD; their relationship has been strained by differing interpretations of rights and responsibilities under the communal forest lease contract. The BFD district office believes the KEF is still functionally under its authority, but in the past the KEF has negotiated directly with the BFD central office. The KEF believes its agreement with the BFD gives it primary jurisdiction over the communal forest lease area and therefore feels entitled to be consulted on matters concerning the area. Moreover, the KEF feels that the BFD district office should continuously provide technical assistance to the foundation as provided for in the Memorandum of Agreement. The BFD, however, believes that the KEF should also continuously submit their development reports to the district office, rather than to the central office.

The jurisdictional conflicts between the KEF, the local civil authority, and the district forestry office result from problems in integrating new management systems into preexisting administrative structures. The recent routinization of the ISF program and reorganization of the forestry bureaucracy may allow for better coordination between communal management organizations and local forestry offices.

TENURIAL STRATEGIES

Land Claims and Ownership Before the Communal Forest Lease

At the turn of the century, there was open access to the Yangyangan area, which includes Imugan and the outlying villages. Any migrant could clear unoccupied land and cultivate it. This cultivated area is called *kaingin* or *oma*. Open access to land encouraged the immigration of various mountain tribes who later established their livelihood in Imugan and the vicinity.

Like the other cultural groups, the Ikalahans considered land to be common property with members possessing use rather than ownership rights. In the mid-1930s, however, survey teams from the BFD and the Bureau of Lands visited the Yangyangan and later classified and released the flatlands along the Imugan River as alienable and disposable. Around a hundred Ikalahans applied for land titles and before the outbreak of World War II almost all the applicants became private landholders. This began a process of land privatization in the Yangyangan.

In the following years, lowlanders started encroaching on the Ikalahan ancestral lands. In 1963, a number of lowland residents from a neighboring province were able to get land titles for areas in Malico that were declared alienable and disposable. Again, in 1967, some influential lowlanders were able to secure titles for 190 hectares near Imugan. The Ikalahans filed a case for the revocation of these land titles, and they finally won in 1972. In 1973, the KEF was established and the idea of communal forest leases conceived. A year later, the Memorandum of Agreement between the BFD and the KEF was signed allowing the Ikalahans "to retain sole and exclusive authority to utilize and develop 14,730 hectares of their ancestral lands and protect its water resources." At present, the KEF also owns private holdings within the communal forest lease area, including the 2.2-hectare site of the Kalahan Academy and an 8-hectare orchard.

Land Allocation Under the Communal Forest Lease

The granting of a communal forest lease to the KEF legitimized the prior and vested rights of the Ikalahans to their lands by legally recognizing their claims. The board of trustees then allocated parcels of up to fifteen hectares per family, a limit based on the ten- to fifteen-year fallow cycle required for sustaining soil fertility under indigenous rotational agricultural systems. Before allocation, the agroforestry team made sketches using transit and other surveying instruments. The claimants were asked to pinpoint their claims during the survey and they set the boundaries. Established farmers in the area who were cultivating less than fifteen hectares at the time of the survey also claimed the unclaimed farms adjacent to their holdings. Those with more than fifteen hectares generally chose the best parcels and either distributed the excess areas to their children, relatives, and neighbors, or simply abandoned such areas and let the KEF board of trustees apportion them to deserving claimants. For this reason some families received noncontiguous lots. Ikalahans without established farms at the time of the survey had to content themselves with smaller parcels. This explains the differences in the size of farms allocated to the claimants.

Of the 14,730 hectares covered by the communal forest lease, the KEF allocated 2,443 hectares (16.6 percent) to individual claimants representing 398 families (see Table 7.1). It also recognized the rights of private landholders in the area. Private holdings within the communal forest lease area comprise 786 hectares (5.3 percent), including the 8-hectare orchard owned by the KEF. In this orchard, staff are hired by the Foundation to plant and care for trees until they bear fruit. These planter-caretakers are paid on a monthly basis for each tree that survives. As an added incentive, caretakers are given 15 percent of the fruit they harvest. Staff and their children also enjoy free tuition at the Kalahan Academy.

The KEF directly manages nearly 80 percent of the nearly 15,000 hectares covered by the lease, which includes virgin forest (13 percent); parks and wildlife reserve (5 percent); areas for reforestation/watershed development (9 percent); and grasslands/pine and dipterocarp forest (51 percent).

TABLE 7.1
Land uses within the communal lease area

Land Use	Area (Ha.)	Percent of Total
1. Virgin Forest	1950	13
2. Parks and wildlife reserve	777	5
3. Reforestation/watershed development	1303	9
4. Grasslands/pine and dipterocarp forest	7469	51
5. Individual claims	2443	17
6. Privately owned titled lands	787	5
Total	14,728	100

Tenurial Issues and Problems

Emerging tenurial problems in the KEF include boundary conflicts, the entrance of future claimants, land fragmentation, communal titling, and the standing resolution of the Municipality of Santa Fe to reduce the communal forest lease area. The agroforestry team has recorded some cases of overlapping boundaries due to the fact that all farmers were not present during the survey. The agroforestry team's maps are the primary reference in boundary disputes. If conflicts cannot be settled by the persons concerned, the board of trustees mediates and its decision prevails.

When the KEF was established in 1974, not everyone received a piece of land to cultivate. New entrants in the community and newly married couples had no existing farmland to claim. Among these new entrants are the faculty members at the Kalahan Academy and some KEF staff. In response to the complaints, the KEF subdivided an area near Imugan and allocated it by lots. The KEF foresees more entrants to the community in the future and plans to allocate farms to these people, but has yet to determine the location and size of future plots. Newly married couples were generally granted smaller farms of one-half to one hectare. Future marriages among the Ikalahans will cause further fragmentation of the land, a process accepted by the KEF.

Traditionally, the inheritance system among the Ikalahans provides the youngest child the smallest share, while the eldest has the biggest portion, regardless of sex. At present, however, all heirs are given equal shares. The KEF expects parents to apportion parts of their lease once their children start families of their own.

Recently, personnel from the Philippine Association for Intercultural Development (PAFID), a nongovernment community development organization, visited Imugan to explain the concept of communal titling and discuss it with the Ikalahans. Initial interviews with key informants revealed that the Ikalahans' idea of communal titling is still vague. They are unsure whether communal titling would apply to the whole communal forest lease area covering 14,730 hectares or only to the approximately 2,443 hectares allocated to individual claimants. Similarly, they are uncertain whether title would be in the name of the KEF or in the name of the claimants. Because of these ambiguities, there seems no strong reaction for or against communal titling. Those in favor reasoned that a communal title lasts forever; hence their descendants are assured of something to cultivate. Those opposed fear they will have to pay taxes once the land becomes privately owned.

The municipal council of Santa Fe has a standing resolution to reduce the area covered by the communal forest lease from 14,730 hectares to only 100 hectares, and recommends the gradual conversion of individual Ikalahan lease contracts to private land titles. The KEF argues that such a move, if approved, will only enrich the municipality by obliging the Ikalahans to pay taxes. At present, KEF is tax-exempt and all KEF allocatees are exempted from paying the annual tax of ten pesos per hectare.

While tax issues have received considerable attention during the debate over titling, perhaps a more fundamental issue is whether communal management can survive in the face of pressure to privatize and establish individual titles. While the Ikalahan desire individual control over farmlots, communal control of forests and less intensively used land continues to be widely accepted and provides an effective management mechanism for common land. Privatized or individual management of this land would likely lead to more intensive use and misuse, and less equity in access.

PRODUCTION AND TECHNICAL STRATEGIES

Farm Plans

Most Ikalahan farmers use a variety of land-use systems on their farms, including swiddens planted to rootcrops (*oma* or *kaingin*); irrigated ricefields (*talon*); lands under fallow (*kiniba*); areas devoted to upland rice (*bangkag*); second forest growth (*bal-aw*); orchard; and pasture (see Table 7.2). Of the 398 allocatees, nearly 60 percent have *oma*, *kinaba*, and *bal-aw*. Thirty-seven percent have orchards and 14 percent *bangkag* and only 10 percent have pasture lands and *talon*. Aside from individual pasture lands, the KEF maintains a communal pasture area where interested members can graze their cattle. To do so they must secure a permit from the agroforestry team and pay an annual pasture lease fee of 5 pesos per head.

A few years ago, the KEF board of trustees and staff observed that some members were not making permanent improvements on their farms. Hence, the board required all members to prepare individual farm plans and submit them to the agroforestry team. The farm plan is prepared either individually by KEF members or by the agroforestry team personnel

TABLE 7.2
Land uses of allocated farms

Land Use	Area (Ha.)	Percent of Total
Oma	278	12
Talon (Irrigated Ricefields)	44	2
Orchard	130	5
Bangkag (Upland Ricefarm)	119	5
House	24	1
Kinaba (Land under fallow)	860	35
Balaw (Second growth forest reserve)	766	31
Pasture land	212	9
Total	2433	100

in consultation with the members. The members decide what crops to plant; cash crops that command a high price at the time of planning are usually preferred.

All KEF members are required to implement their farm development designs and the board of trustees may impose sanctions for failure to follow the plan. At the end of each year, the board of trustees tours the farms to assess how far each member has proceeded with the development plan. Based on the trustees' evaluation, the three most outstanding farmers are awarded with farm implements (*e.g.*, a shovel) as prizes. However, a member who has failed at the end of the year to do what he had planned is not allowed to cultivate an *oma* or *kaingin* for a year. If the claimed area is not significantly improved in two to three years, the size of the allocated farm will be reduced. Aside from these sanctions, the board of trustees can determine others for noncompliance with the farm plan. Since May 7, 1985, there have been seven KEF members who have not received permits to operate a *kaingin*, one of whom was assessed a fine in pigs by the board of trustees.

Cropping Systems

The KEF farmers themselves decide what crops to plant in their farms. In the *oma*, planting is usually done during the rainy season after the area is cleared, burned, and cleaned. Ginger or corn is commonly planted in the boundaries, while rootcrops, specifically *taro (pitik)*, are grown within. After these crops are harvested, sweet potato *(camote)* is planted, followed by beans. The land is used as *oma* for about two to three years, after which it is fallowed and becomes a *kinaba*. The usual fallow period is five years, which is believed to be sufficient time for the soil to regain its fertility.

In the *bangkag*, rice is planted in May and harvested in October, after which vegetables are grown, followed again by rice. In the *talon*, rice is planted in March. The varieties grown in the irrigated ricefields are a combination of traditional and new varieties such as *malagkit, pula,* and other high-yielding seeds. Harvesting is done in July or August.

For the orchards, the KEF provides free seedlings of passion fruit and lemon. The fruit is contracted to the KEF food-processing plant. Pomelo, citrus, coffee, and dagwey (a wild fruit similar to the raisin) are also commercially grown. Because of the commercial value of fruit trees, the Ikalahans are eager to plant them.

Soil Conservation Methods

As conservation measures, the KEF reintroduced old strategies the Ikalahans had stopped practicing, including *balka* or *barikes, gengen,* and *day-og. Balka* or *barikes* means "belt." The practice involves planting tiger grass, alnos, citrus, and pomelo along the contour to prevent soil erosion. In *gengen,* sweet potato vines derived from the harvested crop are laid laterally and covered with soil. *Gengen* is a technique of composting on the contour that rebuilds fertility while protecting from erosion. *Day-og* is similar to *gengen* but is generally practiced on level or flat lands.

SOME LESSONS FROM THE KEF EXPERIENCE

In conclusion, the Kalahan experience indicates that communal forest leases can be a viable tenurial option in the uplands. The KEF has shown that the socio-economic development of upland communities can be pursued in conjunction with environmental protection and conservation. The role of an organizing force (in the KEF case, the missionary) is critical. This role can be assumed by nongovernment organizations, but development of community leadership should be pursued at the outset. Indigenous institutions, leaders, and rules can provide functional and effective organizational frameworks for resource management. Indigenous conservation strategies can also anchor environmental protection and conservation functions of land management systems. Perhaps the most important lesson from Kalahan was that providing tenure security to a community of farmers in general, and to individual farmers in particular, through a variety of tenurial mechanisms, allows for better integrated agroforestry development and land management.

NOTE

Authors' Note: The authors would like to acknowledge the assistance of Francisco R. Calixto and Reynaldo P. Elma in collecting and analyzing some of the information included in this chapter.

CHAPTER EIGHT

Identifying Appropriate Agroforestry Technologies in Java

Carol Stoney and Mulyadi Bratamihardja

NATURAL TROPICAL FORESTS in Southeast Asia exist in a variety of forms. Forest ecosystems are biologically diverse and dependent on complex interrelationships. Because of this complexity and a lack of understanding of natural forest regeneration processes, early forest management systems converted land use to single-species timber stands. The development of single-species forest systems often was also stimulated by demands for a few commercial forest products to support the colonial economy. The rise of independent nations, growing populations, land hunger, and industrial development led to a demand for a wider range of forest products, more forest-sector jobs, and income-earning opportunities. In response to these needs, forestry agencies began experimenting with multipurpose agroforestry systems. Early attempts to develop polyculture management systems for state forest lands borrowed heavily from indigenous Southeast Asian agroforestry technologies. In this chapter we will examine the conceptual issues underlying agroforestry system design and then discuss how these concepts affect decision making in the recent evolution of agroforestry technologies on Java.

The Indonesian State Forest Corporation (SFC) manages approximately 2.9 million hectares of forest land on the island of Java. An estimated 30 percent of the forest land in Java is degraded or marginally productive, including 230,000 hectares which are unproductive. The forest lands managed by the SFC are dispersed throughout the island, and their boundaries are usually contiguous with village settlements. About 21 million people live in or near state forest in over 6,000 villages. Almost 60 percent of this population depends on agriculture as their primary source of income. Average land ownership is about one-third to one-half hectare per family, and landlessness is rising. Low household income levels and small agricultural landholdings cause agricultural labor surplus and high unemployment. These conditions place increasing pressure on the forest. The forests on Java have long been important to the welfare of the local inhabitants, who benefit from the use of the forest land and its products. Increasing population pressures in Java are causing forest land use to be both redefined and intensified through innovative silvicultural and agricultural technologies. The result is a move towards more appropriate agroforestry systems, which are being tested as part of a social forestry program.

In general terms, agroforestry on state land in Java can be defined as a forest management system incorporating tree species with agricultural crops, livestock, and/or fisheries, with the goal of productive forest sustainability. An intercropping system, called *tumpangsari* in Java, is commonly used in reestablishing teak plantations. *Tumpangsari*, similar to the type of agroforestry system known as *taungya*, has been used in Java since 1856;[1] in recent years the use of *tumpangsari* has been expanded onto non-teak forest areas as well. Conventional *tumpangsari* takes place during the establishment of plantations, when farmers are granted access to forest land. In exchange for site preparation, planting, and tending the forest trees, the farmers are allowed to cultivate food crops between the rows of the timber species. Under conventional *tumpangsari*, farmers are only permitted to grow rice and corn as the intercropped species, and the duration of the intercropping period is limited to the first two years of the rotation of the main tree species.

The conventional *tumpangsari* system has been modified, however, to reflect changing needs. New agroforestry approaches, while modeled after *tumpangsari*, are no longer limited to food crop production for home consumption, but can be commercially oriented for increased income earning. The agricultural component has been diversified to include horticultural species, fodder, and fuelwood crops. The duration of *tumpangsari* intercropping can also be prolonged until the end of the rotation of the main tree species. The combination of plants is dependent on land suitability, climatic conditions, and local land-use traditions.

Given the need to improve forest management, new silviculture and agriculture technologies are needed to achieve better, sustained yields. Furthermore, rural people living near the forest area need to be included and involved as partners in forest development. Following a year of diagnostic studies, the SFC began to implement a social forestry program with the support of the Ford Foundation. The program seeks to help forest farmers organize groups to facilitate better relations between the SFC and the target community, and create equal, legal partnerships between the two parties, and encourage the adoption of agroforestry techniques that can provide an optimal species mix for both the agency and participating farmers.

Agroforestry models are evolving and will continue to develop as forestry and agricultural technologies improve. Because each plant species requires specific conditions for optimum growth, appropriate silvicultural systems, agricultural technologies, and the plant's characteristics need to be properly understood and utilized. To develop agroforestry systems responsive to local ecological and economic conditions, the SFC and the forest farmer groups decide together on the plant composition for each site.

KEY CONCEPTS IN AGROFORESTRY SYSTEM DESIGN

Although agroforestry can be defined very broadly, several common features characterize most agroforestry systems. Agroforestry systems generally are typified by greater species diversity than other agroecosystems. Their spatial structure changes dramatically over time. They provide a variety of products and serve multiple land-use functions. Agroforestry systems enhance the income and food security of rural families because farmers do not have to depend on a single crop. Further, intercropping with perennial species can protect and ameliorate soil quality and enhance other environmental conditions. These characteristics often make agroforestry systems appropriate in areas suffering from environmental and socio-economic stress.

Ecological Diversity

Indigenous knowledge of agroforestry in Java makes the island an ideal laboratory for developing social forestry production systems. Javanese farmers have developed highly complex home gardens, with hundreds of productive plant species found in a single village.[2] Indigenous agroforestry systems often imitate the floristic diversity of natural forest ecosystems, although the actual species composition may be very different. This ecological diversity contributes to overall system stability. An agroecosystem made up of a number of different species is often more resilient to environmental stress than monoculture. For example, in a single-species stand of trees or in a rice paddy, a pest or disease can spread rapidly through the plant population in a short time, damaging the entire crop. In a plant community with a diversity of species, it is more difficult for diseases and pests to spread and it is likely that some of the crops will be immune. A complex agroecosystem is also more likely to support predator species, which can help keep pest populations under control.[3]

Stratification

Different species have different requirements for light, nutrients, and moisture, which determine the necessary growing space for each. Spatial stratification is the arrangement of various plants within a unit of land.

An agroforestry system should maximize the use of available resources through stratification of the various components. Another approach, chronological stratification, changes the composition of the stand over time. Spatial stratification can be described in both horizontal and vertical terms. The arrangement of species within traditional home gardens may appear almost random, although placement of plants is often based on indigenous knowledge of species requirements and compatibility.[4] A more plantation-like approach may consist of alternating rows of perennial and annual species, as in *tumpangsari* systems. Horizontal stratification is often diagramed as in Figure 8.1. Vertical stratification is also an important consideration for analyzing competition between plants. Below ground, plants compete for nutrients and moisture. Above ground, plants also compete for sunlight, although some species thrive in the understory, by absorbing light filtered through the canopy. Because species have different light requirements, the most efficient use of space is to strategically place shade-tolerant species in the understory. The canopy of an agroforestry system can include several layers, as diagramed in Figure 8.2.

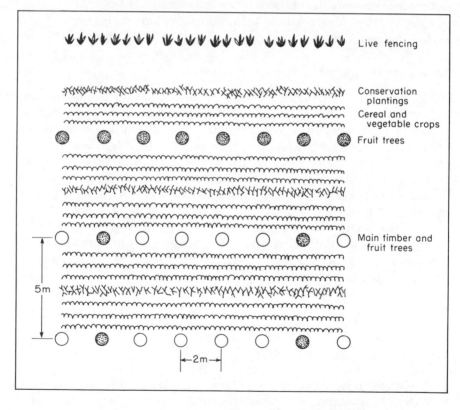

Figure 8.1. Javanese agroforestry plot diagram

Stratification of an agroforestry system may come about as the system progresses through various chronological sequences. Some of the factors that determine changes over time include competing demands for growing space as certain components mature, differential height growth and crown development, the removal of components as harvestable products, or the need for a fallow period. These factors may result in the replacement of one crop by another, continuous rotation of components on a single unit of land, or a system of alternating land uses. For example, once the canopy begins to close, shade-tolerant fodder crops or medicinal plants can be used to replace cereal crops, as illustrated in Figure 8.2. Yields from these crops can be supplemented by fruit trees, which can bear fruit within two to ten years.

Multiple Use

Multiple use is a basic tenet of forest management. Forest land in Java is managed by the SFC to provide a sustained yield of forest products that generate revenue for the nation; to protect soils and water supplies through conservation of forest land; and to provide employment and a source of income to local communities. Thus, the forest serves several important functions and benefits different segments of the population in different ways. Multiple use is also a concept implicit in agroforestry design, in that agroforestry systems provide a variety of products and services. New agroforestry models provide farmers with more land-use options and a wider array of crops for home consumption or sale.

Sustainability

Like multiple use, sustainability is a key concept in forest management and rural development, as well as in agroforestry. The concept of sustainability is also used in agroecosystems analysis. Conway defines it as an agroecosystem's ability to permanently maintain a certain level of productivity, even under conditions of stress or disturbance.[5] One of the objectives of the SFC's social forestry program is to regenerate lands that have been degraded through unregulated use. To achieve sustainability, however, agroforestry systems must be both ecologically stable and provide forest and community managers with a steady flow of products and income to encourage them to protect the system from overuse and degradation. Agroecosystems must be sustainable with respect to soil and water conservation and to nutrient cycling and energy balances within the ecosystem. Sustainable agroforestry models are crucial to the success of the social forestry program.

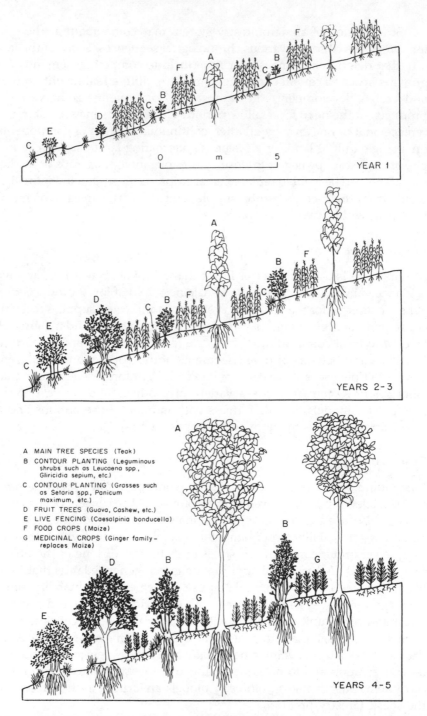

A MAIN TREE SPECIES (Teak)
B CONTOUR PLANTING (Leguminous shrubs such as Leucaena spp, Gliricidia sepium, etc.)
C CONTOUR PLANTING (Grasses such as Setaria spp, Panicum maximum, etc.)
D FRUIT TREES (Guava, Cashew, etc.)
E LIVE FENCING (Caesalpinia bonducella)
F FOOD CROPS (Maize)
G MEDICINAL CROPS (Ginger family – replaces Maize)

Figure 8.2. Changing vertical stratification in a Javanese agroforestry plot

CONSTRAINTS AND OPPORTUNITIES FOR AGROFORESTRY DEVELOPMENT IN JAVA

Improving Tumpangsari Systems

Many forest farmers on Java are no longer satisfied with the traditional two years of forest access offered under conventional *tumpangsari*. Their shrinking private landholdings no longer fulfill their daily needs for food, fodder, and fuelwood. Reforestation often fails on sites near village settlements because of livestock grazing, forest fires, firewood cutting, and other forms of encroachment. These disturbances usually occur after the plantation is two years old, when farmers' cultivation rights to the reforestation site have ended. The SFC recognizes that on forest sites where local use pressure is high and reforestation has repeatedly failed, traditional *tumpangsari* cannot meet forest farmers' increasing needs for job opportunities and income.

Conventional *tumpangsari* policies created a seemingly unbridgeable gap between the SFC and poor, landless farmers. The following concerns have been identified:

(1) The duration of the *tumpangsari* period is limited to two years; and because new sites do not continuously become available, and the supply of forest land for *tumpangsari* no longer meets the demand for access. This shortfall is exacerbated by the ever-increasing rural population.

(2) Long-rotation silvicultural systems limit opportunities for intercropping because the farmers' legal period of access occurs only at the time plantations are established. Teak rotations, for example, vary from 60 to 120 years.

(3) Only about 60 percent of forest land area is actually available for intercropping because of the space taken up by the main tree species, which are planted quite close (usually 3m × 2m; 3m × 1m; or 2m × 2m).

(4) Intercropped species allowed in *tumpangsari* are restricted to rice and corn.

The SFC's objective is to manage forest areas efficiently and economically. At the same time it must provide land for forest farmers to intercrop and must create more job opportunities without threatening production and conservation goals. Innovative agroforestry systems implemented as part of social forestry programs seem to be the best solution to the problems occurring on forest sites near village settlements in Java. Agroforestry technologies are expected to meet forest farmers' needs while maintaining the long-term sustainability of the agroecosystem.

The Social Forestry Program

Agroforestry systems hold promise for optimizing yields and benefits for both the government and local people. The problem is to operate these systems on forest land in an effective and efficient manner that will guarantee the sustainability of the forest. The aims of the SFC's social forestry program are (1) to achieve successful reforestation on unproductive and degraded land to improve multiple-use forest functions, (2) to create job opportunities and increase the income of forest farmers, and (3) to improve the relationship between the SFC and forest farmers and create an equal partnership in forest development for mutual benefit.

After two years, the SFC recognizes that social forestry as a program and as a participatory forest management approach is still developing, and that its success depends on adjusting forest policies. Social forestry differs from existing traditional *tumpangsari* policies in emphasizing (1) villagers' active role in forest management as part of an equal partnership in forest development, (2) bottom-up extension methods and active farmer participation in the planning process, (3) optimum use of forest lands through multiple agroforestry models, and (4) implementation of social forestry on state forest lands in the form of participatory forest management.

One of the underlying assumptions of the Java social forestry program is that landlessness is highly correlated with dependence on forest lands for fuel, fodder, and other forest products. This assumption is based on studies undertaken during the diagnostic research phase prior to implementation of the program.[6] Including the landless and lowest-income households in the program is necessary to ensure that their needs for forest access are directly addressed. To maintain farmers' commitment to the program, yields from the crop components of the agroforestry systems must provide an adequate income on a regular, uninterrupted basis. Proper implementation of the program thus depends on designing agroforestry models that can provide an optimal combination of products for both the SFC and participating farmers. Agroforestry development is therefore intended to (1) improve the utilization of forest land so that it is more sustainable and responsive to local needs, (2) make more arable land available to absorb the excess agriculture labor in areas surrounding the forest and provide these people with additional income, (3) support development through a balance of environmental quality and growth, (4) successfully reforest and maintain forest lands, and (5) develop harmonious cooperation between the SFC and the surrounding communities.

In implementing the social forestry program, the SFC has had close cooperation from related agricultural agencies, the Department of the Interior, and nongovernment organizations (NGOs). It has also begun to readjust forest policy and silvicultural techniques in the following ways:

(1) Selection of the main timber tree is shifting from such long-rotation species as teak to short-rotation species such as Periserianthes falcataria (*Albizia falcataria*), *Acacia mangium,* and *Gmelina arborea*. Rotation lengths for these species can be eight years to fifteen years, depending on the targeted yield or product.

(2) Greater latitude in species selection is also allowed for cash and food crops, fodder, medicinal plants, firewood, and fruit tress as auxiliary agroforestry components.

(3) Farmers receive subsidies for 50 percent of the cost of fertilizers used (beginning in 1989 farmers will receive a 100 percent subsidy for fertilizers). SFC timber growth improves as farmers fertilize crops surrounding the trees.

(4) Seeds for annual crops, and seeds or seedlings for perennial species are distributed by the SFC.

(5) The length of the *tumpangsari* period is based on long-term contracts, which can be extended up to the end of the forest tree rotation period.

(6) The spacing of forest trees is wider, usually 4m × 2m, 5m × 2m, or 6m × 1m, depending on the site quality and the characteristics of the main tree species.

(7) The SFC also provides funds for land rehabilitation and soil conservation on sites where soil conditions are too poor for reforestation.

In addition, the SFC helps forest farmer groups market their products after harvest to ensure a better price for their yield. Program planners are also trying to provide credit to forest farmers who want to plant high-value crops, which usually require high levels of inputs.

Technical Constraints and Opportunities

Site selection is fundamental to the success of social forestry projects. Under the adopted criteria, acceptable sites must be unproductive lands on which standard reforestation approaches have failed due to encroachment by surrounding communities. An estimated 10 percent of Java forest land meets these criteria, and the SFC is currently collecting more accurate information about the exact locations and condition of such sites. Many of the most critical sites are located where it is easiest for people to enter the forest or where forest land borders community lands. On some sites, however, reforestation efforts have repeatedly failed, not only because of socio-economic pressures from surrounding communities, but also because of extremely poor biophysical conditions that prevent successful forest regeneration. Without adequate tree cover to protect and restore the soil, some sites have experienced severe erosion and need special rehabilitation efforts. If the biophysical site conditions are known to be difficult, the site's suitability for social forestry needs to be carefully evaluated. To sustain the participating farmers' commitment to the social forestry program, the site must be able to provide an adequate income.

Another important constraint on agroforestry systems is rotation length. Under conventional *tumpangsari* systems, species such as teak *(Tectona grandis)* are produced on 60- to 120-year rotations. Some soil erosion may occur at the time of plantation establishment, during which farmers are allowed to cultivate cereal crops for a period of two years. Over the length of the rotation, however, the long subsequent fallow period eventually ameliorates the effect of initial soil disturbances. Social forestry contracts, on the other hand, allow farmers to continue to grow food crops past the two-year limit of *tumpangsari,* sometimes up to five years. In addition, a recent policy decision allows reclassification of certain teak sites to shorter rotation species such as *Gmelina arborea* and Periserianthes falcataria *(Albizzia falcataria),* which can be grown on eight- to fifteen-year rotations.

Shorter rotations and longer cropping periods will benefit participating farmers by increasing the forest lands available for intercropping, which in turn will effectively increase overall yields from agricultural crops. As changes in rotation length result in longer periods of intensive cultivation, soil conservation measures and site selection criteria gain importance. On severely degraded forest lands, soil rehabilitation programs must be given initial priority over intensive agroforestry systems development.

Competition between plants can also pose problems in agroforestry systems. It is important to maintain a balance between different species, as well as between individuals of the same species. Competition can be manipulated, however, to produce positive effects. Shade-intolerant species are often characterized by early rapid height growth, which enables them to compete successfully with their neighbors and emerge into the canopy. This growth pattern results in straight, clear stems, which are preferred for timber. As the growing space is filled, growth rates usually slow. Over-use of the growing space can result in stagnation of the stand.

Most of the main timber species used for reforestation in Java are shade-intolerant, although some, such as damar *(Agathis spp.),* tolerate shade in their juvenile stages. As the main timber trees mature, however, they begin to overtop most of the other components of the agroforestry system. Some auxiliary fruit species may also emerge into the higher canopy layer, for example durien *(Durio zibethinus)* and randu *(Ceiba pentandra).* Although other fruit tree species can survive in the understory, they may not receive sufficient light to flower and bear significant quantities of fruit. This concern is being tested by intercropping cashew *(Anacardium occidentale)* with teak on social forestry sites in East Java. The teak will eventually overtop the cashew trees, but teak has both a narrow, high crown, and a deciduous habit during the dry season, which increases the available light. The degree to which this stimulates flowering and fruiting of cashews in the understory will determine the feasibility of this intercropping pattern.

In addition, shade-tolerant grasses and leguminous fodder/cover crops, medicinal plants, and herb and spice crops show promise for providing additional income to farmers while providing ground cover for soil conservation. Cardomon *(Amomum carclamomum)*, turmeric *(Curcuma domestica)*, and various other members of the ginger family *(Zingiberaceae)* are particularly interesting due to their potential as valuable cash crops. At several project sites farmers began cultivating these herbs and spices in their home gardens for urban and export markets, and have expanded their production onto social forestry sites.

A new policy decision will allow farmers to plant horticultural crops such as coffee and cacao in the understory. Both species are somewhat shade-tolerant. Annual yields from coffee and cacao grown under shade may be lower than plants grown in full sunlight, but shaded plants are reported to be more pest resistant, and they may live and produce longer.[7]

Competition occurs in the root zone as well, but this can be minimized by selecting species with different root formation patterns. For example, the conventional *tumpangsari* approach uses deep-rooted main tree species intercropped with shallow-rooted annuals. During the first year of intercropping, some competition may occur as both the food crops and the trees draw moisture and nutrients from the top soil layers. For this reason, forest farmers are not allowed to sow crop rows too near the tree rows, and are expected to tend the trees to keep down the growth of grasses and other weeds. Once the deeper root system of the main tree species begins to develop, competition at this level becomes less significant.

The new agroforestry technologies being tried under the social forestry program are more complicated than conventional *tumpangsari* in terms of root-zone competition because they include additional species. Fruit, fodder, and fuelwood trees in particular can develop deep or laterally spreading root systems. Farmers, for instance, do not favor the use of *Acacia villosa*, because the roots concentrate in the areas reserved for interplanting cereal crops. The tough roots of the acacia compete with the shallow-rooted annuals for moisture and nutrients and make cultivation more difficult. On a number of sites, grasses are set out in contour rows between the trees for soil conservation. Farmers can, however, control the spread of the grasses so that they do not compete with food crops.

Technical Approaches to Solving Agroforestry Design Problems

One of the most critical issues now facing the Java social forestry program is the need to ensure that yields from agroforestry systems can be maintained at sufficiently high levels to provide an adequate, consistent income to the farmers. The project is completing the third planting season, and on some sites the trees already have begun to shade the understory plants. Once the canopy begins to close, farmers will no longer be able to culti-vate light-demanding cereal, legume, and vegetable crops and will need alternative sources of revenue. On several sites, guavas are already be-ginning to bear fruit two years after planting. Most of the other fruit tree species are expected to become productive within five years of planting. Economic studies are being undertaken to project the farmers' return on fruit and other alternative crops.

New social forestry policies now encourage foresters to select from a wider range of main timber species, and farmers may incorporate a greater variety of different species into the agroforestry system, including fruit trees and other horticultural species, fodder and fuelwood crops, medicinal herbs, and fiber crops. This increases species diversity in agroforestry systems on social forestry sites. The discouraging experience with lamtoro *(Leucaena spp.)*, has reinforced the importance of including a variety of species within each component.[8] Lamtoro was widely adopted in Southeast Asia almost to the exclusion of other potentially valuable spe-cies. Most of the lamtoro planted on social forestry sites has been damaged or killed by the jumping plant lice insect *(Heteropsylla cubana)*, which rapidly spread throughout Asia and the Pacific. The problem of being too depen-dent on one all-purpose species is now apparent, and current efforts strive to combine several different species to meet a variety of needs. Resistant varieties of lamtoro are now being tested, and other multipurpose annual and perennial species such as *Gliricidia sepium, Calliandra calothyrsus, Flemingia spp., Acacia villosa, Panicum maximum, Setaria spp.,* and *Ananas comosus* are being planted to diversify the agroforestry design.

Initial spacing and thinning are other considerations in designing agroforestry systems. Wider spacing between rows increases the amount of land available for food crops and delays crown closure, allowing farmers to continue to cultivate cereal crops for three to five years. Understanding spatial and chronological stratification is important in predicting changes over time as these new agroforestry models develop. Recent research on teak stand development indicates that wider initial spacing for teak may be more appropriate on poor sites where teak does not use growing space efficiently.[9] Early thinning can also increase the space available for intercropping.

Forest plantations are normally thinned to relieve competition so that overcrowding does not unduly reduce the growth rate or lead to stagna-tion of the stand. Selective removal of inferior stems provides the needed growing space for the higher quality individuals. The SFC uses thinning schedules developed for different species and site conditions. Frequency and intensity of the thinning depend on the site index and the age and condition of the stand. Generally, teak plantations are first thinned five years after planting, and again approximately every five to ten years, until a final stocking of about 100 trees per hectare is reached. Thinning schedules for main tree species planted on social forestry sites need to account for the wider initial spacing pattern and other innovations in the agroforestry design, such as the inclusion of other tree species that compose 20 percent of the stand.

To provide high-quality lumber, a tree should have a clear, straight stem, free of branches, knots, and other defects. Usually trees grown in a plantation arrangement will not produce many persistant lateral branches, because the close spacing encourages suppression and natural pruning of branches, rather than development of a spreading crown. In some silviculture systems where natural pruning does not occur, trees are hand-pruned to increase their value, but this is costly. In Java, natural pruning is generally sufficient for most forest tree species. Because the new agroforestry designs for social forestry involve wider spacing of the plantations, there is some concern that the trees will be spaced too far apart for natural pruning to occur. If certain main tree species, particularly teak, develop more persistent branches than usual, the quality and value of the lumber may be significantly reduced.

People living near teak plantations have traditionally been permitted to remove leaves and small branches from the lower stems of young teak trees. Farmers prefer to pick the young, tender leaves, which are used as a wrapping material, especially for packaging foods to be sold at market. Many foresters in Java apparently believe that this practice adversely affects tree health.[10] With wider initial tree spacing, however, collecting leaves and lower branches has an effect similar to pruning, thus reducing the possibility of poor form development. Farmers should be allowed to prune leaves and small branches from the lower part of the main stem once the trees are at least four meters high and ten centimeters in diameter. Consequently, increasing spacing of main timber species may have dual benefits for forest farmers: allowing the longer light availability for growing other species and greater opportunities to gain income through pruning teak and other timber species.

BALANCING ALTERNATIVES

In its stewardship of forest lands in Java, the SFC must balance a number of potentially conflicting management objectives. The critical condition of social forestry sites requires that several objectives be given priority. To prevent further degradation of these sites, changes have already been made in forest policy, agroforestry and silvicultural technologies, and in the roles of foresters and forest farmers in the planning process. This process still involves difficult decisions, however, and it may be necessary to trade one benefit for another. An ongoing discussion of these issues is therefore important so that each may be analyzed as it becomes apparent. A problem-solving approach is needed that can weigh the various trade-offs, which include direct benefits to the farmers, indirect benefits to society, forest production targets, watershed management and conservation goals, equitable access to benefits, and long-term economic effects. Many of these trade-offs can be described and compared using economic concepts, although economic justifications cannot always determine final natural resource policy decisions.

Maximizing System Sustainability

Technical considerations in agroforestry design often overlap with socio-economic and institutional processes. In Java, farmers' satisfaction with the program is largely based on good yields of rice, corn, and other high-value food crops. A fundamental assumption of the project is that farmers will be able to substitute food crop harvests with fruit, fuelwood, fodder crops, medicinal plants, and other products once shade from the closing canopy makes it impossible to grow light-demanding annuals. Yields from these later harvests must provide income comparable to that from the initial cereal crops for farmers to remain committed to the program and the management of reforestation sites.

In upland Java, agricultural sustainability is closely linked with soil and water conservation. Over-intensive use of fragile sites can trigger a process of degradation leading to soil erosion, poor water infiltration, and low soil moisture retention. These conditions adversely affect tree seedlings planted to rehabilitate the area. The result is a cyclic pattern of failed reforestation and continued degradation. Even where soil loss is not a problem, soil quality may gradually deteriorate due to the continuous removal of nutrients from the site in the form of crop residues, tree leaves, bark, and dead branches and twigs used for fuel, fodder, and medicines. The result is a net drain of nutrients and organic matter unless they are replaced by manures or other fertilizers.

Other trade-offs include accepting reduced revenues from the main tree species due to wider initial spacing, shorter rotations, and selection of lower-value species to reduce the high cost of reforestation projects. Furthermore, although the individual revenue yields of timber, resins, gums, and other products may be lower, total site productivity can be higher.

Another trade-off that foresters and forest farmers now face concerns the balance of power in technical decision making. To increase farmers' participation in designing agroforestry systems, foresters are now trained in extension and communication skills, the organization and training of forest farmer groups, and use of social forestry planning procedures. Often foresters feel compelled to veto farmer suggestions for species they think will be unsuitable due to a site's soil or climatic conditions or for other reasons. There is evidence, however, that SFC staff and forest farmer groups are beginning to discuss these issues more openly. Criteria are currently being developed for evaluating agroforestry systems on different sites. The technical and socio-economic issues cited here are fundamental to the development of these criteria.

Program Needs

Because the social forestry program is complex and interdisciplinary in nature, almost every facet of it requires more information, particularly in the field of agroforestry technology. Policy makers need accurate information from the field, foresters in the field need technical guidelines, and farmers need advice on how to grow new crops. Technical evaluation criteria and methods, agroecosystems research, species selection, and agroforestry design materials for training and use in the field are being developed to meet these needs. Scientists and technicians from the SFC's agroforestry advisory team are attempting to develop a range of agroforestry systems suitable for varying site conditions. They are also developing guidelines that allow a wider range of appropriate species for each agroecological zone, while permitting farmers maximum flexibility in adapting systems to unique local conditions. The State Forest Corporation needs to actively seek and ensure the participation of other government technical agencies in the development of agroforestry systems. Forest use systems must be designed to respond to the needs of the poorest farmers in the program. Special attention must be given to fast-maturing crops and initial income subsidies, since low-income families depend on daily wage labor for their livelihood, and often cannot afford inputs and the costs involved in site preparation.

Just as environmental factors such as soil type, topography, soil fertility, climate, and local pest and plant diseases differ for each location, so do the economic and infrastructural conditions. Agroforestry systems design must also consider infrastructural factors such as road conditions, the availability of inputs and credit, market proximity, and harvest prices in each village. An analysis of private land-cropping practices, agroforestry composition, and recent innovations can help farmer-forester design teams evaluate the economic viability of proposed crops. Farmers need to be allowed to determine the balance of products for home consumption or cash crops.

Traditional planting systems and soil conservation techniques also need to be better understood, and beneficial techniques incorporated into emerging agroforestry systems. Research is required to determine the effect of certain species on soil conservation and erosion, the growth rates for various species combinations, the compatibility or competition between species, and the appropriate spacings, thinning cycles, and rotations. Experience with agroforestry technologies on Java indicate they have the potential to exceed traditional monoculture timber stand production in net revenues, labor absorption, and local income generation. To achieve these goals, however, systems must be fine-tuned to meet site-specific biological, marketing, and labor conditions. Agroforestry technology development must be combined with program flexibility to adapt production systems to local needs and opportunities. Scientists, foresters, and farmers must cooperate in developing effective agroforestry research programs to meet those needs.

NOTES

1. Wiersum, K. F. 1982. "Tree Gardening and Taungya on Java: Examples of Agroforestry Techniques in the Humid Tropics." *Agroforestry Systems* 1:53–70.

2. Christanty, L., O. S. Abdoellah, G. Marten and J. Iskandar. 1983. Traditional Agroforestry in West Java: The Pekarangan (Homegarden) and Kebun Talun (Perennial Annual Rotation) Cropping Systems." Working Paper, Environment and Policy Institute, East-West Center, Honolulu, Hawaii; Michon, G. 1983. "Village-Forest-Gardens in West Java," in *Plant Research in Agroforestry.* Huxley, P. A. (ed.). Nairobi: ICRAF, pp. 13–24; Stoler, A. 1978. "Garden Use and Household Economy in Rural Java." *Bulletin of Indonesian Economic Studies.* Vol. XIV, No. 2., pp. 85–101; Wiersum, K. F. 1980. "Possibilities for Use and Development of Indigenous Agro Forestry Systems for Sustained Land-Use on Java." *Tropical Ecology and Development,* pp. 515–521.

3. Altieri, M. A., Letourneau, D. K., and Davies, J. R. 1983. "Developing Sustainable Agroecosystems." *Bioscience* 33:1:45–49.

4. Christanty, Linda, and Johan Iskandar. 1985. "Development of Decision-Making and Management Skills in Traditional Agroforestry: Examples in West Java," in *Community Forestry: Socio-Economic Aspects.* Y. S. Rao, N. T. Vergara, G. W. Lovelace (eds.). Bangkok: FAO/RAPA, pp. 198–214.

5. Conway, Gordon R. 1986. *Agroecosystem Analysis for Research and Development.* Bangkok: Winrock International.

6. Peluso, Nancy Lee. 1986. *Report on Social Forestry Field Research in West and Central Java (October 1984–October 1985).* Prepared for the State Forestry Corporation and the Ford Foundation.

7. Opeke, L. K. 1982. *Tropical Tree Crops.* New York: John Wiley and Sons.

8. Serrano, R. C. 1988. "Alternative to Ipil-Ipil for Agroforestry." *The PCARRD Monitor* 16:3:1, 10.

9. Larson, Bruce C., and Zaman, M. N. "Spacing and Thinning Guidelines for Teak *(Tectona grandis L.).*" TRI Working Paper No. 2. Yale School of Forestry and Environmental Studies.

10. Peluso. *Report on Social Forestry Field Research in West and Central Java (October 1984–October 1985).*

Part III

Empowering
Communities
Through
Social Forestry

Introduction

Mark Poffenberger

MANY DEVELOPMENT INITIATIVES are undermined by the inability to learn from past experience. Few practitioners would dispute that rural development planning and implementation is a complex process with frequent failures. Project planners, whether working for a local or international nongovernment agency, a bilateral donor, multilateral bank, or a government development bureaucracy, are often under pressure to design and implement projects with little time to reflect or study prior experiences. Because projects require years to mature, each stage of planning, implementation, and expansion usually involves different individuals. Staff turnover and time constraints make it difficult for administrators to draw from past activities to improve project effectiveness and efficiency.

Part III examines the implementation and impact of social forestry projects conducted in Southeast Asia over the past decade, drawing on the experiences of national social forestry programs and local projects in developing collaborative management systems. Each national program discussion is followed by a chapter reviewing a specific social forestry project. Chapter 9 reviews the evolution of collaborative forest use systems in Thailand. Pragtong and Thomas begin by examining the political forces which have shaped forest management policies in Thailand over the past century. They review some of the events which have encouraged the Royal Forestry Department (RFD) to begin experimenting with new policies and procedures to respond to growing population pressures in forest areas and discuss the lessons that foresters have drawn from these experiences.

They note that while Thai environmental groups lobby for the strict protection of national forest lands and the conservation of watersheds, other interests support the development of intensive tree production systems and the privatization of forest lands. Strict conservation may offer hopes of protecting tracts of natural forests, but staffing constraints limit this approach to a relatively small area of prime national park lands. Privatization, while appealing to the interests of large commercial forestry enterprises, is no guarantee that forest cover will be maintained. Further, the transfer of forest use rights to the private sector threatens the interests of local communities and could create political problems for the RFD and the government. The authors stress the need to explore the feasability of smaller-scale production and management systems responsive to rural needs before privatization is initiated. They argue that community-managed mixed agroforestry systems more closely reflect the natural forest ecology than do monoculture timber plantations. The authors point out that past attempts to respond to rural needs through work with individual households could be made more effective by developing tenurial arrangements for villages or groups of households. To effectively develop community management systems, the RFD will need to continue to expand the analytic, organizational, and technical tool kit available to foresters. In concluding, the authors describe recent RFD initiatives in developing a new generation of social forestry projects that allow forest farmers greater participation in designing and implementing forest management systems.

Chapter 10 focuses on the RFD's experiences in implementing community forest management systems in two forest communities in Northeast Thailand. An integrated village project was begun in 1978 and, in a neighboring village, a forest land stewardship project (STK) was started in 1981. By comparing these two activities, the authors assess the projects' success in helping community members to shift from swidden cultivation and forest resources harvesting to intensified agriculture. The projects were ultimately intended to stabilize migration onto state forest lands, an objective the RFD failed to achieve.

To illuminate the projects' shortcomings, Hafner and Apichatvullop analyze agency constraints, the projects' failures to respond to community needs, and the wider political context and agenda of the time. They note that centralized planning prevented these projects from exploiting the indigenous knowledge, institutions, and values of the participating communities. Further, the authors contend that the RFD did not sufficiently develop management skills within the community and that social and technical components were often poorly integrated in community forest project initiatives. These problems are common in community forestry projects; however, through documentation and discussion, Thai social foresters are developing new strategies for working more effectively with forest dwellers.

Chapter 11 describes an ongoing program within the Indonesian State Forest Corporation (SFC) to help the agency work with forest villages in jointly managing state lands. The Java social forestry program is divided into three phases. The first stage involved diagnosing the growing tensions between the SFC and forest communities. The authors cite three factors causing much of the conflict: (1) long-standing disputes between the government and villagers over forest land and tree tenure, (2) a history of bureaucratic misbehavior such as corruption and theft, and (3) the failure of forest policies to respond to diverse ecological and socio-economic conditions in forest villages. After identifying these problems, the SFC began a second phase: pilot projects to resolve disputes, improve villager-staff relations, and increase responsiveness to local forest use needs. The innovative strategies used in pilot projects include training foresters in community organizing techniques and providing villagers with longer, renewable forest use leases, credit, agricultural inputs, and fruit tree seedlings. The agency's problems in implementing the new social forestry strategy are also discussed. In the final section the authors examine the social forestry initiative's shift from a pilot project to an island-wide program.

While most analyses of rural development activities focus on the village, this chapter examines a forestry bureaucracy's problems in reorienting its policies, procedures, and staff attitudes. By following a program from the time management problems were identified through research, pilot projects, and expansion phases, the authors are able to identify some of the organizational problems and constraints which emerged as the agency attempted to develop new methods to work with forest communities. While the Java social forestry program did not solve all the problems identified in one phase before moving to the successive stage, a working group that continuously monitored the program kept attention on strategic weaknesses and the search for possible solutions.

Chapter 12 shifts the discussion from the densely populated island of Java to Irian Jaya, where foresters are working with tribal communities to establish a buffer zone around the Cyclops Mountain Conservation Area. With few professional foresters and over 250 ethno-linguistic groups scattered through rugged, heavily forested terrain, Irian Jaya represents a complicated management problem. Conventional custodial management systems hold little promise in the near future for the large areas recently declared protected forest and national park land. Since boundaries between state forest and tribal lands have never been negotiated, the implementation of government management control has led to conflict. In this chapter the authors describe a program designed to develop collaborative tribal-government management systems. The program assumed that the ancestral land rights of tribal communities living around the reserve must be recognized under any management system. They describe the process of helping tribal leaders to map their lands and gain legal recognition of their usufruct rights. By describing how the program was implemented in three different tribal communities, the authors demonstrate how the strategy had to be refined to meet local needs. They describe problems in gaining local and central government support for the effort and show how assumptions carried over from the Java program undermined its relevance to the Irian scene. Yet, they conclude that the best hope for protecting the rich tropical rainforests in Irain Jaya lies in enhancing tribal land-tenure security and helping Irianese farmers to intensify agroforestry systems.

Chapter 13 chronicles the history of Integrated Social Forestry Program (ISFP) in the Philippines. Nowhere in Southeast Asia has social forestry received as much political support, financial backing, and technical advice as in the Philippines. The Philippines was the first nation in the region to begin a land-lease program for forest dwellers and the only country that also offers communal leases to community groups. This chapter describes the conditions under which the ISFP was formulated and its strengths and weaknesses. Considerable attention is given to the Uplands Working Group, which has advised the ISFP since its inception. The working group was intended to help an old organization move in a new direction and evolve a new structure. The chapter details the working group's strategies and problems in guiding the forestry agency toward greater collaboration with upland forest communities. The authors describe the working group's utility and limitations in influencing the agency, and the ways in which political change in the Philippines could affect the program. The chapter concludes that the working group has helped create a pool of experience, tools, and talent well suited to resolving upland management problems, but that ultimately the success of more effective management systems depends on the political will to decentralize land resource control.

In the final chapter, Salve Borlagdan describes a social forestry project in upland Cebu in the Philippines. She reviews the project from its initiation, discussing mistakes and problems encountered and actions taken to resolve them. Issues of land tenure, stewardship certificates, agroforestry technologies and soil conservation measures, and community organization are discussed. She describes how project staff expanded the participation of community members in land surveys, planning sessions, and agroforestry enterprises, which made the program more accepted and more effective.

As a group, the chapters in Part III provide a review of selected social forestry strategies initiated in Southeast Asia over the past decade to respond to environmental degradation and the growing conflicts between governments and forest communities. These cases illustrate the political, organizational, and socio-economic problems encountered in assisting natural resource management bureaucracies to work with, rather than against, rural people. Most importantly, they demonstrate that, given the time and the will, rural communities, forestry agencies, planners, and scientists can develop solutions to forest management problems.

CHAPTER NINE

Evolving Management Systems in Thailand

Kamon Pragtong and David E. Thomas

CRITICS OF CURRENT forest management practices often blame defor-estation on forest agencies, which they see as closed, conservative groups resistant to change. This chapter, however, is based on the premise that Thailand's Royal Forestry Department has long been responsive to fac-tors beyond its immediate control. The forestry profession seeks to apply ecological principles in managing forest resources to meet societal goals. But as an agency of the government, a forest department is both empo-wered and restricted by policies of higher governmental authority, which are themselves influenced by events, movements, interests, and personal-ities in the larger society. A forest agency's institutional survival depends to a large extent on its ability to respond to such mandates.

Forest production is a long-term enterprise, especially when compared to the more volatile economic and political arenas, where a wide range of interests make claims on forests, forest products, and forest lands. Thus, periods of rapid social, economic and political change may lead to periods of conflict, uncertainty, and instability in forest management systems. Thai-land, along with many other countries, is now in such a period.

The fact that collaborative forest management systems are being de-veloped in various countries is indicative of similar evolutionary trends. But the specific form of new systems will vary according to the charac-teristics of each society. The first part of this chapter examines the past evolution of the Royal Forestry Department as it adapted to changes in Thai society, culminating in the emergence of a need for collaborative management systems. The second part of the chapter presents an exam-ple of current Thai efforts to reach a collaborative forest land use synthe-sis, and issues which are yet to be resolved.

PAST EVOLUTION OF THE ROYAL FORESTRY DEPARTMENT

Thai state regulation of land and forest use has been evolving for centu-ries. During the Sukothai Period (1238–1350), land law centered on the

1292 inscriptions of King Ramkamhaeng, and during the Ayutthaya Period (1350–1767) it was based largely on the Land Code of 1360. During these periods, people were few and resources were plentiful, and the central focus of government was on control over people rather than land. Vast forest areas were largely an untamed frontier.

During the Rattanakosin Period (1782 to the present), however, as colonial powers extracted timber from neighboring countries, the commercial value of forest resources increased rapidly, especially in the northern teak forests. Until the end of the nineteenth century, land-use rights were allocated by still relatively autonomous local nobilities, many of whom began profiting from logging contracts with European companies. The central government watched these developments, and under the administrative reforms of King Chulalongkorn employed the British forester H. Slade to study the situation. Based largely on Slade's recommendations, the Royal Forestry Department (RFD) was established in 1896 (with Slade as chief conservator) in an effort by the government to accomplish at least three goals: (1) to regulate harvests of valuable tree species, primarily teak; (2) to capture a portion of the benefits from tree harvest for the central government through royalties and taxes; and (3) to assist in the consolidation of central authority over regional nobilities.

The following discussion outlines the evolution of forest administration and management activities under the RFD since 1896. We see the evolution as passing through four general phases, the last of which is still in progress. In discussing each phase, an attempt is made to describe how the agency has adapted to changes in the macro-forces which shape and direct its micro-policies and programs.

PHASE I, 1896–1953: FOREST HARVEST
IN THE NATIONAL INTEREST

Initial government mandates for the RFD focused on the regulation and taxation of valuable commercial species. Forest legislation began in 1897 with forest and teak tree protection acts, followed by an act prohibiting illegal marking of timber. In 1899, forest ownership was formally claimed by the central government, and teak extraction without payment of royalties was prohibited. Scattered teak harvest leases were consolidated into larger contiguous areas, with fifteen-year leases covering half of each area. The second half was leased as harvest if the first half was completed, followed by reopening of the first half. These efforts were almost exclusively in the native teak forests of the North, while in the dry evergreen and dry dipterocarp forests of the Northeast and the moist evergreen forests of the South, local authorities and populations continued their traditional relationships with the land and forests.

RFD personnel performed primarily regulatory duties, as officers selected and girdled trees to be harvested, and inspected, measured, and taxed logs as they were transported from the forest down major river systems to port cities, primarily Bangkok, for export. The first RFD experimental forest plantation was established in 1906, using the Burmese *taungya* forest species/annual crop intercrop system. This early precursor of agroforestry systems was employed to meet subsistence needs of local laborers in remote areas. While more extensive plantation development began after 1940, by 1956 the total area planted to teak was only about forty square kilometers, with another twenty square kilometers planted to nonteak species.

The scope of central government forest regulation gradually expanded. The Forest Care Act of 1913 brought selected species other than teak under central government control, and in 1900 and 1921 laws were promulgated to conserve wild elephants. The central government also began collecting royalties on minor forest products, with annual revenues approaching 1.5 million baht in 1949, before dropping to 0.5 million baht by 1953. Although in 1916 the government adopted a policy aimed at establishing reserved forest lands, rather than just species, another twenty years were required to enact implementing legislation.

During the decade following the 1932 transformation of Thailand into a constitutional monarchy, more fundamental change began to occur. The RFD was reorganized in 1935 to include four technical divisions with duties related to forest control, silviculture, forest products research, and forest schools. The number of Divisional (regional) Forestry Offices was expanded from twelve to twenty-one, and the RFD chief conservator was elevated to director-general. Legal reform began in 1936 with revision of the Forest Care Act. Permanent production forest reserves were first authorized by the 1938 Protection and Reservation of Forests Act, but procedures required about a decade to complete.[1] Other forest laws were revised in the 1941 Forest Act and its amendments in 1948 and 1951. In 1947, a separate RFD forest production unit known as the Forest Industry Organization (FIO) was established, and by 1952 it was annually cutting 50,000 cubic meters of timber, including 20 percent of the total teak harvest. The government moved into wood processing by establishing the Thai Plywood Company in 1951. Training needs expanded with RFD responsibilities and in 1952 the United Nations Food and Agricultural Organization (FAO) began a technical assistance project, including overseas education and training of RFD staff in intensive forest management practices.

Relationships between the RFD and local communities centered on regulation, labor, and accommodations for local use. Problems related to the requirements of nearby local communities emerged as the RFD began allocating logging concessions to foreign companies. In response, the RFD began reserving 50 percent of concession trees to work itself, using local labor, with the goal of providing stable local employment while increasing state revenues. RFD officials also resolved problems with local loggers, by allowing royalty-free grants for harvest which did not enter into export trade. By 1953, RFD was annually documenting free grants of 0.5 million cubic meters of saw timber, 1.2 million cubic meters of fuelwood, and nearly 1 million cubic meters of charcoal for local consumption.

Throughout this phase, forests and land were in abundance and population densities were still relatively low. By 1953, about 60 percent of the total land area of the Kingdom remained in forest, with regional levels ranging from 50 percent in the Northeast and the South, to about 60 percent in the Central Region and 70 percent in the North. Harvest concessions covered about 40 percent of the land in the North, and very little elsewhere. Population density averaged about thirty-three persons per square kilometer, ranging from twenty-one in the North to fifty-one in the Central Region. Recognized farm holdings covered about 14 percent of the Kingdom, with a low of about 7 percent in the North, to a high of 19 percent in the Central Region.

PHASE II, 1954–1967: STATE ALLOCATION OF LAND FOR ECONOMIC DEVELOPMENT

The focus of forest management activity shifted during this period from consolidation of central authority and royalty collection to management of centrally allocated lands to facilitate economic development. The phase begins with the 1954 Land Act, which provided the legal basis for most land classification and ownership in the Kingdom, established the National Land Allocation Committee, and revised the Protection and Reservation of Forests Act. Two years later, the Forest Industry Organization became a semiautonomous corporation, independent of the RFD.

Change proceeded slowly, however, until the political rise of Field Marshall Sarit Thanarat in the late 1950s, after which the government began a strong push for economic development. Sarit's often authoritarian approach included national five-year plans for economic development, and gave central planning technocrats more authority in deciding how resources would be allocated. It also included establishment of the Forest Police. An important underlying reason for this thrust in national policy was the perception of a growing threat to national security posed by communist liberation movements in neighboring Indochina. Sarit and his immediate successors allied themselves with the U.S., sent troops to battle in Viet Nam, and mounted counter-insurgency programs in the Northeast and the North.

Several important policies and legislative acts were formulated as the nation launched its first five-year plan (1962–1966), including revisions of the Forest Act and passage of wildlife conservation and national parks acts. A land classification committee was established to implement provisions of the 1954 Land Act, and the Land Development Department was established to conduct a detailed soil survey of the Kingdom. While the first five-year plan adopted a 1948 FAO-recommended reserved forest target of 50 percent of the land area, implementation proceeded slowly, despite regulation revisions. Finally, in 1964, the Protection and Reservation of Forests Act was replaced by the Reserved Forest Act, which reduced procedures for classifying land as reserved forest. As forest cover dropped under 50 percent, the forest target was revised to 40 percent of the land area with the 1967 initiation of the second five-year plan.

In line with government policy, the RFD's orientation toward land area was clearly consolidated. Forest management continued to focus on concession administration and harvest regulation, but with foresters' skills upgraded by overseas training, much larger replanting programs began in 1961. As officials returned from overseas, they argued successfully for legislation and establishment of the Parks, Wildlife and Watershed Management sections of the Silviculture Division. The first national park was established in 1962, and establishment of wildlife sanctuaries and watershed conservation units began a few years later. The National Parks Section became a Sub-Division in 1965. After 1964, the push to rapidly gazette large areas of reserved forest land required a major agency effort.

While relationships between the RFD and local communities continued to enter on regulation, taxation, and accommodation, this phase marked the emergence of ambiguous and conflicting land ownership claims between communities and the central government. Free grants of timber not entering export trade were abolished in 1960, although harvest permits for household consumption could still be requested. The 1964 Reserved Forest Act provided for rapid declaration of reserves by reducing land claim verification requirements. RFD officials realized that reserved areas included some existing villages, but they assumed procedures would be established for processing claims to previously held lands. In mountainous areas, however, many ethnic minorities had no legal status in Thai society, and claims to lands under shifting cultivation and forest fallow were difficult to fit under lowland Thai land legislation. In 1967, the FIO began to work with villages inside forest lands under a new program of integrated forest village development. As in early RFD concession and plantation management programs, the dominant concern of this innovative program was a stable supply of labor in remote areas.

Transformation of the landscape began to accelerate during this period. By 1967, forest cover dropped to 48 percent of the Kingdom's land area, while farm holdings grew to 26 percent and population density rose to over sixty-two persons per square kilometer. The rate of change was slowest in the mountainous North, which retained over two-thirds of its area under forest cover, had an official population density of only 45 persons per square kilometer, and where recognized farm holdings covered only 15 percent of the region. Declared reserved forest covered about 15 percent of the nation's land, including 10 percent of the Northeast and nearly 20 percent of other regions. Harvest concessions continued to occupy 40 percent of the North, but little area elsewhere. National parks and wildlife sanctuaries occupied less than 1 percent of the land area.

PHASE III, 1968–1980: THE VANISHING FOREST FRONTIER

This phase begins with the 1968 decision to extend long-term harvest concession leases throughout the country. The motivation for this change had its roots in Phase II and the government's push for economic development. In addition to accelerated declaration of reserved forest, the RFD was directed to declare concession areas containing sufficent compartments for thirty years of harvest. This program resulted in more than 500 concession areas covering half the land area of the country, including overlapping concessions for teak and nonteak species. Provincial logging companies were established to harvest the concessions, with capital mobilized on the basis of renewable fifteen-year concession contracts. Tree replanting requirements were mandated in 1970, and by 1973 provincial logging companies were paying a fee to the FIO to perform the task for them. While this may have seemed a progressive effort to mobilize forest resources in support of economic development, its scale was based on ambitious optimism that did not allow for the events and social turbulence which were to follow.

In 1973, as the United States was winding down its Indochina war effort, a student-led rebellion against the authoritarian military regime resulted in the formation of a democratic government. While the new government had difficulty maintaining political stability, it managed to initiate a number of policies and programs, including reestablishment of relations with China and a request for the withdrawal of U.S. military bases, before it ended in 1976 in a violent military coup. Domestic policies during the democratic period gave increased emphasis to the plight of the rapidly growing poor rural population: they included central government funding of local projects, and Prime Minister Kukrit Pramoj's 1974 declaration of amnesty for those residing in reserved forest lands. The growing importance of land issues was reflected in the establishment of the Land Consolidation Commission and the Agricultural Land Reform Committee. Growing concern with environmental deterioration resulted in the National Environmental Quality Act and establishment of the National Environment Board in 1975. The planning approach to resolving land-use conflicts was reflected in the 1975 Town and Country Planning Act.

These events affected the RFD in several ways. While the national parks unit obtained Division status in 1972, the democratic period brought rapid expansion of the national park system, and international cooperation leading to initiation of Biosphere Reserves. Wildlife conservation and watershed management sections were also upgraded to Division status, and the National Forest Land Management Division (NFLMD) was established to develop programs in deteriorated and occupied reserved forest lands. The government's concern for rural people living within reserved forest gave rise to the NFLMD's Forest Village Program and the Watershed Management Division's Watershed Development Units. Both of these programs were strongly influenced by the technocrat-planned integrated approach to rural development then in vogue with progressive development agencies around the world. Virtually all of the new RFD programs, however, were directed toward reserved forests already blanketed with concession contracts.

The military coup of 1976 resulted in a wave of student activists seeking refuge in the forest. While some joined militant units, most began local political organization campaigns in sympathetic remote villages. Buoyed by the U.S. retreat from Indochina and reassertion of military rule in Thailand, externally supported militant groups stepped up anti-government activities. While battles raged in remote areas of the Northeast and the North, improved relations with China brought decreased external support and splits within the primarily Maoist militant opposition. Seizing the opportunity, military leaders began an amnesty program for rebels, who began surrendering to be reintegrated into Thai society. Parliamentary elections were held in 1979 under a newly modified constitution, and the communist movement began to collapse. As violence subsided, government attention shifted to rural political stabilization and economic development, including continuation of several programs begun during the democratic period. Military focus shifted to security problems along the Kampuchean border after the 1979 Vietnamese invasion of Kampuchea, and to continued security problems in the South.

Again, RFD programs reflected external events. The military government supported the centrally organized forest village concept, which was extended in the Watershed Management Division's Hilltribe Forest Village Program in 1977. The militant opposition, however, used local land conflicts related to reserved forests and logging concessions to seek support in remote areas and, as violence increased, small, scattered RFD units found a natural alliance with military units. By 1978, this was formalized in a forest village program under the Local Development for Security Project. Thus, RFD duties expanded to include a wide range of community planning, infrastructure construction, and rural development activities, despite a lack of training in these areas and the local perception of RFD officials as agents of the opposition in land-use conflicts.

As the political climate in remote areas began to stabilize, flows of migrants into reserved forests increased sharply. Although the national family planning program was showing remarkable success by this time, the number of young households looking for land was still growing rapidly. The extent to which the influx was stimulated by Kukrit's 1974 amnesty proclamation is often debated, but an unwillingness to use police or military force against rural populations in formerly sensitive areas is still a characteristic of government and military policies. Prompted largely by security and stabilization interests, the Interior Ministry continued to register new villages within reserved forests, allowing them to qualify for government service programs. The military itself appears to have participated in, or at least encouraged, forest conversion and settlement in some areas, especially during periods of jungle warfare. The well-known, but very shadowy efforts by "influential persons" to profit from illicit logging and upland cropping operations within forest areas became an increasingly significant problem in several areas.

Construction of strategic roads was a central element of the government's strategy throughout the 1960s and 70s, particularly in the "Troubled Northeast." Whereas in 1954 villages were an average of 14.5 kilometers from an all-weather road, by 1980 the region had over 200 kilometers of roads per 1,000 square kilometers of area, and at least 96 percent of the villages in each Northeastern province were within 1 kilometer of a road or access road.[2] Roads provided military and government access, routes for commercial market expansion, and transportation routes to increase villagers' mobility. Since strategic roads often penetrated remote forests, they also facilitated illicit logging, upland crop production, and establishment of new villages.

As rural conditions were stabilizing in Thailand, victorious communist regimes in Laos and Viet Nam sought to consolidate their control over mountain ethnic minorities, many of whom had assisted in fighting against liberation forces during the war. Several border areas were ambiguous due to Franco-Thai negotiations during French colonial expansion, and Indochina ethnic minorities began crossing the border to seek sanctuary in the mountains of northern Thailand. While many entered refugee camps, many others quietly swelled already rapidly growing populations of their ethnic kin in Thailand's mountain hinterlands. (Similar, but even less obvious flows of uncertain magnitude have resulted from conflict between the lowland government and remote ethnic minority groups in Burma.)

After the 1979 parliamentary elections, the growth of civilian voices in the government brought increased concern with land conflicts, and the first survey of landlessness. As it became clear that land-use conflicts and occupation of reserved forest lands were growing more rapidly than government capacity to address the problem through expensive integrated rural development programs, government leaders began to focus on land tenure as the most important issue. Accordingly, the Cabinet authorized the issuance of long-term land-use certificates for agricultural lands within reserved forest.

By 1980, reserved forest covered 36 percent of the Kingdom, with national parks and wildlife sanctuaries occuping 6 percent. Most of this area was also covered by harvest concessions, although minor withdrawals were made for national security considerations in highly sensitive areas. Deforestation, however, had accelerated, leaving only 32 percent of the Kingdom still under forest cover. A national forest deficit had emerged. Rates of loss were highest in the Northeast and Central regions, with forest cover levels falling to 17 percent and 28 percent, respectively. The North, however, registered the most dramatic loss, with forest cover dropping to 54 percent. The end of the land frontier was now a popular issue among resource analysts and national planners.

PHASE IV: TRANSITION TO
COLLABORATIVE FOREST MANAGEMENT

This phase begins with implementation of the fifth five-year plan and the return of political stability, accompanied in recent years by rapid industrialization and economic growth. Deforestation, occupation of forest lands, land-use conflicts, and environmental deterioration have become major issues in an increasingly pluralistic political arena.

During the early 1980s, government leaders began recognizing the magnitude of land problems. Pursuant to the 1979 Cabinet authorization, the National Rural Development Committee established a sub-committee for land and recommended a policy allowing villagers presently in forest reserves to remain. The next year a land-use and ownership policy was adopted, an inventory was ordered of remaining forests, and reclassification into agricultural and nonagricultural land was ordered for 9.6 million hectares of encroached reserve forest and land intended for reservation.

The RFD responded with a program to survey occupation of reserved forests and issue STK land usufruct certificates to households present before 1982. STK land-use rights are similar to those issued under the Forest Village Program, but the program does not include infrastructure development and government services, which were to come later under regular rural development programs. An STK Program Office was set up within the NFLMD to administer the massive job of surveying lands and issuing certificates. Since 1982, the RFD has surveyed most of the nation's reserved forests and issued over 800,000 land-use certificates for more than 700,000 households to use 11,500 square kilometers of land.

In another response to the problem, the NFLMD in 1981 launched a program of pilot village woodlot projects on community lands in the Northeast. This was an effort to assess the potential for villages outside reserve forest boundaries to increase production of forest products for local needs, thereby relieving pressure on reserved forests. Supported for two years by funding from U.S. Agency for International Development (AID), the program was constrained by its focus on fuelwood and by a project life sufficient only for planting trees, without follow-up studies and development of community management systems.

Despite such efforts, it was clear by the mid-1980s that the forests were still vanishing. The extent and regional distribution of forest change during each phase from 1953 to 1985 are indicated in Table 9.1. High deforestation rates during Phase III are clear in all regions. Although Phase IV deforestation rates appeared to be slowing, they were still high in the urbanizing Central Region and in the mountainous forests of the North. Deforestation rates were dropping more quickly in the South and the Northeast, where growing, dispersed populations were associated with

TABLE 9.1

Forest lands, forest cover, farm holdings and population, 1985

	Whole Kingdom	Central and East	North	Northeast	South
	—percent of total land area—				
1985 Forest lands					
Reserve Forest Land	39	28	58	30	35
Parks and Wildlife	9	17	9	5	11
Concessions	31	32	38	26	31
Remaining Forest Cover	29	24	50	14	22
80–85 Annual Change	−0.6	−0.7	−0.8	−0.5	−0.4
67–80 Annual Change	−1.2	−1.4	−1.1	−1.5	−1.0
53–67 Annual Change	−0.3	−1.1	−0.2	−1.0	−0.9
Farm Holdings	40	45	28	53	34
80–85 Annual Change	+0.6	+0.0	+0.6	+1.0	+0.6
67–80 Annual Change	+0.8	+0.9	+0.7	+1.1	+0.5
53–67 Annual Change	+0.9	+1.0	+0.6	+1.1	+0.8
	—persons per square kilometer—				
Population Density	101	163	61	107	91
80–85 Annual Change	+2.7	+4.8	+1.6	+2.8	+2.3
67–80 Annual Change	+1.9	+3.3	+1.0	+2.1	+1.8
53–67 Annual Change	+1.4	+2.2	+1.0	+1.6	+1.3
	—hectares per person—				
Forest Area per capita	0.4	0.2	0.9	0.3	0.4
Farm Area per capita	0.4	0.3	0.4	0.5	0.4
	—percent of total population—				
Urban Population	18%	39%	8%	6%	12%

forest cover levels approaching or below 50 percent of the area officially reserved for forest.

It became apparent that the magnitude of deforestation within reserved forest boundaries was too great for the RFD to correct by itself. Assuming that all remaining forest cover was within parks and reserved forests, the area of deforested reserves was so great by 1986 that if all 7,355 RFD officers and 4,765 permanent employees were to do nothing but plant forest plantations for forty hours a week using standard RFD techniques, it would take forty-one years to complete the job. If they were all paid at the US$1.40 daily local labor wage rate, the planting costs alone would consume the entire RFD agency budget for thirty-six years, or the land-use improvement budget for 369 years. Yet there was very little prospect for major increases in either manpower or budget allocations.

As they examined such issues, government policy makers began recognizing the complexity and magnitude of the forest crisis and the urgent need for a broader, more systematic government policy for managing forest lands. To address this need, the National Forest Policy Committee was established to formulate a unified government forest policy.

The resulting National Forest Policy of 1985 is the clearest statement of government policy to date and includes several new directives. The forest reserve target of 40 percent of the national land area is retained, but further articulated to include 15 percent in protected national parks, wildlife sanctuaries, and watershed headlands, while the remaining 25 percent is reserved for "economic" forest. Short-, medium- and long-term plans are mandated for development of forest lands and the forest industry, with administration to be adjusted accordingly. Forest laws and regulations are to be thoroughly reviewed and revised, and the RFD is directed to encourage local community participation, to identify and apply new technological innovations, to cooperate closely with the private sector, the universities, and other government agencies, and to conduct public awareness, education, and information programs. In short, the policy urges all components of government and society to collaborate with the RFD in defining and maintaining a forest resource base which can support the needs of society.

The RFD and other government agencies soon attempted to respond to the new national policy. Protected parks and wildlife areas were expanded to cover about 10 percent of the land area of the country, and pilot management plans began to be developed with assistance from nongovernment organizations. Nongovernment organizations (NGOs) also began pilot projects in villages bordering some important national parks, and an AID-funded project was designed to include support for cooperation with the U.S. National Parks Service in further developing protected area management programs. A watershed classification system was developed, based on physical characteristics, and a nationwide mapping program has now been completed. Reclassification of reserved forest lands was accelerated, and planning began for a major degazetting effort. Implementation of the STK Program was accelerated. The Ministry of Interior stopped registering new villages located within reserved forest in 1986, and began a pilot project to develop provincial-level natural resource management plans.

In addition to accelerated RFD planting programs, large tree planting and forest plantation programs began to be proposed by the military and the private sector. In 1987, the military began a major rural development program for the heavily deforested Northeast Region. Known as the Green Northeast (Isan Khieo) Project, plans included massive forest replanting programs. Private-sector initiatives began with several large corporations submitting proposals for major forest plantation schemes on degraded reserved forest land. The Asian Development Bank also began lobbying for a government-guaranteed loan for medium-scale private forest plantations on deteriorated reserved forest land.

Although limited by budget and personnel constraints, the RFD also strove to improve its capacity for outreach and cooperation. In 1986 the NFLMD established a Forestry Extension Office and began developing a nationwide forestry extension programme. Under this program, existing district forestry officials are trained in extension techniques, supported by mobile extension units and a network of agroforestry demonstration centers. The Community Forestry Section also developed "interest-group desks," responsible for developing support programs for organizations such as temples, schools, and nongovernment organizations, and a central publication and audio-visual production unit. Other officers were assigned to develop agroforestry and community woodlot technologies and management systems. The National Parks, Wildlife, and Watershed Management divisions also began developing relations with NGOs interested in helping to protect and manage areas under their jurisdiction.

Meanwhile, a loosely knit national environmental movement began demonstrating its growing power. Government plans to construct the large Nam Choan reservoir and hydroelectric facility within the Kingdom's largest wildlife sanctuary were twice stopped by widespread mobilization of public opposition, which included reemerging organized student protests and support from academics, politicians, nongovernment organizations, and even some government agencies, including the RFD.

Implementation of new policies was difficult, however, and by 1988 the RFD felt engulfed in contradiction, conflict, and criticism. Many long-term harvest concessions included areas now designated as protected areas. Vast areas of reserved forests, including logging concessions, were occupied by registered villages receiving services under government programs. With about 1.2 million households (about 10 percent of the nation's population) occupying lands within reserved forest boundaries, it was not possible to relocate more than a small percentage to sites outside the reserved forest. Villagers were advancing their claims on forest resources through elected politicians, newspapers, and nongovernment organizations. Swollen ethnic minority populations in the mountains were pushing their swidden agriculture systems beyond the limits of sustainability, which increased conflict among groups and with lowland populations. Some opium crop substitution projects had introduced heavy pesticide use and erosion-prone cropping systems into critical watershed headlands. Other government agencies continued to demand reserved forest land for land reform, reservoir construction, and other projects. Newspapers alternately accused the RFD of loving trees more than people and of failing to protect the environment. Powerful people at all levels were involved in illegal logging and land use. Accusations of RFD malfeasance and corruption became commonplace; the director-general was suspended under investigation, and his first temporary replacement was soon replaced by a second.

Finally, in November 1988, an unusually heavy rainstorm in the politically sensitive South induced a wave of floods and landslides, destroying villages and leaving more than 200 dead. Extensive media coverage linked the tragedy to encroached and deforested watershed headlands, triggering an unprecedented public outcry. Public outrage grew as the nation mounted a massive relief effort and environmental groups publicized the extent of forest destruction resulting from illegal logging and concession abuse. The Minister of Agriculture responded in January 1989 with a nationwide emergency ban on commercical logging in reserved forests, and promised to revoke all concessions. Rumors soon spread that powerful interests, including politicians connected with logging companies, would attempt to block the effort. When Parliament reconvened in May to consider legislation to revoke concessions, intense public interest prompted the first live televised broadcast of parliamentary debate in the nation's history. The bill was passed by a large majority, and opposition was limited to procedural objections. Virtually the entire basis of public forest land management is now subject to reorganization.

To compensate for the commercial logging ban, Thailand reduced log import tariffs and opened all borders to timber imports. The government claims these are temporary measures during the reorganization and rehabilitation of Thai forest reserves, but critics fear the action will result in accelerated forest destruction in neighboring countries. (Indeed, the unpopular Burmese regime has increased its fighting with ethnic minority rebels over timber export routes in forested areas near the Thai border. Laos is taking a more positive approach, responding with a huge tax on log exports, coupled with plans to improve its forest managment capability and an invitation for Thai industry to invest in wood-processing facilities for export to Thailand.)

With growing domestic and international political pressure to find solutions for the Kingdom's deforestation problems, proposals are being forwarded to change a wide range of forest land policies, laws, and regulations, accompanied by much debate on the appropriate role for the private sector in reserved forest management. The next few years will undoubtedly result in many substantial changes, shaping the future of forest management in the Kingdom.

TOWARD A COLLABORATIVE LAND USE SYNTHESIS FOR RESERVED FOREST LANDS

With logging concessions revoked, attention is now focused on the millions of villagers living within reserved forest boundaries. It is a primary task of the RFD to find innovative solutions to deforestation problems in occupied reserved forest lands. As discussed in Chapter 4, past efforts such as the Forest Village and STK Land Certificate programs have often resulted in increased inmigration and forest deterioration. The government's assumption that usufruct certificates alone would reduce deforestation appears to have been too simplistic, and a study suggests that without strict enforcement land usufruct certificates appear to have no particular value.[3] Yet the political sensitivity and logistical impossibility of enforcing many forest regulations suggest that strict enforcement measures are not feasible, at least in the near future. It is this recognition that has provoked the search for programs which, in place of negative reinforcement, provide positive reinforcement of desirable behavior.

In 1984, with support from the Ford Foundation, a multiagency working group organized by the Kasetsart University Faculty of Forestry began studying deforestation problems in reserved forests of the Northeast.[4] After an assessment of deforestation trends, the Khon Kaen University Faculty of Humanities and Social Science helped conduct case studies in three critical areas.[5] Results from one of those areas are discussed in Chapter 10. Similar case studies were conducted in mountainous areas of the North by the Faculty of Social Sciences at Chiang Mai University.[6] Based on these studies and in collaboration with the three universities and with support from the Ford Foundation, the RFD in 1987 began a program of pilot projects aimed at developing practical field methods for RFD-community collaboration in developing land-use management plans and activities which meet both local needs and the objectives of national resource management policies.

Known as the Thailand Upland Social Forestry Project, the program employs a collaborative strategy at two levels. At the program level, the RFD is collaborating with policy advisors and university forestry and social science faculty and research staff, in both central and regional universities, with some assistance from nongovernment organizations. At the local level, the RFD is collaborating with local communities in formulating mutually acceptable land-use plans and in exploring the potential for community management of nearby reserved forest resources.

Implementation of this strategy is through a learning approach centered on community organizer and working group concepts. Resident village community organizers (COs) are agricultural vocational school graduates trained by staff from various RFD offices, universities, and a nongovernment organization. Community organizers are supported by RFD field project officers and each month they discuss their progress, problems and ideas, and develop rolling plans for the next month in an informal working session with local, regional, and central RFD staff and university staff and faculty. University staff also analyze progress and problems across pilot villages in each region, and conduct applied research to support project implementation. Their findings are integrated into monthly meetings, where new issues are raised for further work. These informal collaborative monthly working group sessions are a critical central element of program implementation.

In the Northeast, three types of pilot villages were selected: forest villages established under programs of the NFLMD, villages participating in the STK Land Certificate program, and villages located in reserved forest where no RFD programs are currently operational. The project seeks collaborative solutions for increasing the effectiveness of STK and Forest Village programs in the first two types of villages, and explores the potential of CO-initiated programs alone in the third type of village.

Pilot villages in the mountainous North focus on the problems of villages located in watershed headlands. Settlement and agricultural activities are prohibited in first-class watershed headlands under the national watershed classification scheme. Since detailed mapping has often resulted in a mosaic of first-class lands mixed with categories where more intensive land use is acceptable, however, the project seeks to minimize the need for resettlement through collaboration between the RFD and local villages in developing local catchment land-use plans acceptable to both parties in mixed zone areas.

Initial community organizer activities focus on establishing rapport and learning from villagers. Rapid rural appraisal techniques and tools such as sketch maps and labor and land-use calendars have been useful.[7] As problems and options are discussed and plans are developed, COs assist in establishing community-owned and operated nurseries to propagate trees selected by villagers. Initial selections are usually trees yielding horticultural products. Demonstration and propagation stock plantings are often associated with temples, schools, or other village public areas. Various village interest groups have been identified, and more detailed investigations of production technologies, market potentials, and tenurial arrangements are underway. Villagers are also helping identify areas for protective forests and alternatives for their maintenance.

As the RFD undertakes these efforts to collaborate with local communities, it is learning some important lessons. Perhaps the most important lesson is the need for true collaboration in working with villagers. Past efforts, even when well-intentioned, have used agency-centered decision making with little local participation in planning and implementation. This has followed from (1) the rise of "expert" planning approaches to development, (2) public forest administration approaches learned from Western agencies and forestry schools, and (3) the traditional role of government officers in rural Thai society. Foresters working in social forestry are now recognizing the value of local knowledge and experience in understanding local land characteristics and the needs of local communities. Since local resource use patterns usually reflect resource, labor, and market conditions, collaborative planning with local communities appears to be a promising way to resolve and prevent land-use conflict between local communities and national policies.

A second lesson relates to local community production objectives. Programs to meet the needs of local communities tend to focus on single-use subsistence objectives; village woodlots for fuelwood production are an example. While under some conditions communities may support fuelwood plantings, in most villages fuelwood is considered a by-product and fuelwood plantings are considered a very odd idea.[8] Trees rendering a range of "horticultural" products are usually prefered by villagers for planting in and near villages, often in tree gardens mixed with annual crops or with livestock grazing. Under these conditions, promotion of sustainable, spatially integrated tree production for other products is probably the best way to stabilize or increase the fuelwood supply.

The common focus of forestry programs on subsistence needs is often a patronizing view of village life. While there may be a few very remote areas where the cash economy has yet to be strongly established, most rural people feel a growing need for cash income. Upland crop production, sales of timber and minor forest products, and seasonal migration for wage employment reflect villagers' efforts to meet this need. Under these conditions, subsistence production may be promoted as a means of increasing disposable cash income by decreasing subsistence costs. If forestry programs are to mobilize substantial amounts of village labor, however, much more effort must be devoted to developing village forest-based production systems as a serious commercial enterprise. There is no reason to doubt that villagers would plant and protect trees if it were to their economic advantage.

A third lesson has come from attempts to impose bureaucratic organization under village conditions. Many communities in reserved forest areas are either relatively new settlements, or have recently experienced growth from inmigration. Such villages are often characterized by more factionalization and less community cohesion than older villages in long-settled areas. Various ethnic minority populations also have different approaches to social organization. In either case, there is little reason to believe that government-mandated village-level committees and organizations will necessarily have enough shared interest or mutual trust to function smoothly as units of organization for local resource management. While there is still a feeling that village-level organization should be promoted whenever possible, smaller groups of households based on kinship or production interests, or even individual households, may sometimes be more appropriate. Foresters are appreciating the need to approach the problem of community organization with an open mind and a variety of organizational options from which local communities can select those most appropriate for their social conditions.

As the RFD shifts from a regulatory approach toward forest management programs focused on developing incentives for behavior that accords with national policies, it is finding a need to develop analytical capabilities in subjects not traditionally found in the forester's toolkit. Foresters collaborating with local communities need to understand the local political economy, community social structures and organizations, household and community economics, production and marketing microeconomics, and communication and extension methodologies. Collaborative land-use planning methods, small-scale forest production technologies, and legal and institutional arrangements still need substantial refinement, while much biological and ecological work remains for fields such as agroforestry.

While the forestry agency must rely on collaboration with other institutions for many of these tasks, they must also develop internal capacities sufficient to operate coherent programs and formulate policy recommendations. In order to develop these capacities, the RFD needs to draw systematically from a mix of sources, including (1) short courses, such as those being offered by international organizations (recognizing limitations in language and depth of training), (2) expanded forestry university curricula brought by newly-hired graduates, (3) graduate programs in social science undertaken by appropriate agency foresters, and (4) a few strategic new positions within the RFD requiring skills other than forestry. Thus, a systematic program for personnel development will require collaboration with universities and the civil service commission.

UNRESOLVED ISSUES
FOR COLLABORATIVE FOREST MANAGEMENT

At this point in the evolution of Thai collaborative forest management systems, many issues remain unresolved. While their resolution will largely be determined outside the Royal Forestry Department, the outcome will have a substantial impact on the nature of forests and forestry programs in the years to come. We close this chapter with three examples of such issues. Comments and suggestions regarding these issues are very welcome.

(1) *To what extent should economic forests emphasize natural forest management or intensive tree production?* This issue emerges from conflicting views on how a forest is defined. By most ecological measures, there is very little difference between intensive monoculture plantations of exotic "forest" species, and "agricultural" plantations of tree crops such as para rubber. Indeed, rubber plantations are accepted by the RFD as forest cover. Critics argue that intensive monoculture "forest" plantations are really a form of agriculture, and that "forest" means mixed communities of flora and fauna. Their argument is supported by villagers arguing for the right to plant fruit trees and other multipurpose economic plants rather than exotic "forest" species such as eucalyptus. Industrial producers of eucalyptus, on the other hand, seek promotion of their plantations under the banner of reforestation.

Perhaps such issues must be resolved by more articulate definitions of the objectives for reserving various types of land. If watershed protection is the objective, then any management system capable of providing sufficient protection should be acceptable, regardless of the product. If timber production is the goal, timber and growth characteristics must be considered. If preservation of species diversity or wildlife habitat is the objective, other criteria would prevail. If multiple objectives are desirable, a minimum set of requirements must be used in screening management systems. Articulation of objectives beyond "economic" forests will be required to resolve this issue.

(2) *To what extent should public forest lands be privatized?* Now that logging concessions are revoked and the government seeks to collaborate in managing the nation's forest resources, several interest groups are calling for privatization of ownership, or at least private management of large portions of "economic" forest reserves. Most agree that village agricultural lands settled before declaration of reserves should be degazetted. New policy proposals would place areas farmed for many years, but only after reserve declaration, under recent land reform legislation or the STK program. More recent settlers could enter lease agreements to continue using land for acceptable purposes. Indeed, local communities would be encouraged to lease reserved forest land for sustainable production of forest products.

Many academics and NGOs argue that this is not enough, that "the forests should be given back to the people," and they advocate splitting reserves into titled parcels for local residents. Such parcels would presumably be owned by individual households, but the government could establish regulations allowing village ownership. Opponents argue that transfer of reserved forests to private village ownership would only encourage large-scale land purchases and further occupation of reserves in hope of further privatization. Such "magnet effects" have already surfaced in STK program areas, where land-use rights fall short of full title, and large private land purchases by speculators are already a problem in many areas.

While large companies are not publicly requesting private ownership of reserved forest land, it is no secret that they would like it. Their approach, however, is to request long-term leases of exclusive rights over large parcels, to be used for private forest plantations. Their main obstacle is that large-scale transfer of land or land-use rights to private companies would face the potentially serious political problems of villager eviction, presumably with a concomitant expansion of landless rural laborers. In order to get villagers to relinquish claims peacefully, one large company is even offering to purchase villagers' informal (technically illegal) claims to reserved forest land.

Much of this debate relates to societal objectives for forest areas and whether those objectives are best met through public or private ownership. Regulated private management of public lands is a likely compromise for many areas. Yet, if ownership is to remain public, more effective measures must be developed for collaborating with villagers and private industry in their management.

(3) *What scale of management units should be emphasized in private-sector collaboration?* Although landlessness is on the rise as frontiers for new settlement disappear, Thailand is primarily a society of small landholders. Psychological feelings of security, self-sufficiency, autonomy, and "stake" in social, political, and economic systems are closely intertwined with land ownership and control. Some observers believe Thailand's ability to reestablish rural political stability is related to dispersed ownership and control of land.

In its first bids to participate in reserved forest management, the private sector proposes large- and medium-scale production units under their centralized control and management. They see no forestry precedents for alternative modes of industrial organization such as those associated with many agricultural crops, wherein large processing facilities are supplied by many small-holder production units; however, there appear to be no intrinsic characteristics of forest production which require large-scale production units.

Given Thailand's social, cultural, and political history, as well as its current rural economic development and forest policies, a forest industry based on small-scale village forest management units needs to be thoroughly evaluated before large areas of occupied reserved forest land are allocated to concentrated control by private interests. Currently policy proposals for establishing local industry centers, perhaps with FIO taking the lead, appear to be a step in the right direction. If Thai society could view villagers as serious partners with private industry and the RFD in managing national forest resources, it could bring new vitality to existing collaborative efforts and incentives for public assistance in maintaining and protecting the Kingdom's forest lands.

NOTES

Author's Note: The views and opinions expressed in this chapter are those of the authors, and do not necessarily reflect the official positions of the Royal Thai Government, the Royal Forestry Department, or the Ford Foundation. The authors also gratefully acknowledge the assistance of former RFD Deputy Director-General Dr. Tem Smitinand in reviewing a preliminary draft of this paper.

1. Chuntanaparb, Lert, and Henry I. Wood. 1986. *Management of Degraded Forest Land in Thailand*. Northeast Thailand Upland Social Forestry Project Final Report, Vol. 1. Bangkok: Faculty of Forestry, Kasetsart University, p. 80

2. Binswanger, Hans, Kosit Panpiemraj, *et al.* 1983. *Growth and Employment in Rural Thailand*. Report No. 3906-TH. Washington, D.C.: East Asia and Pacific Regional Office, The World Bank.

3. Chalamwong, Yongyuth, and Gershon Feder. 1986. *Land Ownership Security and Land Values in Rural Thailand*. World Bank Staff Working Paper No. 790. Washington, D.C.: The World Bank.

4. Wacharakitti, Sathit, *et al.* 1985. *Land Use and Resource Management in Northeast Thailand*. KU/Ford Northeast Thailand Upland Social Forestry Project. Bangkok: Department of Forest Management, Faculty of Forestry, Kasetsart University.

5. Subhadhira, Sukaesinee, Yaowalak Apichatvullop, Prasit Kunurat, and James A. Hafner. 1987. *Case Studies of Human-Forest Interactions in Northeast Thailand*. Northeast Thailand Upland Social Forestry Project Final Report Vol. 2. Khon Kaen, Thailand: Khon Kaen University.

6. Tan-Kim-Young, Uraivan, Anan Ganjanapan, Shalardchai Ramitanondh, and Sanay Yanasarn. 1988. *Natural Resource Utilization and Management in Mae Khan Basin: Intermediate Zone Crisis*. Chiang Mai, Thailand: Resource Management and Development Project, Faculty of Social Sciences, Chiang Mai University.

7. For more information see: Khon Kaen University. 1987. *Proceedings of the 1985 International Conference on Rapid Rural Appraisal*. Khon Kaen, Thailand: Rural Systems Research and Farming Systems Research Projects, Khon Kaen University.

8. See also: Subhadhira, Sukaesinee, *et al.* 1987. "Fuelwood Situation and Farmers' Adjustment in Northeastern Thai Villages," in Khon Kaen University, 1987. *Proceedings of the 1985 International Conference on Rapid Rural Appraisal*.

CHAPTER TEN

Migrant Farmers
and the Shrinking Forests
of Northeast Thailand

James A. Hafner and Yaowalak Apichatvullop

*Years ago the forest was so thick with large trees, vines, wild animals and
filled with malaria that only a few hunters had the courage to enter. When
Mr. Oon came to settle with his family his ponies were frequently frightened
by the dark forest. In time, however, it was the terrorists who brought fear
to the farmers who migrated to the Dong Mun. —a Phu Hang villager*

TODAY, APPROACHING THE last decade of the twentieth century, the
Dong Mun forest in Northeast Thailand bears little resemblance to the
environment which confronted the first settlers less than twenty-five years
ago. Many of the changes affecting this national reserved forest have undoubtedly been repeated elsewhere throughout the country. Yet, the questions presently confronting government officials and villagers differ strik-
ingly from those which existed when the first settlers entered the forest
in 1960. Growing shortages of arable land, instability of agricultural markets and prices, government efforts to limit forest access, and concern over
future availability of land and security of land tenure are much more the
questions of today than of the past. Although it is difficult to separate
these issues from the rapid postwar social and economic changes in Thailand, they have distinct historical origins. The macro-level forces and policies which have affected forest and land-use change in the Northeast were
examined historically in Chapters 4 and 9. This chapter explores some of
these issues in the context of two forest land management programs recently implemented in Phu Hang and Non Amnuay villages in the Dong
Mun National Reserved Forest in Northeast Thailand.[1]

THE DONG MUN NATIONAL RESERVED FOREST

The past twenty years have brought significant social and economic change
in Thailand. Progress toward planned targets for economic growth and

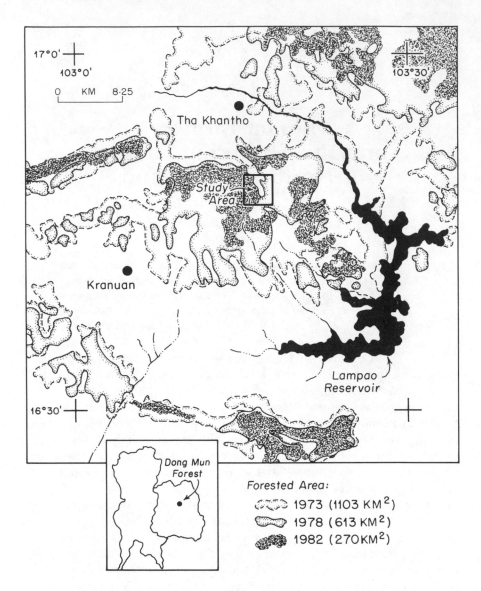

Figure 10.1. Change in Dong Mun Forest area, 1973–1982

development, however, is increasingly affected by problems with the use and management of basic natural resources. One symptom of these problems has been the accelerated depletion of forest resources. In Northeast Thailand, the largest and poorest region of the country, high rates of postwar population growth, instability in the region's rainfed farming systems, and a shrinking amount of arable land have made reserved forests the final resource frontier for many poor and landless rural households, giving these forests the highest rates of illegal encroachment and deforestation.

In 1964, the year of the most recent Thai legislation creating national reserved forests, the Dong Mun forest encompassed 590 square kilometers of the upper Lam Pao watershed in Kalasin and Udornthani provinces. The following year approximately 414 square kilometers of the forest were designated as the Dong Mun National Reserved Forest.[2] Between 1961 and 1974, annual deforestation rates by province varied from 1 to 5 percent throughout the Northeast and generally exceeded 4 percent in the Korat Triangle. A more recent analysis of land use by watershed area between 1973 and 1983 shows that these high rates continued through 1978, but have generally declined since then.[3] One of the few notable exceptions to this trend has been in the Lam Pao subwatershed, which includes the Dong Mun forest (Figure 10.1). Here, the area of reserved forest declined between 1973 and 1978 at an annual rate of 8.9 percent, significantly above the regional rate for Northeast watershed areas. Over the next five years this rate accelerated to 11.2 percent per year, leaving undegraded less than one-half of the area originally designated as reserved forest.

The Dong Mun is primarily a dry dipterocarp forest. Above 500 meters there is some dry evergreen forest, at least 30 percent of which is deciduous. The dry dipterocarp forest covers the lower elevations between 200 and 500 meters and is comparatively lower in height, and almost 90 percent of the trees are shedding species. At one time the forest contained valuable stocks of commercial grade hardwoods, a diverse and abundant wildlife, and a variety of edible foods such as honey, mushrooms, fruit, and wild vegetables. Although now vastly depleted, tigers, elephant, barking deer, wild pigs and chickens, monitor lizards, monkeys, gibbons, and many bird species once inhabited the forest in large numbers. Logging concession rights in the Dong Mun forest were originally granted to two saw mills in 1961, but were later cancelled in 1965 when the area was declared reserved forest. New thirty-year concession rights for an area of 590 square kilometers of the forest were granted in 1975 to the Kalasin Lumber Company.

The topography of this area is dominated by a series of mini-watersheds and uplands which cover the upper Lam Pao watershed (Figure 10.2). Elevations reach 500 meters in the northwest and diminish to around 200 meters near the Lam Pao reservoir in the east. Two smaller streams, the Huai Diak and Huai Lao drain separate mini-watersheds west of these villages and have been important in the settlement, forest clearance, and political history of this part of the forest. The principal soil types within the forest are clayey paleustults on lower and middle terraces and a generally undefined slope complex of hill soils on steeper slopes and at higher elevations. Loamy paleustults and paleaquults, which will sup-

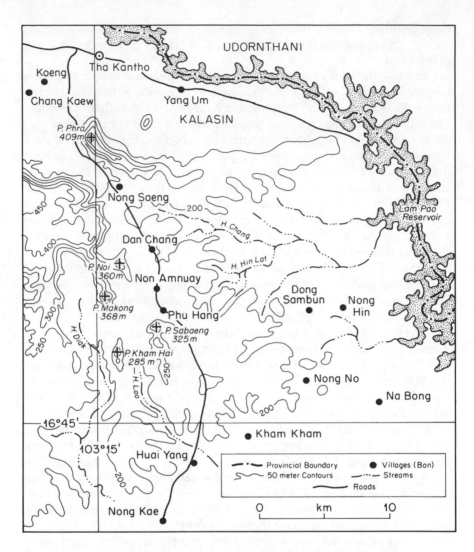

Figure 10.2. Environs of the forest village and STK study sites in the Dong Mun Reserved Forest

port irrigated rice and some sugar cane, are also found along the Huai Hin Lat and smaller streams. Elsewhere, soils in areas of cleared forest on upper terraces and lower slopes retain moisture better and have been used almost exclusively for field crops. Annual precipitation is between 1,300 and 1,400 millimeters, although the distribution and amounts of rainfall for much of this area vary in a way typical of the entire Northeast.[4]

Despite the visible evidence of deforestation and timber harvesting in the Dong Mun forest, the social forces that accompanied these processes are not so easily recognized. Immigration and encroachment on forest land accelerated early in the last decade and continued intermittently throughout a period of political instability in the 1970s when much of the forest was controlled by leftist guerrillas. The guerrillas' influence adversely affected settlement, commercial logging, private control of land, and even the villagers' personal safety. The government's initial response to these conditions was an anti-terrorist campaign within the forest by the army and Border Patrol Police. In 1975, an amnesty for illegal residents of reserved forests contributed to new waves of immigration, settlement, and encroachment. Over the next five years, two new forest land management programs were implemented in Phu Hang and Non Amnuay: the Forest Village Program and the National Forest Land Allotment Project. These projects have reduced rates of forest encroachment and population growth, but they have also limited individual landholdings, prohibited some residents from obtaining land, and fostered social and economic conflicts that continue to plague these communities. The following sections outline the design and objectives of these forest land management programs, and the turbulent settlement history that preceded their implementation.

FOREST LAND MANAGEMENT PROGRAMS IN PHU HANG AND NON AMNUAY

Deforestation and illegal encroachment on forest land have led to several new initiatives to improve government control and management of these important resource systems. In 1975 the Thai cabinet approved formation of the National Forest Land Management Division (NFLMD) within the Royal Forestry Department (RFD) and the Forest Village Program, responsibility for the administration and implementation of which was given to the NFLMD. Two years later the NFLMD received cabinet approval to implement the National Forest Land Allotment (STK) Project. The Thai cabinet then gave amnesty to all illegal residents of reserved forests, an action intended to facilitate these projects. Both projects share common goals of limiting forest land degradation, restricting illegal encroachment on reserved forest lands, consolidating residents into permanent settlements to facilitate provision of government services, and furthering the government's national internal security policy. Thus, direct government intervention was framed in terms of national security and the need to distinguish between terrorist elements and legitimate villagers loyal to the government. These programs have slowed encroachment on reserved forest lands, controlled the process of land occupancy, and imposed limits on the amount of land households may use for agriculture. This has also created sharply different reactions among the residents of these two villages.

The Forest Village Program in Phu Hang

In 1978, Phu Hang was formally designated a "development village," which enabled the NFLMD to implement the Forest Village Program. In preparation for this program, the area and its population were surveyed, a five-year plan of operations was developed, and principles were established to determine which resident households were qualified to join the project. A total of 2,320 hectares of degraded forest land was set aside as the project area: 1,120 hectares for agriculture and 1,200 hectares for reforestation. The type of forest village model implemented in Phu Hang provided for (1) improvement of the existing village, (2) provision of infrastructure and basic village services, (3) participation by all households residing in the project area before 1978, and (4) the allocation of 2.4 hectares of forest land per household (2.32 hectares for agricultural activity and 0.08 for houselot area). Agricultural land allotments included cultivation, occupancy, and inheritance rights, but not formal ownership. These conditions were defined in use certificates issued to each household that remained valid for five years. Community services to be provided by appropriate government agencies included agricultural cooperatives and extension services and a program of agricultural credit and loans set up by the Bank for Agriculture and Agricultural Cooperative (BAAC). Reforestation activities were to provide paid employment in tree seedling production, planting for forest restoration and community forests, and distribution of tree seedlings for planting on private land.

The National Forest Land Allotment (STK) Project in Non Amnuay Village

Continued forest land encroachment and problems in implementing the Forest Village Program prompted renewed consideration of alternative solutions to these problems. In 1981 the Thai cabinet granted formal approval of the National Forest Land Allotment (STK) Project as a remedial solution. This project was primarily motivated by the slow progress in developing new forest villages, the high costs of establishing these villages, and inadequate budgets for this work.[5]

The STK Project has had objectives similar to those of the Forest Village Program: to grant agricultural land entitlements in reserved forests, promote reforestation and conservation of degraded forest land, improve relations between forestry officials and local residents, and discourage repeated migration and encroachment on reserved forest land. A committee of local and provincial officials, with the provincial governor, coordinated these projects. Special STK Centers were established in RFD regional offices to plan, monitor, and implement activities in specific project locations. (The STK Center responsible for the Non Amnuay project was located in Khon Kaen.) Of particular importance in these planning activities were (1) meetings with local residents to explain the project, advise them of the qualification requirements, and discuss application procedures, and (2) surveys of the site to determine that land for which entitlement applications had been received was clearly demarcated from adjoining plots and no other claims existed to that land.

The STK Project is based on a system of land entitlements for crop agriculture on degraded forest lands. These entitlements provide legal rights of use, but prohibit subdivision of the land or its transfer except by inheritance. The primary requirement for obtaining an entitlement was demonstration of residence or cultivation of land prior to January 1, 1982. Qualified households were granted 2.4 hectares of land and STK 1 certificates granting land-use rights and other conditions of their land entitlement. Violation of the terms of these certificates incurred their cancellation and the loss of any legal rights to contest this decision.

The STK Project in Non Amnuay has differed from the Forest Village Program in Phu Hang in a number of important respects. No land was identified or allocated for houselots, village paths and roads were not developed, and no village infrastructure or services were provided. Land allocations were limited to a maximum of 2.4 hectares per household, but previously claimed and cleared land could continue to be cultivated by paying an annual fee of US$12 per hectare. Further, this land was not confiscated for reallocation, which allowed many of the original claimants to retain the right to use land in which they had already invested labor and capital.

In short, both of these programs share common goals and objectives, but differ in their land allotment procedures, the extent of government involvement in village affairs, and in the provision of village infrastructure. These differences, however, provide only a partial explanation for the villagers' somewhat polarized view of these projects. Factors such as historical settlement patterns, attitudes toward land and forest resources reflected in traditional tenure systems, political unrest, and the effects of immigration on village social and economic organization have been equally important. These factors influenced the circumstances under which these forest land management programs were implemented in ways examined in the following section.

THE SETTLEMENT OF PHU HANG AND NON AMNUAY VILLAGES

Free Occupancy

Until the early 1960s, the Dong Mun forest remained almost entirely undisturbed by human activity. Occasional visits by small groups of hunters and the presence of a few itinerant Buddhist monks represented only a transient human presence in the forest. The dense forest, wild animals, and malaria appear to have effectively discouraged neighboring forest-margin communities from claiming land and clearing it for cultivation. The subsequent settlement history of this area can be divided into three stages based on the type and conditions of land claims, the rate and composition of settlement growth and forest clearance and the extent of government intervention in the area. The details of this process provide a framework central to understanding the motives behind government intervention programs, their impacts, and the type of system that is evolving in the villages of Phu Hang and Non Amnuay.

In 1961, the government established the district of Tha Kantho and granted exclusive logging rights to areas of the forest to two companies in Kalasin and Udornthani. These developments may have precipitated the first phase of forest land claims that ultimately led to new settlements. This period may be characterized as one of free occupancy, during which forest land was claimed by exercising squatter's rights, marking boundaries of these claims by notching trees, and inserting bundles of twisted grass (yakha) to identify informal ownership rights. A few officials from Huai Yang Dong village on the southern edge of the forest established this type of claim to areas of forest land between their village and the present site of Phu Hang, but none of this land was actually occupied or cleared, and none of these claims were formally recorded.[6] Control over this land was exercised through cab cong rights embodied in traditional, informal land-tenure systems.[7] In 1961, eight households from Tha Kan and Chang Kaew villages established a small hamlet at Nong Saeng on the northern edge of the forest and claimed large tracts of land as far south as the Huai Hin Lat. A few subsistence crops were planted in forest swidden and later, as more lower terrace land was cleared for cultivation, irrigated wet rice was planted. When the Dong Mun was declared a reserved forest in 1964, Royal Forestry Department officials evicted these households from their land for violating the new laws. Each household was fined and prohibited from cultivating land they had already cleared. Encroachment into the forest ceased for the next six years, although these settlers continued to cultivate this land secretly while living in the nearby village of Koeng.

Increased migration and establishment of the first permanent settlement (around 1970) marked the beginning of a second phase in land occupancy and settlement. Villagers defined this process as forest land pioneering, which involved occupancy of land rather than simply claiming land. The terms of informal land-tenure systems continued to govern land claims, but as more settlers arrived the sale of land and its clearance for agricultural activities increased.

In 1971, a Mr. Oon and nineteen members of his extended family from Udornthani province reached the site of Phu Hang village. His primary reasons for coming to the Dong Mun forest were land shortages in Kumphawapi district, Udornthani, the flooding of his land by the Lam Pao reservoir, and the inadequate compensation and resettlement opportunities provided by the dam authorities.[8] The settlers immediately built some small houses without walls near the Huai Hin Lat, claimed large tracts of land, and began to clear forest swidden for crops. Over the next eighteen months Mr. Oon convinced nine additional households to immigrate to Phu Hang from their villages along the southern edge of the forest. In 1972, these settlers had their first contact with members of a leftist guerrilla band who came to assist them in harvesting rice.

Guerrilla Control

By 1973, settlement patterns, rates of forest clearance, and individual flexibility in claiming land had begun to change. These changes were associated with renewed commercial logging activities, rising immigration rates, and the increased assertion of land control by leftist guerrillas. Two commercial logging companies from Nam Phong and Yang Talad districts actively began to harvest timber on concession areas and extended the logging road reaching into the forest from the north. Almost immediately, twenty new households arrived to settle near Phu Hang. The largest group was from Loei, but others came from Udornthani, Nakhorn Ratchasima, Khon Kaen, Mahasarakham, and Kalasin provinces.[9] Many of these early settlers confirmed that their decision to migrate to the Dong Mun forest was influenced by rumors that leftist guerrillas were allocating forest land. A year later Mr. Oon encouraged another fifty households from nearby forest-margin villages to settle in Phu Hang by giving each 3.2 hectares of the forest land he had claimed previously. No formal title documents or certificates of occupancy accompanied these land transfers, which quickly became a source of conflict between settlers and the leftist guerrillas. Because of the large amount of land distributed by Mr. Oon, the guerrillas warned the villagers that all land claims must stop, private distribution of land must first have their approval, and all claimed land would be subject to confiscation. Rumors threatening the conscription of village youths prompted a general exodus of many older students and the school teachers. Meanwhile, the original settlers of Nong Saeng had returned to that village, accompanied by thirty households from the villages of Chang Kaew, Yang, and other communities in Kalasin, Udornthani, and Mahasarakham. This quickly brought the size of Nong Saeng to over 200 households. Land sales began as the original settlers transferred control of some of their *cab cong* holdings to new immigrants at prices reported to have been between US$60 and US$90 per hectare. However, the guerrillas again intervened to prohibit land sales, threatened to appropriate all individual land claims, and began to relocate land on the basis of four hectares per household. Apparently this enforced "land reform" program was partly intended to strengthen the guerrillas' prohibition on forest clearance and thus protect the location of its base camp in the forest.

Increased immigration during the mid-1970s accelerated land conflicts with the guerrillas and resulted in open confrontations and the deaths of several people. By 1975, the guerrillas had forbidden all transactions involving the sale or transfer of land, villagers were prohibited from claiming or clearing forest land, and all privately controlled land was appropriated by the leftists for redistribution on the basis of 3.2 hectares per household. Border Patrol Police (BPP) were posted to the area and fighting intensified over the next several years between the guerrillas, the BPP, and supporting units of the Thai army. A year later conditions had so deteriorated that Phu Hang had declined from 105 to 60 households and immigration had stopped entirely.

Despite continued fighting, some villagers indicated that a fragile accommodation was reached with the guerrillas. The present site of Non Amnuay village was first occupied around this time by Mr. Oon and several members of his extended family. During frequent trips to Nong Saeng, he often noted the large areas of unsettled and as yet unclaimed land north of the Huai Hin Lat. In the mid-1970s, accompanied by a few family members, he built a small hut in this area and began to clear some land. In 1979 he was joined by ten households from Mukdahan and Nong Khai provinces who were relatives of his son-in-law. A few years later, other households dissatisfied with the land controls imposed on Phu Hang by the Forest Village Program joined Mr. Oon at this small hamlet.

Throughout the 1970s, the rate and pattern of forest clearance were direct results of immigration and the level of political stability (see Figure 10.3). This process represents the direct actions of villagers in cutting timber for domestic use and commercial sale, and the expansion of agricultural activity rather than timber harvesting by logging companies. The spatial configuration of this process also illustrates the guerrillas' growing influence, their prohibitions on clearing forest, and the political instability in this area during the 1970s. Between 1971 and 1973 the area of cleared forest spread over lower and middle terrace lands to a distance of several kilometers around Phu Hang village. Timber was used for house construction and the land was devoted to small garden plots for vegetables, swidden for rice, and houselot areas. Forest land continued to be cleared to the east and south of Phu Hang even as open confrontations between the guerrillas and units of the Thai army and Border Patrol Police intensified. However, little land was cleared in the uplands along the Huai Diak until after 1980, when fighting had ceased. Timber then began to be cut in the areas west of the village, and upland swidden were developed for the cultivation of rice and corn. The forest margins also began to recede northward as settlement and forest clearance expanded around Non Amnuay.

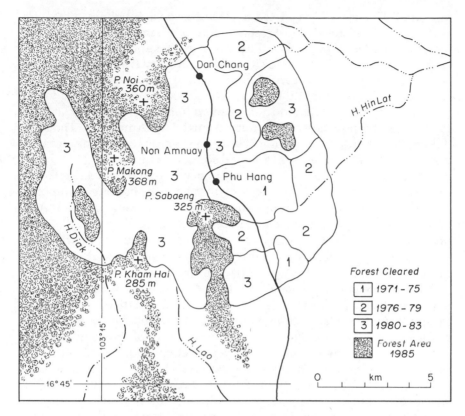

**Figure 10.3. Forest clearing near Phu Hang and
Non Amnuay, 1971–1983**

By 1985, large areas of the upper slope west of both villages was partially deforested to a distance of four kilometers, and most of the remaining land had been converted to agriculture. The small remnants of the original dense forest are now found only at higher elevations and in the undulating landscape of irrigated rice and field crops that stretches eastward toward the Lam Pao reservoir.

Government Control

The most recent phase of settlement and land occupancy began toward the end of the last decade. This period is characterized by greater government intervention, the introduction of two new forest land management programs, increased controls on forest land encroachment, a rapid acceleration in the rate of immigration, and a return to open sales of land. As fighting drew to a close around 1980, both villages began to grow from migration. This trend was related to (1) improved accessibility, (2) a 1978 amnesty for illegal residents of reserved forests, (3) implementation of the Forest Village Program (FVP) in Phu Hang in 1978 and the National Forest Land Allotment Program (STK) in Non Amnuay five years later, and (4) the end of open conflict with leftist guerrillas. Access improved when the laterite road linking Phu Hang to Nong Kung Si was extended to the provincial capital in 1978 and resurfaced with asphalt two years later. In 1983 the northern section of this route through Non Amnuay to Tha Kantho was also resurfaced to permit year-round vehicle traffic. The amnesty granted to illegal residents of reserved forests was intended to stabilize forest land encroachment, but appears to have had the opposite effect in the Dong Mun forest. After news of the amnesty became commonly known, many of the immigrant households in Phu Hang and Non Amnuay believed that by claiming land in reserved forests they would receive title to the land. Consequently, the amnesty and subsequent announcements of the FVP and STK programs caused immigration to rise dramatically, which had an immediate impact on the local land market.

Despite the political instability of the 1970s, an active land market had developed based primarily on sales of land to new settlers. The average sale prices for forest land, cleared forest, and field crop land between 1970 and 1984 are shown in Figure 10.4.[10] Sale prices for all types of land appear to have remained below US$25 per hectare through 1972, although there are indications of an upward trend in land prices. Forest land continued to be "sold" during the next several years, especially in the area west of Phu Hang, where a second group of immigrants from Loei paid from US$36 to US$42 per hectare for uncleared forest land. Open sales then declined as leftist guerrilla influence increased and by 1974 even land sold secretly was only bringing US$5 per hectare. This situation continued until 1977 or 1978, when land transactions and prices began to rise dramatically. During the next six years the price for houselot land, previously occupied freely within the village, rose from US$800 to over US$2,400 per hectare and the cost of one hectare of cleared swidden and uncleared forest land rose from an average of US$50 to over US$200 by 1982.

Several factors influenced these changes in the local land market. First, immigration following the amnesty for illegal residents of reserved forests and the creation of the Forest Village Program increased the demand for land and drove up local market prices. Second, the prospects of having land confiscated by the Forest Village Program, which restricted the size of household land allocations, prompted many older residents to sell surplus cultivated lower and middle terrace land and claimed but uncleared areas of reserved forest. Third, topographic conditions limited the area of lower terrace land suitable for irrigated paddy cultivation, which tended to increase the value of such land as immigration swelled the populations of both communities. Finally, as the basis of household economy shifted

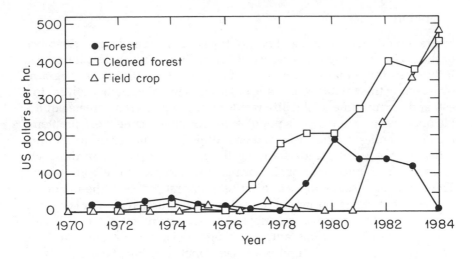

Figure 10.4. Land market prices, 1971–1984

from subsistence cultivation to the production of cash crops, more cleared land was transferred into field crop production, enhancing both the value and prices for this land. Thus, for various reasons, the price of land rose, even though land transactions during this period of growth took place entirely within the context of informal tenure arrangements.[11]

From a small cluster of houses without walls, these communities have emerged as permanent settlements on the margins of a rapidly receding forest. In less than fifteen years the original nucleus of 21 households that established Phu Hang had grown to over 600 households with a total population of 4,000 residents. In 1985, Non Amnuay included 200 households, composed primarily of the families from Phu Hang and Nong Saeng who founded the village and more recent immigrants. The villagers, with initial help from the Border Patrol Police, have built some community facilities, a small reservoir, a community road network, a health center, and a new school. By 1983, residents of Nong Saeng began to resettle in Non Amnuay and this rapidly growing hamlet was officially recognized as a village. Two Buddhist temples have been built on land donated by a former Nong Saeng villager on the eastern edge of the village and a temporary branch of the Nong Saeng school occupies two new buildings that accommodate over 300 students and seven teachers. Migration has contributed significantly to the growth of these villages and has affected the socioeconomic fabric of both communities, the villagers' reactions to the Forest Village and STK projects, and the long-term prospects for the success of government forest land management programs.

Migration

Migration has been an integral part of the settlement and forest clearance of the Dong Mun and other reserved forests in the Northeast. It has also influenced the initial success of the forest land management programs by affecting their ability to provide sufficient land allotments, control forest land encroachment, stabilize resident populations, and create equitable opportunities among this population. To some degree these problems are also manifest in the social and economic instability of these communities. Consequently, understanding the migration process in these villages and its implications for similar programs in the future is important. The following discussion examines the temporal profile of the migration process, the origins of migrant households by source region or last place of residence, the objective and subjective bases for migrant decision making, and the effects of migrants on village social organization. We have not neglected rates of natural population increase, but these have been difficult to determine. We have accepted a rate of 3 to 4 percent per year based on analogous data for neighboring forest-margin villages, sample fertility-mortality data for some households, and estimates provided by local officials.

As indicated in the previous section, peak periods of immigration in Phu Hang and Non Amnuay have coincided with (1) the slowing of hostilities between leftist guerrillas and the Thai military, (2) initial governmental actions opening the forest to settlement, and (3) the implementation of the Forest Village and STK programs (see Figure 10.5). This process has been dominated by interprovincial migrants, who account for over 60 percent of the current village populations. The decline in migration after 1982 suggests that the cumulative effects of the government programs began to be reflected in subjective conditions for immigration to this area of the Dong Mun forest. That is, government controls on access to forest land, the effects of land allotment programs, and knowledge about opportunities in this area began to influence the decisions of potential immigrants to these villages.

Loei, Udornthani, Khon Kaen, and Nong Khai provinces have been the main source regions for interprovincial migrants to Phu Hang and Non Amnuay (see Figure 10.6). The reasons for this pattern include distance, patterns of intraregional migration since 1965, the spread of cash cropping, instability in areas of rainfed paddy production, and government policy decisions opening reserved forests to settlement. The relative location of the Dong Mun forest with respect to the volume of migrants from adjoining provinces indicates distance had been one factor in this process. Improved accessibility has at the very least facilitated these movements. Moreover, the long-term trends in intraregional, rural-rural migration since 1965 have been out of the Korat Triangle to the north and west.[12]

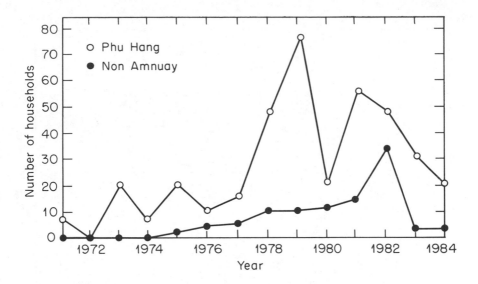

**Figure 10.5. Interprovincial migration to Phu Hang and
Non Amnuay, 1971–1984**

This can be partly attributed to land shortages in the more densely settled areas of the Triangle, instability in the system of rainfed rice farming,
and market and price incentives supporting the growth in cash cropping.
Thus, marginal uplands and unoccupied forest lands less suitable for
paddy production have offered opportunities for cultivating kenaf, maize,
and cassava.[13] This may be especially important in the context of the
phenomenon of chain migration illustrated in the data for Phu Hang and
Non Amnuay. Household interviews and registration records show that
(1) more than 75 percent of the migrant households have come from only
four provinces, (2) 40 to 68 percent of these households came from three
or fewer districts in these provinces, and (3) the households from these
districts came from fewer than five villages.[14] In short, the success or relative satisfaction of early movers to the Dong Mun has encouraged others
to follow, often from the same villages as those earlier households.

First-time migrants to both villages have come primarily for social reasons: to maintain social bonds with family and friends, accompany parents, marry, or meet social obligations to family and friends. This group
represents a clear minority of all migrant households. Most immigrants
were highly influenced by personal expectations of increased income and
economic security through the land entitlement programs in the Dong
Mun forest, and by communications about land fertility, access to forest
resources, and the opportunity to obtain title to land (although many
migrants acted on incomplete or incorrect information about the qualifi-

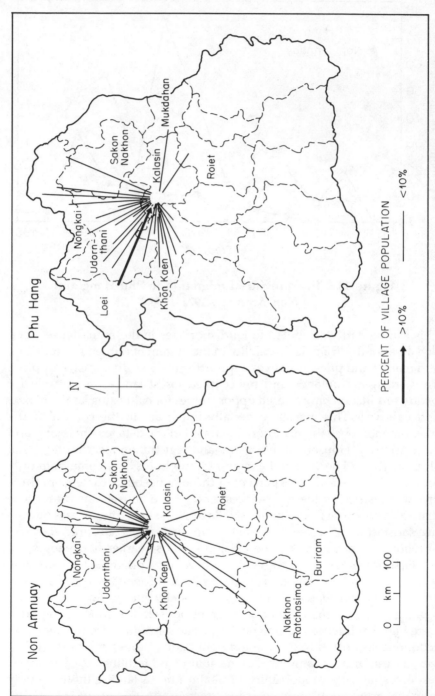

Figure 10.6. Origins of interprovincial migration to Non Amnuay and Phu Hang

cations for land entitlements in both villages). The majority of households moving to Phu Hang and Non Amnuay have migrated more than once, and 25 percent have moved as often as five or six times. These households have migrated mainly for economic reasons, especially poverty, land shortages, low agricultural yields, and the associated effects of drought and flooding, factors consistent with the known conditions and stability in rice farming systems in the areas from which they emigrated. Whether or not these households have lacked sufficient knowledge of upland farming methods to achieve some level of economic success in these locations is unclear; however, this has clearly not affected their adaptation to conditions in the Dong Mun.

The influence of migration can also be seen in the social fabric of both villages. The mechanics of migration to these villages has involved two general patterns. Among the earlier migrants, one or more male household heads visited the area to evaluate land availability and settlement conditions, and later returned with other household members, kinsmen, and friends. Subsequent communications between residents and nonresident kinsmen and friends have also contributed to the process of chain migration, a process typical of the majority of movements to these villages in the last decade. This tended to reinforce a certain local selectivity in the migration process, which has in turn contributed to the rather fragmented social fabric of these villages. There are at least twenty-four separate neighborhood groupings in Phu Hang's two subvillages, ranging in size from ten to over seventy households. Each neighborhood is identified with a specific group of immigrants who share common kinship and past-residential affiliation, although these groups usually comprise a minority of neighborhood residents. Internal economic and social cooperation within groups/neighborhoods is generally strong, but relations with other neighborhoods in the village are at best weak, and often hostile. This diversity of the village population, reflecting the migration process, has affected social and economic conditions and produced different reactions to the two land allocation programs in Phu Hang and Non Amnuay.

The history of these two communities illustrates a pattern of pioneering land settlement on Thailand's final resource frontier, its forest lands. In general, settlement has resulted from interprovincial migration fostered by serious population-land pressures, low productivity and instability in the system of rainfed farming, and market and price incentives linked to the production of field crops. Government policies giving amnesty to residents of reserved forests and the granting of land entitlements have attracted large numbers of immigrant rural households to these areas of reserved forest land. This situation has clearly contradicted policy objectives concerned with reducing forest land encroachment and controlling the illegally resident population in reserved forests. These communities have also evolved in areas where the modern institutions of the Thai state are weakly established, traditional attitudes governing access to undeveloped land and forest resources remain strong, and land control and rights of use are defined by informal tenure systems. This experience also suggests that the government has failed to understand adequately the nature of its population and land problems in the Northeast and their implications for its new programs granting land entitlements in reserved forests.

FARMING THE FOREST:
AGRICULTURE AND FOREST RESOURCE HARVESTING

The earliest settlers in the Dong Mun forest confronted an ecosystem rich in timber, edible forest products and wildlife. Increased human settlement has sharpened the boundaries of that system, reduced the number of natural components, inserted man as a key regulator of important interactions, and reintroduced complexity in the form of social, cultural, and economic institutions. The transitional ecosystem that is emerging combines properties of both the natural forest ecosystem and the rainfed cropping systems typical of Northeast Thailand. Productivity is based primarily on crop production and forest product harvesting, although total production varies considerably between socio-economic groups and villages. These variations are to some extent attributable to the influences produced by the Forest Village and STK projects.

Patterns of Agricultural Production

Village economy in Phu Hang and Non Amnuay is based on the cultivation of cash field crops, subsistence rice production, harvesting of forest products, and wage labor. Once the government imposed restricted access to forest resources, agricultural production became an increasingly important component of the village economy. However, land distribution has been uneven, leaving many households without the opportunity to participate in the intended transition from a forest- to agricultural-based economy.

The median farm size varies from 2.9 hectares in Phu Hang to 3.3 hectares in Non Amnuay. Households in the medium and large farm size categories in Non Amnuay generally cultivate more land than their counterparts in Phu Hang. There are also proportionately three times as many small farmers in Non Amnuay as in Phu Hang, and considerably fewer landless households. The primary reason for this is that the STK Project has allowed households not qualifying for land allotments to rent-in land, and those granted land entitlements to exceed the 2.4-hectare limit by paying user fees for additional land. As a result, over 60 percent of Non Amnuay households cultivate more than 3.2 hectares, as opposed to only 7 percent in Phu Hang. Furthermore, the large-scale landless population in Phu Hang must depend primarily on legal and illicit forest product harvesting and wage labor to meet their basic household subsistence needs. These differences have also been affected by the larger amount of middle and lower terrace land available in Non Amnuay, which allows for more frequent double cropping, relatively higher yields, and a higher average household income from crop agriculture.

The pattern of agricultural land-use in both villages includes cash crop production on 60 percent of the crop land, paddy on 30 percent, and the remainder in agroforestry, fish ponding, and livestock grazing. No common village or public use land areas exist in either village and few farmers use any types of commercial fertilizer or herbicides. Rice is the basic food staple crop and every household with agricultural land cultivates some irrigated or upland rainfed paddy. However, total village rice production remains below current demand, a problem due less to low yields than to the limited amount of suitable paddy land.

The area and types of field crops cultivated have tended to vary considerably with changing market prices and shortages of draft animals. The main field crops are kenaf, cassava, corn, soy beans (*Glycine max.*), black gram (*V. Sinensis*), and sessame (*Sesamun orientale.*). Kenaf is presently grown by one-half of all landed households and by almost two-thirds of the farmers in Non Amnuay. Until recently, cassava was the field crop preferred by a majority of households, but planted area has declined by 50 percent since 1982 due to depressed market prices and the high costs of renting draft animals. This situation has been especially difficult for landless households which have relied on wage labor in cassava cultivation.

District agricultural officers have encouraged crop diversification and intercropping by introducing a number of new crops to both villages. However, success with these efforts has been quite uneven. The promotion of sugar cane and soy beans has been unsuccessful due to high transport costs, low market prices, and inadequate water supplies. Sessame has been adopted for intercropping with corn by almost one-half of the farm households, and black gram has been successfully grown and marketed since 1982 when it was first introduced as a substitute for cassava. Perhaps, the most successful of these new crop innovations has been young corn, introduced by the Laplae Canning Company from Khon Kaen. Its popularity has been based on a short forty-five day planting to harvest period, firm market prices, and a ready market.

The only other forms of noncrop production found in either village are modified forms of agroforestry, fish ponding, and livestock raising. Fruit trees are occasionally grown along field boundaries where soils and drainage are suitable, but this is not a common practice. The intercropping of fruit trees and field crops represents the only type of agroforestry found in either village, although it is a full-time activity by only four households in Non Amnuay. More widespread adoption of this practice has been hampered by a lack of technical knowledge and experience, high prices and shortages of tree seedlings, and occasional theft of fruit trees. The shortage of livestock, especially water buffalo, is a special problem in both villages. Few animals are available, grazing area is limited, and most households have insufficient capital to purchase draft animals. Consequently, one-half of all households must hire water buffalo from neighboring villages and seasonal hire-rates are as high as US$58. Fish culture in 12m × 12m ponds has been started by ten households and village-wide interest in fish ponding has grown. Because fish stocks in local streams are already depleted and villagers are forbidden to fish in the Lam Pao reservoir, the initial success of these ponds has encouraged talk of establishing a communal village fish pond.

Both forest management programs have sought to provide residents with an agricultural alternative to forest product harvesting. Most farmers with middle- and large-size farms have made this transition, although the small size of land allotments and their capability to sustain productivity under present cropping conditions may yet be a serious problem. However, the large number of small farmers and landless households have been provided with few alternatives and their continued dependence on cutting and harvesting forest resources is unlikely to change under present conditions. Despite village interest in agroforestry and some limited initial success with tree crops, project officials and extension agents have done little to promote this technology.

Forest Resource Harvesting

The harvesting of forest resources is a key component of village economy. Indeed, for many of the smaller farmers and landless households, wage labor and harvesting of forest products are both year-round activities and their primary if not sole sources of income. In general, this population has gained the least from the new forest land management programs, and is the most dependent on the wages and income earned for the legal and illegal harvesting of these resources. The major forest harvesting activities include timber cutting, gathering fuelwood, charcoal production, hunting, and collecting edible plants, fruit, and herbs. Most of these resources are consumed within the village, but some are used to produce handicrafts, furniture, and rough-sawn timber for sale locally or in nearby markets.

Timber cutting is widely practiced in both villages, except by the few households cultivating larger amounts of land. Logs and rough-sawn timber are used primarily for local house construction and secondarily for sale. The principal buyers of timber in recent years have been villagers from Mahasarakham and Roi Et provinces, where fuelwood and lumber are already scarce. Most timber cutting is done during the rainy season because of lower agricultural labor demands and the reduced risk of arrest by Forestry Department patrols. If demand is high, however, contract cutting of timber may continue all year. This work is usually done in groups of two to six people drawn from several households. During 1982 and 1983, a particularly active period of timber harvesting, members of these groups could earn at least US$6 per day and single logs were being sold for US$11 to US$13. Timber cutting also increases when crop yields are low and the demand for wage labor in the village declines. In 1985 almost 20 percent of all households in Non Amnuay, especially the landless and wage-laboring families, cut timber on a regular basis. The areas where timber is cut have constantly changed with expanded settlement and forest clearance. Households in Non Amnuay are still able to cut timber on Phu Noi and Phu No, within two to four kilometers of the village, but the residents of Phu Hang must now travel to the uplands beyond the Huai Diak to find timber, a distance of three to seven kilometers. Since 1978, when timber cutting on reserved forests lands was prohibited, illegally harvested logs have been moved to the village only after dusk to avoid detection by RFD officials.

The main use for timber in both villages is for house construction. Between 1983 and 1985 a total of sixty new houses were built in Non Amnuay, mostly for new immigrants. Current forestry law allows trees to be cut for domestic house construction, but prohibits all forms of private logging for commercial sale. However, a clause in the law enables timber cut for domestic house construction to be sold after that structure has been standing for at least two years. Villagers have exploited this loophole in the law by using reserved forest timber to construct "houses built for sale." This involves building the structural framework of a house without siding, walls, or permanent roofing. After standing for a two-year period, the house may be dismantled and the timber sold. The average prices for these house frames have ranged from US$115 to US$385, although a few built with better quality and larger timber have been sold for US$1,000 to US$1,500. In late 1987, there were seventy-nine of these structures in Phu Hang and thirty in Non Amnuay. A small number of landless households in Phu Hang are also involved in purchasing, disassembling, and selling the timber from older homes that have been replaced or abandoned. After these structures are disassembled, the timber is transported to other provinces where it may be sold for as much as three times the purchase price. These activities illustrate several fundamental problems arising from the high levels of immigration and the limited access to land imposed by the Forest Village and STK programs.

Timber for local house construction has recently been scarce, especially in Non Amnuay, where immigration has been high since 1982. New immigrants who lack sufficient cash may have to wait an entire year before they can purchase enough timber to build a house. Timber shortages are the result of more careful monitoring of forest clearance by the RFD, the income which can be earned from selling timber outside of the village, and the dependence of poorer landless and small-size farm households on timber income to purchase rice. Because the Forest Village and STK programs have limited farming and other economic opportunities, landless households have begun to sell their houses and move elsewhere. Many of these households even suggested that they would move to other areas of reserved forest where they might find land. Such behavior, to the extent it typifies similar situations in other forest land management communities, raises important questions about land allocations systems, economic equity within these programs, and how effectively they resolve the problems of forest land encroachment.

Almost all households engage in gathering greenwood and deadfall wood from the forest for cooking, heating in cooler months, and resale or processing into charcoal. Villagers in Phu Hang prefer fuelwood to charcoal for cooking, while the opposite is generally true in Non Amnuay. This difference is unrelated to current availability of fuelwood or charcoal, labor supplies, or preferences in food preparation; it is rather a measure of length of residence, adaptations made to local fuelwood conditions, and previous experiences with fuelwood shortages in other places. Beginning in 1982, charcoal production in Phu Hang expanded rapidly as increased immigration in Non Amnuay created a larger demand. Ovens or kilns were built to produce charcoal and the price per bag has remained around US$1.35, rising to US$1.50 during the rainy season. Production has declined, however, as the distance to available fuelwood supplies has increased and RFD officials have more closely inspected timber cutting and as landless households have shifted from charcoal production to wage labor in harvesting cassava and retting kenaf.

Villagers collect other forest products for local handicraft activities and to supplement household food supplies. Several households in Phu Hang have received permission to cut timber on reserved forest land to make furniture and flooring for houses. Thirty households in Phu Hang also weave mats from local grasses (*Pennisetum pedicellatum*) and sedge (*Cyperus corymbosus, Cyperus diffusus*) to supplement household income on an irregular basis. Wild grasses are also collected to make and repair roof thatching. Hunting and collecting edible forest products have always been important postharvest activities in both communities. Chickens, wild boar, rabbits, and occasionally deer were killed in the nearby forest and edible forest plants, mushrooms, fruit, herbs, honey, rattan, and rubber oil have been harvested from the forest, primarily for household consumption. Hunting, however, due to over-exploitation and government controls, has decreased in frequency and increased in length of time and distance. Even the collection of edible forest products by women and younger children now requires them to travel deeper into the forest to find some of these resources.

Forest Resource Dependency

The preceding discussion illustrates the integral part forest resources play in Phu Hang and Non Amnuay. In combination with crop agriculture, they define the total resource base for these populations. Forest resources have diminished in relative importance as this human-forest system has changed with increased settlement, population growth, the expansion of cultivated land, and the controls imposed by the Forest Village and STK programs. Dependency on forest land remains high, however, especially among some segments of the village population, raising questions about the design and implementation of these forest land management programs relative to their stated goals, and about the broader issue of Thai forest policy.

Forest land dependency is defined as the total volume or percentage of annual household consumption needs obtained from forest resources and products harvested from forest land. Values for forest land dependency were obtained in 1985 for a stratified random sample of 2 percent of all households in both communities. Despite problems with methodology and verifiability of data, this index is considered an acceptable measure of dependency.[15] The combined dependency value for both communities is 66 percent (73 percent in Phu Hang and 58 percent in Non Amnuay) (see Figure 10.7). That is, two-thirds of the mean annual household consumption needs in both communities have been obtained from forest resources. This level is the highest among the six forest-margin communities recently studied at three different locations in the Northeast. This degree of dependency in part reflects the transitional state of these human-forest systems. The major changes accompanying this transition include greater definition of systems boundaries, a reduction of natural or biological components, greater human regulation of interactions, and the creation of a new order of complexity and systems properties linked to peoples' cultural, social, and economic activities in the forest.[16] A key question in designing new social forestry initiatives is how to manage these transitional systems to increase productivity without jeopardizing stability, sustainability, or equity in the distribution of the products of these human-forest systems.

It is also possible to interpret this index in the context of the two villages and their separate experiences with the Forest Village and STK programs. Evidently the socio-economic status of households in both communities is inversely related to their dependence on forest resources. Those households with larger amounts of land are less dependent on forest resources than those with little or no land at all. Further, regression values

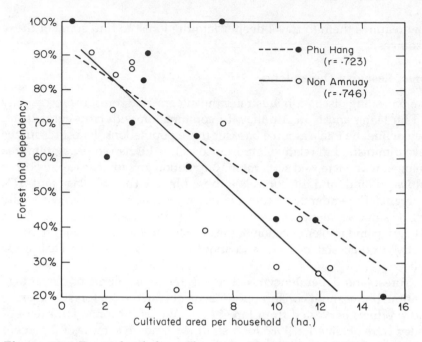

Figure 10.7. Forest land dependency in Phu Hang and Non Amnuay

and the slope of the trend lines suggest this relationship is somewhat stronger in Phu Hang than in Non Amnuay. This reflects historical patterns of land claims and occupancy, different conditions for land allocations under the Forest Village and STK programs, and the failure to anticipate the economic needs of households excluded from the land distribution process. Indeed, the gap between the two estimated regression lines may reflect the effects of these programs in both communities. More importantly, this relationship may imply that those lower on the socio-economic spectrum will continue to exert the most pressure on forest resources and pose the greatest threat to the objective of stabilizing forest land encroachment. Until program design and implementation are adjusted to compensate for this situation, many of these and other villagers residing in reserved forests will continue to depend on harvesting forest resources.

These patterns suggest the types of changes and trade-offs afforded by varying traditional agricultural systems. Swidden cultivation techniques and forest product harvesting, land-tenure practices, and low population densities fostered sustainability and considerable equity in distribution. This appears to have continued through the late 1970s, despite some growth in population. However, implementation of the two forest land management programs and related population growth have adversely affected both the stability and sustainability of established systems. Paddy yields have generally failed by an average of at least 10 percent with increased frequency of field use, the shift of paddy cultivation from uplands to lower terraces, and decreasing access to land. Enforced land allotments and increased immigration have created inequity in the access to and distribution of production, and consequently increased the exploitation of forest resources. Even here, signs of depletion of some forest products are beginning to appear. Although field crops are highly productive, stability is low due to irregular water supplies and fluctuations in market prices and demand. Also, the newly imposed formal tenure systems granting land-use rights have significantly lowered equitability, which has not been buffered by increased use of agroforestry technology. Institutional controls imposed by the Forest Village and STK programs have created many of these changes in the systems structure, which reflect inevitable trade-offs between productivity and stability on one hand and sustainability and equitability on the other. This situation is also manifest in the fabric of social organization and patterns of cooperation in the new institutional structures created in these communities.

SOCIAL AND INSTITUTIONAL ISSUES OF FOREST VILLAGE AND STK PROGRAMS

The importance of institutional and socio-structural issues in developing alternative forest management strategies has often been neglected. Although there is no single set of social and institutional factors which should be considered for every project, some of the more essential ones include: population size, growth, and homogeneity; patterns of land use, ownership, and distribution rights to resources; labor; and modes of social organization, leadership, and mechanisms for collective decision making and mobilizing group action.[17] Perhaps the most important element in designing the social strategy for these projects is properly identifying the unit of social organization or structure that can sustain the social innovations needed to change forest use and management practices. The experience of the Forest Village and STK projects in Phu Hang and Non Amnuay clearly illustrate the significance of these issues and the ways in which their neglect can influence project success.

The basic foundations of social organization in Phu Hang and Non Amnuay are in general the same as in other Thai-Lao villages in the Northeast. A typical community may be characterized as one which is a distinct ecological entity, with a bilateral kinship structure, and where people have a large number of both cognitive and affinal kinsmen in the community.[18] Villages are organized into neighborhoods or *khum*, which may be occupied by several domestic groups, but do not function to regulate marriage, control property, shape economic cooperation, or worship common ancestors. Domestic groups cannot be equated with households, but rather are groups of kinsmen bound by shared needs for social reproductivity and cooperation in agricultural production.

Although the populations in Phu Hang and Non Amnuay share these general attributes, they do so as immigrants in communities which are patchworks of many domestic and kinship groups from disparate locations throughout the Northeast. Village social structure and organization in Non Amnuay is more consistent with the normative foundations of village life in the Northeast outlined briefly above. This is due to the fact that almost 60 percent of its residents formerly lived in Nong Saeng village, its four neighborhoods tend to be dominated by a single domestic or kin group, and immigration has not fragmented these domestic groups and weakened the bases for traditional social and economic cooperation. The more flexible land-allocation policies of the STK program have also minimized access to land as a divisive community issue. In Phu Hang a decidedly different situation exists. The vast majority of village neighborhoods are small, seldom are they dominated by a single domestic or kin group, and residents have few kinsmen elsewhere in the village. Consequently, the role of kinship in reinforcing communal solidarity and cooperative agricultural activities within neighborhoods is much weaker. Where these residential areas are composed of small farmers and landless households, the capacity for economic cooperation within domestic groups has been diminished by their limited land and labour resources. This has also contributed to their relative poverty and under-representation in group decision making on village committees and organizations.

A number of local governance, village development, and self-defense organizations have been established in both communities. These institutions assist village officials in managing community affairs, encourage participation in community-wide development activities, and promote the government's social, economic, and internal security policies. The model used in designing the Forest Village Program has provided for a government-appointed village headman, a village committee and development fund managed by elected neighborhood members, a rice bank, young adult club, agricultural credit program, and four paramilitary organizations created under the national program of Political Groups for National Security.[19] The STK Project did not provide for any of these village organizations, but district officials have appointed a headman and formed a village committee and development fund. Most neighborhoods also have informal leaders who help resolve social conflicts over land rights, broker marriages, and assist with private financial problems. Their influence in village affairs tends to vary in relation to the size and relative prosperity of their domestic groups and the roles they play in institutions of village governance. Several examples may help to clarify how these social and institutional structures have affected village cohesion.

The government's appointment of headmen for Phu Hang's two sub-villages has been a central issue in a number of continuing disputes. These individuals represent two separate domestic neighborhood groups whose members include many of the older and more prosperous middle- and large-size farm households. Villagers assert that their influence on a decision by the village committee to locate new cooperative stores in their own neighborhoods shows favoritism and mismanagement of village funds. The headmen have also imposed a users fee for fishing in the village pond. This decision exerts a heavy burden on the poorer and landless households who, without livestock or other sources of meat, rely heavily on fishing in the pond. Prominent among this group is a cluster of forty-five households that immigrated in 1979 expecting to acquire land in the village. Less than one-third of these households have land, much of which is unsuitable for paddy production, and most are rather poor. Other village institutions, such as the young adult club and village committee, have become ineffective or had been disbanded by 1985 due to mistrust and a lack of cooperation among their members.

A rice bank was formed in Phu Hang in 1979 by the Border Patrol Police (BPP) to provide need-based loans of paddy stock to village residents. The bank has been managed by a BPP-appointed committee, although many of the smaller neighborhoods are not represented. In the past seven years it has given 120 loans, 70 percent of which have gone to recent immigrants, small farmers, and landless households. Almost one-half of this group have remained in debt and defaulted on their loans, while 10 percent have emigrated without repaying loans. The poorer farmers, often the bank's main clients, have land holdings which are too small and incapable of producing a subsistence yield, even in years of good harvests. In 1985 the bank committee resigned amid disputes between neighborhood groups and committee members over mismanagement and depletion of the bank's paddy stocks.

The Forest Village Program has also been plagued by conflicts between villagers, foresters responsible for managing the program, and district officials. These disputes illustrate a variety of problems with poor communication about the program's goals and objectives, implementation policies, and the responsibilities of different government agencies. In 1985, for example, newly arriving immigrants continued to encroach on the reserved forest because the area set aside for land allotments was already occupied and district officials lacked authority to withdraw additional forest land for agricultural allocations. The 465 hectares of project land reserved for reforestation have been badly degraded by village livestock and partially cleared for cultivation. This has occurred because no common land or grazing area was provided for the village, and some project participants have been unwilling to claim their alloted land due to fear of retribution from households that still claim informal squatters rights to this land. In fact, eighty households were sold land in the reforestation area by older residents who feared their informal claims to this land would not be honored and the land would be confiscated by project officials. Many of these disputes remain unresolved, and are often manifest in the social conflicts between neighborhoods and within village institutions.

The distrust which characterizes relations between villagers and project officials has been partly fostered by poor communications. Inequities in land allocations have made many villagers doubt the sincerity of official arguments that reforestation is in their interest. They have rejected proposals to plant eucalyptus trees on their land to promote reforestation, improve rainfall, and increase soil moisture. On occasion some villagers have even burned and uprooted new tree seedlings in the reforestation area. They see little benefit to themselves in these activities, especially when they do not have ownership rights to the land, land allotments are often insufficient to meet household subsistence needs, and some have no land at all. Residents of Phu Hang, seeing the distinct advantages of the STK Project, have requested that their village be transferred to this program. Indeed, these villagers frequently commented that even the village institutions established under the Forest Village Program were formed to pursue government interests in reforestation rather than to meet the needs of their community.

In comparison, the STK Project in Non Amnuay has been marked by much less social and institutional conflict. Disputes over original land claims were mainly resolved before land entitlements were granted. The entitlement process has also enabled villagers to retain land originally claimed and developed, to cultivate more than 2.4 hectares, and has given landless households opportunities to rent land. Plans to reforest 320 hectares of village land were cancelled once it became clear that the area of land set aside for agricultural land allotments would not be sufficient for the population. This land remains designated for reforestation, but villagers may use it to plant crops while an area of degraded upper slope land is being reforested. The absence of an externally imposed institutional structure also seems to have allowed villagers to create or request only those organizations which will help meet their needs.

The social and institutional characteristics of these communities illustrate the importance of assessing appropriate social strategies in the design and implementation of alternative forest management prgorams. The social heterogeneity of Phu Hang's predominantly immigrant population and its implications for community cohesion and support for project activities have revealed a central weakness of the Forest Village Program. The externally imposed institutional structure has tended to promote project goals without allowing for the diverse needs of different social and economic groups. It is not surprising that few of these institutions function effectively or enjoy wide support among the various neighborhood groups. Poor communications regarding project goals and how the community will benefit have also compromised the initial success of the Forest Village Program. These problems have also been complicated by poor communications and coordination within and between government organizations, and by a shortage of trained personnel to manage these programs.

Whether the existing institutions of village governance are capable of sustaining these forest management programs remains a serious question. While their structure and authority may be consistent with government policies of creating responsive local government, they are clearly unable to meet diverse community-based needs, build problem-solving capacities, or integrate the technical and social components of these new programs. The lessons from these two projects reemphasize the importance of balancing the socio-cultural and institutional needs of participants with the goals and objectives of this type of alternative forest management program.

MANAGING FORESTS AND PEOPLE

The management of forest resources in Thailand has been dominated by traditional forestry policies emphasizing commercial production, protection against deforestation, and restrictive legislation to discourage encroachment. This approach has been reinforced by a variety of commercial, civil, and land codes that deemphasize preservation and education and create an adversarial relationship between forestry officials and the public. The Forest Village and National Forest Land Allotment programs begun in the Dong Mun forest have emerged from this more orthodox framework as strategies for resolving problems of forest land encroachment, reforesting degraded land, consolidating residents so that government services and programs can be developed, and fostering the objectives of the government's national internal security policy. The historical context and processes surrounding these programs have been examined in this case study for the villages of Phu Hang and Non Amnuay. The design and management problems that villagers have experienced with these programs suggest some larger issues that must be resolved before more equitable and sustainable systems of human-forest management can be realized in Thailand.

A primary goal of these forest land management programs has been to stabilize the population in areas of national reserved forests. The situation in the Dong Mun forest indicates this has been a substantial failure. Both natural birth rates and migration have increased the forest resident population, yet net immigration has been the major component of growth. Indeed, immigration accelerated rather than diminished after these programs began. This appears to have resulted from several factors. The 1978 decision by the Thai cabinet to grant amnesty to residents in national reserved forest encouraged migration to these area. How effectively the details of this decision were communicated to the general public is not clear, but clearly many people understood that by establishing residence in reserved forests they could obtain land from the government. It also appears that policy makers have been poorly informed about the land situation in the Northeast and did not anticipate the demographic implications of either amnesty or the Forest Village and STK programs. The effects of this oversight are evident in the overpopulation of both projects relative to land set aside for allocation in persistent immigration, and in the continuing encroachment on forest lands by this population.

A second goal of these programs was to reduce forest land encroachment, if not completely stop it. Some attribute this problem to the Royal Forestry Department's inadequate budget for recruitment and training of officials to police forest lands.[20] While there is merit to this argument, it may also reflect the persistence of more orthodox forest policy and a failure to acknowledge the social dimension of forest resource management. Land entitlements have been the primary strategy for replacing dependency on forest resources with agriculture. Wage labor in tree seedling cultivation, enrichment planting, forest plantation management, and planting community forests were activities intended to provide residents with other suitable occupations and income. However, forest land encroachment has continued because of inequities in the land allocation process, failures to anticipate demands from the continued flow of immigrants, inadequate opportunities for wage labor, and land conflicts embedded in the population's commitment to informal tenure systems.

The persistence of informal tenure systems also reflects larger structural problems in a society undergoing rapid growth and development. Existing forest laws and land codes, despite numerous recent amendments such as the Agricultural Land Reform Act, remain confusing, contradictory, and inadequate for efficient and equitable land control. On this point, Kemp has noted, "as suitable land for cultivation becomes scarce and increases in value, so the weakness of informal tenures based on common ties of kinship and community identity becomes more significant."[21] This has become all the more severe where requisite land surveys and the issuance of title deeds have been slow and reserved forest boundaries are inadequately marked. The confusion over conflicting legislation has led villagers to mistrust government officials, to fail to understand why conventional acceptance of land tax receipts as proof of ownership is disputed, and, in Phu Hang, even to resist confiscation of that land. The failure of planners and project officials to acknowledge these contradictions and resolve them in an efficient and equitable manner will continue to be a major barrier to innovative land management programs, especially in the Northeast where land pressures have reached serious levels.

That these programs coincided with a period of recent internal instability raises another question about their actual intent. Despite their design and implementation by the National Forest Lands Management Division, there is evidence that the primary if not overriding objective of these programs was to isolate and suppress the leftist guerrillas. Among the more unfortunate consequences of this strategy has been the alienation of precisely those segments of the population which national security policy has been intended to protect. This has been emphasized by the support for paramilitary groups in both communities and the correspondingly low level of investment in helping the villages address social and economic problems. Building more responsive local government and rural development programs appears to have had a lower initial priority than satisfying the goals of national security policy. We do not question the appropriateness of this short-term policy goal, but rather the failure to demonstrate a commitment to the community's long-term social and economic needs.

In the final analysis, these forest land management programs illustrate a fundamental problem in rural development programming. One clear lesson is that planning documents call for a participation of program beneficiaries that is seldom achieved in reality. To a considerable degree, this accounts for the differing responses of villagers to the Forest Village and STK programs, and for the problems encountered in achieving project goals. Korten identifies four lessons that appear to summarize most of the central issues surrounding these new initiatives for forest land management in the Dong Mun forest.[22] First, planning and implementation of participatory programs have relied on centralized organizations unable to respond to diverse community-defined needs or to build on community skills and values. Second, implementing agencies have consistently under-invested in creating community problem-solving capacity. Third, the social diversity of target populations, especially highly stratified village social structures, has received insufficient attention. Finally, the social and technical components of the development effort are poorly or insufficiently integrated. In the case of these and other programs designed to stabilize forest ecosystems and ensure that they become more productive, sustainable, and equitable in the distribution of benefits, learning from past lessons can help us to see both the forest and the trees.

NOTES

1. This chapter considers one of three upper watershed areas in Northeast Thailand investigated in 1985–1986 by an interdisciplinary research team supported by the Developing Countries Program of the Ford Foundation. The institutions cooperating in this study were the National Forest Lands Management Division, Royal Forestry Department, the Department of Social Sciences, Khon Kaen University, and the Faculty of Forestry, Kasetsart University.

2. Thailand, The Royal Gazette. 1968. Ministry Regulation 741. Vol. 82, Section 106. The designation of areas as reserved forest has been made under Sections 5 and 6 of the National Reserved Forest Act of 1964, and as amended by the Ministry of Agriculture and Cooperatives in 1975.

3. Wacharakitti, Sathit, and Lert Chuntanaparb. 1984. *Land Use and Resource Management in Northeast Thailand*. Bangkok: Department of Forest Management, Faculty of Forestry, Kasetsart University.

4. Phien, H. N., A. Arbhabhirame, and A. Sunchindah. 1980. "Distribution of Monthly Rainfall in Northeast Thailand," in *Southeast Asian Studies* 18(1):110–123.

5. Chuntanaparb, Lert, and Henry I. Wood. 1986. *Management of Degraded Forest Land in Thailand*. Bangkok: Department of Forest Management, Kasetsart University.

6. See Chapter 4 for a discussion of the 1954 Land Code and the types of formal land occupancy and ownership provided for in this legislation.

7. The term *cab cong* refers to the act of claiming land under squatter's rights, a condition generally accepted in traditional, informal tenure systems. In the context of these tenure systems this act also acknowledges ownership and the right to hold land for later sale or use, but does not necessarily imply occupancy or clearing of the land for agricultural use.

8. Poorly planned and managed resettlement and compensation programs associated with multipurpose dam and irrigation projects displaced over 15,000 rural households in the Northeast between 1960 and 1970. Two-thirds of these households chose self-managed resettlement, 40 percent of whom initially migrated and resettled elsewhere in the Northeast. Pa Mong Resettlement Research Project. 1976. "Self-Managed Resettlement in the Private Land Market." Working Paper No. 6. Ann Arbor, MI: Department of Geography and Center for Southeast Asian Studies. The University of Michigan.

9. The leftists' growing control over land is suggested by the experience of the sixteen households that emigrated from Loei: upon arrival they were forced to pay an "admissions tax" of US$1.50 per head to homestead land near the Huai Diak.

10. The category, "cleared forest," in Figure 10.4 represents a stage of land use transition between partially cleared but uncultivated *cab cong* land and fields that are fully cleared and under regular cultivation. The term used by villagers to identify this type of holding and identified in Figure 10.4 as "cleared forest" is *bye burg*.

11. Since 1982, most transactions in the private land market have involved land outside of the boundaries of the Forest Village and STK project areas. Those obtaining this land have justified ownership by obtaining PBT 5 and PBT 6 receipts for payment of land taxes, although these documents do not accord ownership or any legal protection of land rights under current land laws.

12. Sternstein, Larry. 1974. "A Critique of Thai Population Data," in *Perspectives on Thai Population. Research Report No. 11*. Bangkok: Institute of Population Studies, Chulalongkorn University; and Pa Mong Resettlement Research Project. 1976. "Self-managed Resettle-

ment in the Private Land Market," Working Paper No. 6. Ann Arbor, MI: The Department of Geography and Center for South and Southeast Asian Studies. The University of Michigan.

13. Arnold, Fred, and Susan Cochrane. 1980. "Economic Motivation Versus City Lights: Testing Hypotheses Interchangwat Migration in Thailand." World Bank Staff Working Paper No. 416. Washington, D.C.: The World Bank; Rigg, Jonathan. 1987. "Forces and Influences Behind the Development of Upland Cash Cropping in North-East Thailand," in *The Geographic Journal* 153,3 (November): 370–382.

14. The importance of communications between past and potential migrants as a factor in "follow-on" migration has been well documented in the process of self-managed resettlement in the Northeast. (See Gosling, L. A. Peter, et al. 1976. *Pa Mong Resettlement: Final Report*. Ann Arbor, MI: The Department of Geography and Center for Southeast Asian Studies, University of Michigan.)

15. Sample methodology was based on a four-way matrix with variables for cultivated area, household size, length of residence, and size of household labor force. However, these variables somewhat undervalue dependency since wages and/or income derived from forest product harvesting are not included.

16. Conway, Gordon R. 1986. *Agroecosystem Analysis for Research and Development*. Bangkok: Winrock International.

17. Cernea, Michael M. 1985. "Alternative Units of Social Organization Sustaining Afforestation Strategies," in *Putting People First: Sociological Variables in Rural Development*. New York, N.Y.: Oxford University Press, pp. 267–293.

18. Keyes, Charles. 1976. "In Search of Land: Village Formation in the Central Chi River Valley, Northeast Thailand," in *Contributions to Asian Studies*. vol. 9, ed. James Brow, 45–63; Keyes, Charles, 1975. "Kin Groups in a Thai-Lao Community," in *Change and Persistence in Thai Society*. G. William Skinner and A. Thomas Kirsch, eds. Ithaca, NY: Cornell University Press, pp. 278–297.

19. The Village Scouts, Thai Volunteers for Country Protection, Voluntary Development for Self-Defense, and Reinforcement for National Security paramilitary organizations are supported by the Border Patrol Police and regional units of the Thai Army. Only the Voluntary Development for Self-Defense group was formed in Non Amnuay.

20. Chuntanaparb, Lert, and Henry I. Wood. 1986. *Management of Degraded Forest Land in Thailand*. Bangkok: Department of Forest Management, Kasetsart University.

21. Kemp, Jeremy H. 1981. "Legal and Informal Land Tenures in Thailand," in *Modern Asian Studies* 15, 1:1–23.

22. Korten, David C. 1984. "Rural Development Programming: The Learning Process Approach," in *People Centered Development. Contributions Toward Theory and Planning Frameworks*. David C. Korten and Rudi Klauss eds. West Hartford, CT: Kumarian Press, pp. 176–188.

CHAPTER ELEVEN

Reorienting Forest Management on Java

Nancy Lee Peluso, Mark Poffenberger, and Frances Seymour

FOREST RESOURCES IN developing countries are under immense pressures from state institutions charged with their profitable management and also from rural people seeking access to forest products and land for subsistence. Changing demographic, political-economic, and environmental circumstances require forestry bureaucracies to adjust to those changes or risk obsolescence and failure. Management of forest resources therefore not only presents technical challenges to policy makers and planners, but increasingly requires creative sociological thinking on the nature and objectives of forest management. Chapter 11 details the initial phases of a fundamental change in a conservative, Third World forestry bureaucracy. The historical evolution of the organization and its environment made change inevitable; we describe the strategies used to ease the change process.

Java (Indonesia) provides a textbook example of the anomaly of traditional forest management in contemporary circumstances. Although 23 percent of the island is designated state forest land, millions of rural people seek access to this land for fuel and other forest products.[1] Some 21 million people live in Java's 6,000 forest villages, and many of them clamor for limited opportunities to temporarily farm state forest lands targeted for reforestation. Most production forest on Java (over 60 percent of the total forest area) is kept under eighty-year-rotation teak plantations and twenty- to thirty-year-rotation pine plantations, despite these systems' low labor absorption and the island's growing population of land-hungry rural people.

The State Forestry Corporation (SFC; Perum Perhutani in Indonesian) manages all production forest and most protection forest on Java.[2] The SFC is a para-statal organization within the Ministry of Forestry and is mandated to protect forest cover and watersheds, to generate state revenues through forest production, and to stimulate improvements in rural welfare through forest-related earning opportunities. The social forestry program described in this chapter helped the SFC to identify and analyze administrative and field-level management problems and to develop an operational style responsive to rural needs.[3] In Java, such change could potentially revitalize the island's deteriorating watersheds and generate income for the poorest rural people.

Structurally and ideologically, the contemporary SFC shares many similarities with its colonial predecessor (see Chapter 2).[4] The organization is composed of technical forestry specialists, forest police, and administrators whose primary objective is the production of teak and other forest products to generate revenues for its own reproduction and the national development budget. While teak provides 92 percent of the SFC's total income,[5] tradition, as much as financial justifications, supports continuing colonial-style timber stand management. Consequently, SFC foresters remain skeptical of outside studies showing the ecological stability and productivity of indigenous agroforestry technologies.[6]

In the past, community involvement in SFC forest management has primarily been through a reforestation system called *taungya* (or *tumpang sari* in Javanese; see Chapter 8). Begun early in the twentieth century, *taungya* allowed farmers to cultivate agricultural crops between the rows of reforested timber species for two or three years in return for planting and protecting the tree seedlings. *Tumpang sari* plantation establishment was favored by foresters on Java because it significantly reduced their costs. Some also lauded *tumpang sari* as a way to relieve rural land hunger.[7] The system, though relatively successful, took advantage of land-poor farmers, whose poverty had been partially aggravated by the state's bounding of the forest lands and by other colonial policies; it was most successful where land was scarce and labor abundant.[8]

Although rural people on Java still benefit from employment and land access provided by the *tumpang sari* system, they have also become increasingly dependent on forest lands for fuel, fodder, and building materials, the collection of which is in most cases illegal. Thus, they see their survival threatened by the SFC's efforts to enforce central state control over the forest through limiting access. The differences between farmers' and foresters' interests, exacerbated by the confrontational tactics used by the forest police, create tense relations in rural areas. The tension is reflected in the figures on teak theft and forest damage;[9] as recently as 1986, wood theft on SFC land had reportedly risen 50 percent from the previous year, leading the Minister of Forestry to call for a 17,000-man police operation to help guard state forest lands. Local response was swift: in March 1986, an SFC forest ranger was killed by a gang of angry forest villagers.[10]

As early as 1973, in seeming contradiction of its police tactics and control ideology, the SFC began a series of community development programs aiming to increase forest-based employment opportunities and benefits for people living near state forest lands. While these pilot projects reflected mounting political pressure on the SFC to respond to rural needs, they had little effect on the vast majority of forest villagers because the programs never expanded beyond pilot projects. These experiences indicated that, while the SFC recognized the need for better relations with rural people, it had a limited capacity to plan or implement community-based programs.

Established forestry policies did not encourage community-oriented management systems. Although foresters were willing to be concilliatory, they were not ready to give management responsibility to local forest users. After decades of mistrusting rural villagers, forestry professionals were reluctant to allow communities to participate in planning reforestation efforts. Similarly, villagers were suspicious of foresters attempting to elicit their cooperation. While SFC officials talked of community development, mechanization of logging operations displaced laborers who depended on logging income in some forests. Intensified forest policing operations were integrated with the other armed services to "sweep" village homes and fields where teak theft was suspected. As a result, conflicts between foresters and villagers grew more strident, further confounding the modest attempts to establish forest village development programs.

PROBLEM SOLVING STRATEGIES:
A LEARNING-PROCESS APPROACH

Initial discussions between Ford Foundation staff and a few concerned SFC planners and administrators in 1984 indicated the SFC's willingness, though hesitant, to experiment with new strategies to allow greater community involvement in forest land management. Foundation and SFC staff hoped that a process of change could be effected that would give SFC officials a better understanding of sources of and solutions to contemporary forest problems. For senior officials to understand more fully the causes of conflict between the agency and rural communities, new sources of information and opportunities to learn had to be created. Agency staff had to reconsider the roles of foresters and state forestry institutions and the perspectives of forest villagers. They needed to address many procedural and structural issues, both within the SFC and at the village level, with greater objectivity. This required open exchanges with subordinates and rural people, and opportunities to experiment with decentralized community management systems.

How would such an organizational reorientation work? Seeing the bureaucracy itself as the primary obstacle to change, Korten and Uphoff advise developing a "centrally guided bottom-up process of building new approaches to field operations based on field experience."[11] Some of the decision-making power and capacity must be shifted to the lower bureaucratic levels to involve those served by (and therefore outside of) the bureaucracy in the decision-making process. The change process requires analysis of local factors related to field-level management problems and how these are affected by organizational conditions. In effect, the process applies the philosophy and procedures of "action research" to bureaucracies intended to serve as agents of development.

Korten and Uphoff recommend establishing a working group to meet regularly and oversee the involvement of lower-level officials and program beneficiaries/participants. The working group would comprise key players "who devote major portions of their time to working on the problem at hand."[12] This group would preferably have funding—independent of the usual bureaucratic budget—in order to give them maximum flexibility and empower them to make decisions or support programs that might otherwise be lost in the organization's regular routine.

Clearly there are problems, conceptual and operational, with the Korten-Uphoff approach. Critical analysis and alteration of organizational procedures and power structures are contrary to the top-down nature of the bureaucratic structure and process, a problem that Korten and Uphoff admit. To be successful, organizational change strategies require the continued commitment of highly placed officials. In other words, "some 'top-down' effort is needed to elicit and sustain 'bottom-up' activities."[13] Many high-level officials are reluctant to devote much of their time to lengthy analyses of management problems and alternatives that may ultimately erode their own authority. Competent managers also tend to be overburdened by their superiors and unable to devote sustained attention to a single problem. While outside funding may allow the working group greater flexibility in developing alternative management systems, it may also lead to internal jealousies and resistance from other members of the organization and create dependence on outside funding sources. Unless the host agency is willing to commit its own financial resources to the new program, a key pillar of the program falls away when the external funding source withdraws.

Despite these problems, the approach does offer a starting point for efforts to improve the effectiveness of development agencies committed to increasing their effectiveness and responsiveness to their clients' needs. In full awareness of the program's many shortcomings, in this chapter we describe the reorientation process undertaken by Java's forestry bureaucracy.

PHASE ONE: DIAGNOSTIC RESEARCH

In May 1984, Indonesian ecologists, social scientists, forestry planners and policy makers, and foreign consultants met to review major forest management problems, analyze past efforts to overcome them, and develop new plans to address them. The participants agreed that a working group should be established to study forest resource conflicts. Field work would be conducted by an interdisciplinary team of graduate students who would work with senior scientists and report to key policy makers in the SFC. The research was to focus on analyzing the history of human-forest interaction patterns, relationships between foresters and local people, the perceptions of villagers and field foresters towards the forest and forest policy, and the influence of village social structure on patterns of forest access.[14]

Each research team member was responsible for studying a particular forest community. Twelve sites were selected to represent a range of natural and socio-economic environments and management systems, including production forests under coastal mangrove, lowland teak, upland pine, and protection forests in West and Central Java. The sites had varied cultural histories and histories of conflict with the forestry agency. The team spent nine months living in the case study communities. Long-term residence in the study villages helped researchers overcome their assumptions and biases toward particular sites or management issues. It also allowed them to build rapport with forest villagers, most of whom tended to be suspicious of outsiders, especially those affiliated with the SFC.

Throughout the course of the study, the research team, met every three to six weeks to discuss methods and interim findings. Periodically, senior scientists and planners from the working group joined these discussions. As the research progressed, the research design was modified, often in different ways according to a site's characteristics or the experience of the fieldworker. In this way, site-specific problems and issues could be explored in depth. Nevertheless, much of the baseline data was collected for comparison across cases.

Oral histories gave the working group an understanding of the evolution of forest and private land-use systems as well as villagers' relationships with the forestry agency. Similarly, local beliefs about village and forest origins indicated community perceptions of the forest and their relationship to it. In-depth interviews with local SFC staff, village and religious leaders, and community members of all classes, sexes, and age groups provided insights into the different perspectives of villagers involved with the forest in particular ways. Household-income and time-allocation studies examined the ways in which access to and dependence on forest lands varied within communities according to socio-economic status. On-site analyses of existing agroforestry systems and in-depth interviews about land and tree tenure and cropping patterns on private and forest lands served to illuminate different production strategies and priorities within the communities and the local forestry agency personnel.

The diagnostic research found that most conflicts could be attributed to three factors: long-standing disputes between forest villagers and state foresters over forest lands and tree tenure; a history of bureaucratic misbehavior among many field foresters, including corruption, exploitation, and involvement in teak theft; and the failure of the highly centralized SFC to adapt its forest management policies to diverse ecological and socioeconomic circumstances in forest villages.

In all of the research sites where *tumpang sari* reforestation was in progress, the two- or three-year tenure period provided no long-term incentive to forest farmers to pursue such ecologically sound farming practices as terracing, contour planting, or fertilization. Although the primary timber species and the annual crops generally did well during the first two years, once the plots were closed to *tumpang sari* the forest farmers had no interest in protecting young forest species from grazing cattle, fires, and undesirable secondary growth. In some forest districts the SFC had repeatedly planted deforested areas, and each time they were burned or trampled by cattle once the *tumpang sari* period was over. In one Central Java site, forest farmers set nearly seventy-five fires over a five-year period, destroying the reforestation area and requiring the SFC to open a new plot. Though resistance methods differed, sabotage of closed reforestation areas was common in many of the study sites throughout Central and West Java. Unable to demand change openly, forest farmers and other forest villagers expressed their opposition in anonymous, clandestine ways. The failure of such reforestation efforts became a victory for the forest farmers: soon the lands were reallocated for *tumpang sari* reforestation, opening up land for annual crop cultivation.

Research also showed that closing *tumpang sari* had the greatest impact on the household economies of landless or land-poor farmers who depended on reforestation plots for survival. If new blocks were not opened in their vicinity, they lost a major source of livelihood. Some field foresters reportedly manipulated the high demand for access to *tumpang sari* by auctioning off access rights, transferring cultivation rights to wealthy farmers in the community, or requiring that forest laborers perform extensive voluntarily labor. In one case, entrepreneurial foresters auctioned off land which had not been slated for reforestation.

Research revealed that much of the antipathy between forest police and community members stemmed from the people's beliefs that the foresters misused their authority. Field foresters reportedly exacted illegal fees and accepted bribes (for access to land or "purchase" of seedlings), underpaid forest laborers, and used strong-arm tactics with villagers. Because the SFC did not systematically monitor the field staff's relations with forest villages, and because the agency's own goals (*i.e.*, growing trees)

were couched in physical and technical, rather than social terms, field foresters could exploit forest laborers as long as such exploitation created no
major administrative problems. Transgressors were rarely fired for accepting bribes or otherwise cheating the SFC; rather, they were "contained"
through demotion to desk jobs.

Interviews with foresters at all levels indicated that they blamed
reforestation failures on the villagers. During the early 1980s, for example, when a great deal of national attention was focused on the money
wasted on failed reforestation projects, senior and junior officials alike
pointed at "backward" rural people as the reason, despite considerable
evidence that poor planning and widespread corruption were equally, if
not more, significant factors. The foresters' view of rural people as ignorant
of "the meanings and functions of the forest" was found to be deeply in-
grained and widespread throughout the agency.[15]

Complex agroforestry systems developed by forest villagers on their
private lands showed that they were far from ignorant of the hydrological
functions of forests. In a number of interviews, farmers elaborated reasons why the primary timber species selected by the foresters was inappropriate to the local environment, illustrating their knowledge of local
micro-climatic and soil conditions. However, SFC personnel had been
taught the superiority of their "expert" knowledge to indigenous knowledge, and these teachings were reinforced by forestry decision-making
policies and procedures.[16]

The research revealed that SFC planning procedures structurally reinforced top-down decision making. Twenty-five-, ten-, and one-year plans
had to be made for each district and adhered to as closely as possible.
District management plans were written far from the field, based on theoretical tenets of forestry instead of on the empirical uniqueness of each
field site. High-level officials frequently visited field sites, but they focused
their attention on technical problems and used police methods to handle
conflicts stemming from inadequate or irrelevant management policy. Forest rangers often made heavy demands on forest laborers, but rarely
listened to their problems or advice. Technical goals were never adjusted
to the practical, socio-economic needs of each forest village.

While rigidity and centralized policy formulation characterized the official SFC management system, the case studies revealed that SFC policies
were often adapted to local conditions. Many field foresters desired smooth
relations with the community and overlooked small transgressions, such
as subsistence fuelwood collection, in order to maintain reasonable working relations with local villagers. Yet, while local forest managers acknowledged the inappropriateness of certain policies and procedures, they
were also aware of their inability to influence policy change.

Although some foresters' informal agreements with the community
resulted in mutually beneficial compromise, informal systems of forest ac-

cess control also led to the misuses of power described above. The frequent need for informal arrangements between foresters and villagers reflected both the problems of applying macro-forestry policies across Java and the considerable diversity of circumstances and interaction between forest villages and state forests.

One year after the working group first met, the case study findings, summarized above, were reviewed. The research had achieved its major objective of providing an understanding and documentation of field situations. The working group used that information to urge agency planners and policy makers to look beyond technical management issues to the economic, socio-political, and organizational problems at the root of many forest conflicts in Java. While many of the problems illuminated by the case studies were not unknown to critics inside and outside the SFC, the working group's research reports brought these issues into the open and removed organizational taboos on their discussion with outsiders.

The principal recommendation at the close of the diagnostic research was that the SFC initiate pilot projects in which SFC personnel would cooperate with forest villagers to manage the forests. To meet the SFC's reforestation mandate, degraded forest lands were given priority for proposed pilot project sites. To respond to villagers' needs, structural changes in access controls were to give people longer rights of tenure on reforestation lands and greater involvement in selecting alternative crop species, to which they would also have firmer rights. At the community level, forest farmer organizations would be formed to give farmers a greater sense of collective power and responsibility and a common direction. Finally, some forest rangers would have to exchange their police roles for those of community organizers and assistants. Given the history of forest management on Java, both the bureaucracy and the forest villagers were expected to be skeptical of these kinds of changes.

PHASE TWO: PILOT PROJECTS

To alleviate conflict over forest access, the SFC needed to be able to communicate with rural families and offer land management systems that provided security and income. Based on the findings of the diagnostic research, pilot projects were designed to use community organizers (COs) to facilitate communication between the SFC and pilot villages, extend the tenure period for *tumpang sari*, encourage farmers to plant and retain access to certain perennial species, plan for new annual crops suitable for more mature agroforestry systems, and strengthen the organizational ability of both parties (villagers and the SFC) to collaborate in managing forest lands.

At first, community organizers outside the SFC were enlisted for the pilot projects. In addition, some forest rangers were selected for CO training. By selecting different categories of community organizers, the working group hoped to compare their effectiveness in improving relations between forest communities and the SFC. Selection criteria included empathy for the circumstances of forest villagers and strong communication and problem-solving skills. It was easier to monitor these qualities in the selection of outside CO candidates than in that of SFC personnel.

An Indonesian nongovernmental organization was contracted to train the newly chosen social forestry field staff in community organizing methods. For six weeks, participants and trainers defined the methods to be applied in the coming year to assist communities in establishing agroforestry management systems. The curriculum included ways to rapidly assess the sources of forest-based conflict in pilot sites and formulate new social forestry management systems. The training included lectures, role playing, field exercises, and team planning. Staff also learned diagnostic methods for identifying appropriate agroforestry systems, ways to stimulate group discussions and exchange, and the new administrative procedures that would be required by the SFC.

Community organizers entered the pilot villages in March 1986. They were supported by externally recruited provincial social forestry coordinators who were positioned in the SFC's East, Central, and West Java regional offices. Each coordinator made monthly visits to field sites, held a monthly meeting of community organizers and SFC provincial staff, and facilitated the processing of Forest Farmer Group land-use agreements. The coordinators also acted as a liaison between the central SFC office and the field staff.

During the first two months in the field, the COs identified land-poor households interested in managing agroforestry plots.[17] The CO then helped these households organize a Forest Farmer Group (FFG) to discuss and design a management plan indicating the desired perennial and annual species to be planted. The CO assisted the FFG in taking the proposal to the SFC district office for discussions and possible modifications. Once approved by both the local FFG and the SFC and formalized, the joint management plan entitled the farmers to use the land until the harvest season for the primary timber species, provided they conformed to the agreement. While the initial lease was for two to five years, farmer groups were supposed to have the option of extending their tenure for fifteen to forty years, depending on the rotation cycle of the primary timber species.

This procedure was unique in several ways. First, it put the SFC in a position of approaching the community in a cooperative manner and eliciting their opinions on the types of crops most suited to the environment. Second, it allowed farmers to legally plant fruit tree species on state forest lands for the first time and gave them rights to harvest tree products under the long-term tenure agreement. Having provided or paid for the seedlings, the SFC retained control of the land, the fruit tree itself, and the primary forest species, such as teak. As the COs' rapport with villagers grew and the terms of the project became more widely known in the thirteen pilot project villages, enthusiasm increased. There was a growing belief among farmers in many of the pilot project areas that the SFC was changing. Forest rangers found they were greeted with a growing friendliness. In sites where wood theft and forest fires had been common, the incidence of such transgressions began to fall.

By late May 1986, most participating communities had formed FFGs, formulated management plans, and been allocated ten- to twenty-five-hectare blocks of land, divided into quarter- to half-hectare plots for each household. These lands were cleared in the summer of August 1986. Most FFGs decided to plant combinations of familiar local staple crops such as maize, cassava, dry rice, and groundnuts, which the SFC initially approved. To conform to national agricultural policy, however, the SFC later required farmers in most sites to plant hybrid varieties of maize, using chemical fertilizers and pesticides. In September, just before the onset of the rainy season, the SFC loaned participants the hybrid maize seeds and fertilizer, and provided fruit tree seedlings at no cost. Generally, farmers requested fruit tree seedlings that generated income and were known to produce well in their area, such as mangoes, guava, and durian. Also popular were banana, pineapple, and a variety of fodder and fuelwood species.

The SFC provided the seedlings as a means of retaining control over the trees planted on forest lands. All parties agreed, however, that the goal of increasing village employment and involvement would be best served if the SFC purchased the seedlings from village nurseries, to be established as part of the program. Unfortunately, the SFC's rapid implementation of the pilot program created unreasonable deadlines as the planting season approached. As a result, the SFC purchased fruit tree seedlings from the open market rather than waiting for the villagers to establish nurseries.

By January 1987, farmers were beginning to harvest their staple crops. Yields varied widely: in some areas farmers harvested four to five tons of hybrid maize per hectare, two to three times what they have achieved with local varieties on surrounding private farmlands; in areas with poor soils, *i.e.*, most of the pilot sites, the hybrid maize did poorly. The change in the foresters' attitudes and approach, however, seemed to maintain community support for the program in most villages, even where harvests were poor.

The first-year pilot projects were meant to design and implement, on a limited basis, forest management systems that gave local communities economic incentives to manage degraded forest areas in productive and sustainable ways. Field activities were intended to help participants learn while implementing these participatory management systems, rather than to maximize success in pilot sites themselves. However, foresters at both the field and management levels ultimately focused largely on the successful planting of forest species. The program was also confounded by a new national agricultural program to achieve self-sufficiency in maize, resulting in the forced planting of maize mentioned above. The SFC's actions reflected the foresters' traditional top-down, paternalistic relationship to the community and reinforced farmers' long-held beliefs about the nature of forest management.

Another, more serious, problem generated by the SFC's technical orientation was the manner in which some internally recruited COs selected farmers to participate. Under great time pressure to identify and persuade farmers to participate in the program, many foresters did not select land-poor farmers, but rather farmers who they felt "could do the job." This generally meant the more prosperous farmers, able to perform better because of their access to capital and private resources.

Even when selected for FFG membership, many landless families lacked the resources to invest in tree crops that would generate income only after four to seven years. Waiting six months without remuneration, during the land-clearing and three-month growing periods for annual crops, was also difficult for low-income households. The SFC resisted extending subsistence credit or credit to pay labor and provided credit only on hybrid maize packages that they in turn obtained on credit from the Department of Agriculture. This put poor households, especially female-headed households, at a disadvantage from the start. Not surprisingly, transfers of tree tenure and rights of program participation were reported within the first year. Many poor farmers who tried to participate transferred their plots to farmers with capital to hire labor to farm their own fields while they worked the pilot forest plots. Thus, independent funds for labor costs and household support during the first six months effectively became a prerequisite to participation, hindering the program's ability to improve rural income distribution and poor rural peoples' forest access.

Women, too, were systematically excluded from participation by the FFG selection process, which solicited membership from the head of household, traditionally defined as the husband. A few women, mostly widows, were able to obtain plots in certain pilot sites, but foresters tended not to select women for the new program, and most women were embarrassed to ask for plots. Yet the diagnostic research had shown that women often worked as much as their husbands or sons on their forest or privately held agricultural plots.[18] Female heads of households were not given the same access opportunities as the men. When contracts for access to the fruits and leaves of trees planted on the state forest lands were signed, only the men signed.

Financial and organizational constraints on continuing the program also became evident in the first year. While externally recruited COs were actually more successful in gaining community trust and negotiating between the foresters and the villagers, the SFC decided that the agency could not afford to use outsiders when the program was expanded to all SFC-controlled lands in need of reforestation. As a result, the program would have to rely on forest rangers learning to be community organizers. The CO's self-perceptions and the perceptions of his constituency would be critical factors in the project's success.[19]

Another unforseen organizational problem resulted from the program's reliance on the bottom of the SFC's bureaucratic pyramid. Although several social forestry orientation seminars were held for provincial, district, and subdistrict SFC staff, considerable suspicion and misunderstanding arose among middle-level SFC administrators. In some cases, mid-level SFC personnel were annoyed at being by-passed by senior SFC planners working directly with field staff. To alleviate such suspicion, program planners gave more attention to intensive mid-level staff training and integration in the second year of the program.

PHASE THREE: EXPANSION

From the start of the Java social forestry program, it had been assumed that the first-year pilot projects would lead into a long-term expansion phase that built on the successes and lessons learned from the pilot phase. Encouraged by the initial positive results of the pilot projects, senior SFC administrators indicated that some 250,000 (since revised upward to 300,000) hectares of degraded forest lands, representing approximately 10 percent of the state-controlled forest lands on Java, would be reforested using social forestry management systems over the next five years. Program planners were encouraged by growing political support for the program, but feared that rapid expansion would undermine its quality and integrity. The administrative burden of implementing the still-immature program over such a large area seemed certain to doom efforts to improve the initial design.

The working group agreed to confine expansion in 1987 to the twelve (of a total fifty-eight) forest districts that already had pilot projects. Site selection criteria for new locations included a significant area of degraded forest, surplus labor markets, and supportive SFC personnel. To enhance the supervision of field staff, a forest ranger from each of the twelve districts was trained to serve as social forestry field supervisor. In addition, an NGO advisor in community organizing was seconded to each of the three provinces to implement district-level staff training and to backstop FFG formation. Unfortunately, the plans for controlled expansion were overwhelmed by political pressures for rapid growth. From the original thirteen pilot locations in 1986, the program expanded in 1987 to fifty-seven additional locations clustered around, but not limited to, the twelve target districts. There followed a significant decline in the quality of implementation in the expansion sites.

First, poor site selection led to the inclusion of labor-scarce sites, sites in areas needing only limited reforestation, and sites so degraded as to be virtually nonarable.[20] A central office directive to select "critical lands," meaning areas where socio-economic pressures were greatest, had apparently been misinterpreted by district officials to mean "critical soils." Thus, the program was burdened with a number of sites requiring rehabilitation before they could offer farmers a reasonable income. To address the site-selection problem, a special course on micro-level land management planning for district-level officials was held in mid-1987; it was also proposed that this method be incorporated into the standard SFC planning process.

The second problem encountered at the expansion sites was inadequate field staff preparation. At a number of new locations, field staff formed farmers into FFGs and told them what to plant without seriously attempting to elicit their participation in decision making.[21] The one-week training course for new staff had proven insufficient. As these personnel were all internally-recruited forest rangers and guards, it is likely that they needed more, rather than less, training and socialization than the first cohort, which had received six weeks of training and had included externally recruited community organizers. However, it was not feasible to put all of these personnel (which numbered over 100) through the full six-week course, primarily because there were few capable trainers and only limited time for training during the off-season. In the short term, the SFC has tried to address this problem by conducting additional short courses at the district level, reserving more intensive training for staff with potential to become trainers themselves. In the medium term, the SFC hopes to integrate social forestry curricula into its standard staff training courses.

The third problem encountered during the first year of the expansion phase was an exacerbated friction with mid-level SFC staff who did not yet understand or support the program. Some district-level officials obstructed program implementation by hindering field staff from carrying out their program-related responsibilities. For example, several officials refused to recognize field supervisors' special status and prohibited them from working across forest district boundaries. The SFC central office also encountered problems in mainstreaming the program: officials who had felt left out of initial program discussions were reluctant, for example, to cooperate in modifying the agency's planning process or granting employment tenure to the externally recruited COs.

As program leaders attempted to deal with the many problems that arose during expansion, the inadequacy of management's involvement in the program became clear. To respond to emerging problems and prevent them from becoming crises, program leaders needed time to visit the field, digest reports, lobby for the program within the agency, interact with personnel from other institutions, and plan for training and expansion. However, senior SFC program managers were also handling a range of other tasks as large and complex as the social forestry program, and were often called away from their routine duties to attend national and regional seminars and conferences. Program participants from other institutions were similarly overcommitted, to the extent that scheduling meetings was always difficult. As a result, during the first year of the expansion phase, program managers depended heavily on the informal coordination and field reports provided by an American volunteer associated with the program.

Despite a general recognition within the SFC of the need to address the weaknesses revealed by the program's first year of expansion, pressure to continue rapid expansion was unrelenting. Within a six-month period beginning in late 1987, new leadership assumed office at the highest levels of both the SFC and the Ministry of Forestry. The new leaders were aggressive and self-confident, and saw in social forestry a potential solution to the increasingly apparent problem of forest degradation and fueled hopes for increasing future forest production. Their enthusiasm created additional pressures for rapid program expansion, and sent a signal that provincial- and district-level officials picked up immediately. As a result, program leadership was subjected to irresistible pressure from both above and below to double the program's size in 1988 and open sites in all forest districts. Adding to the management burden, program leaders were also directed to extend the social forestry program to mangrove areas and buffer zones surrounding national parks, even though pilot projects in such areas were among the least successful.[22]

New Ministry and SFC leadership also led to a remarkably fluid policy-making environment for the social forestry program. New policies, such as a decision to switch from teak to short-rotation timber species at social forestry locations, became increasingly frequent. While these new policies almost uniformly supported the program's goals, their rapid implementation raised additional policy issues.

To deal with such questions, the social, economic, and ecological viability of the program's new forest management systems was assessed in greater detail at the national level. In mid-1987, a team of university faculty and students began to monitor progress at the pilot sites and conduct research on socio-economic issues. The program was expected to face its most severe test in the third and fourth years, as the tree canopy began to close and farmers could no longer plant annual crops. In early 1988, a technically oriented team of university-based scientists and agency staff, coordinated by an expatriate advisor, was formed to evaluate ongoing and potential agroforestry systems. The agroforestry team is developing typologies of agroecological zones and determining which annual and perennial species are appropriate to these zones, with the object of helping SFC policy makers, field staff, and FFGs design appropriate agroforestry systems.

REFLECTIONS

Why did this program succeed in influencing a conservative forestry agency to revise its traditional management approach? First, the timing was right. The agency had received increasing pressure to respond better to the needs of rural communities as a way of promoting reforestation efforts. The proponents of change outside the agency identified concerned officials inside the agency and gave them a means to take action. Second, the research team and the working group were strategically placed within the agency, allowing them to channel their findings into the SFC's policy-formulation and program-implementation processes. The program's administrator was an exceptionally able and committed individual, and without his persistence in promoting the program within the SFC, it would surely have floundered. Finally, the donor agency was committed to following up the diagnostic research with pilot projects and support into an expansion period. Planners were encouraged to consider the direction of the pilot projects during the diagnostic research phase. Later, during the pilot projects, they thought about expanding the social forestry strategies into a national program.

It should also be emphasized that the SFC is an exceptionally efficient and effective organization compared with the vast majority of forestry agencies in the developing world. As a state enterprise in a bureaucratic-authoritarian state, it has a clear chain of command and is run with a businesslike bottom-line mentality. This status, as a semiautonomous corporation, lends it a degree of flexibility and independence unknown in regular government line agencies. It is also profit-motivated and the promise of increasing tree production in the long run was appealing. While the social forestry program had to work against the SFC's traditional law enforcement orientation, many other aspects of the agency aided program implementation.

The program's actual successes and failures are both attributable to its social context and the dynamics of the bureaucracy. The agency's decision to give up some of its traditional power by lengthening tenure periods on reforestation plots and allowing FFGs to control nonforest species was a tremendous step forward. The tendency to impose traditional top-down controls at critical points, however, quickly reappeared whenever potential conflicts appeared, as in the selection of the farmers' annual and perennial crops. Thus, despite the efforts of supportive planners and field staff, agency interests often received priority when important policy decisions were made. It is hoped that as confidence in community management ability grows, adjustments will be made to make policies more responsive to community needs.

While supportive policies can be enacted with the stroke of a pen, the development of organizational capacity and attitudinal change are gradual and require long-term internal and external support. The Java experience indicates that change is possible in a conservative, developing-country bureaucracy, provided there are supportive individuals at top levels, mechanisms for opening communication, and opportunities for staff to learn and experiment with management alternatives. Though change is slow and progress incremental, the reorientation of management systems is a strategic means of working within well-established state agencies.

NOTES

Author's Note: A shorter version of this chapter appeared in *Human Organization* (Winter) 1989.

1. Over 85 percent of fuel in rural areas comes from firewood (GOI/IIED, 1985:84), with some forest villages taking 100 percent of their fuelwood from government-controlled forest lands (Kartasubrata and Syafi'i, 1985).

2. Two-thirds of Java's forest land is classified as production forest, composed of teak *(Tectona grandis)*, pine *(Pinus merkusii)*, dammar *(Agathis spp.)*, and rasamala *(Altinggia excelsia)* plantations. The rest are protection forests and national park lands.

3. The program was begun by the State Forest Corporation in 1984 and continues to receive funding and technical support from the Ford Foundation.

4. Peluso, Nancy Lee. 1988. "Rich Forests, Poor People, and Development: Access Control and Resistance in the Forests of Java." Ph.D. dissertation, Cornell University.

5. Radite, D. S. 1985. "Laporan Social Forestry di Desa Tanggel, Randublatung," in *Studi Kasus Social Forestry Berbagain Aspek Tentang Hubungan Interaksi Masyarakat Dengan Hutan di Jawa Tengah*, ed. Tim Social Forestry Indonesia. Jakarta: Perum Perhutani dan Yayasan Ford.

6. Wiersum, K. F. 1982. "Tree Gardening and Taungya on Java: Examples of Agroforestry Techniques in the Humid Tropics." *Agroforestry Systems* 1:53–70.

7. Van Doorn, Z. 1932. "Een Stukje Welvaartspolitiek in Onze Hand." *Tectona* 25:804–807.

8. Onghokham. 1975. "The Residency of Madiun: Priyayi and Peasant in the Nineteenth Century." Ph.D. dissertation, Yale University.

9. Peluso. "Rich Forests, Poor People, and Development: Access Control and Resistance in the Forests of Java."

10. Kompas. 1986. "Ditahan 12 Tersangka Pembunuh Petugas Perhutani" ("Twelve accused of killing Perhutani official are captured"). March 22, 1986.

11. Korten, David C. and Norman T. Uphoff. 1981. "Bureaucratic Reorientation for Participatory Rural Development." NASPAA Working Paper No. 1. NASPAA and USAID. November.

12. Ibid., p. 15.

13. Ibid., p. 6.

14. Vayda, Andrew P., Carol Colfer, and M. Brata Kusumo. 1980. "Interactions Between People and Forests in East Kalimantan." *Impact of Science on Society* 30:3:179–190; Wiersum, Freerk. 1984. "Developing Strategies for Social Forestry: A Conceptual Approach." Working Paper. Honolulu: EAPI, East-West Center; Romm, Jeff. 1986. "Forest Policy and Development Policy." *Journal of World Forest Resource Management* 2:85–103.

15. Blaikie, P. 1985. *The Political Economy of Soil Erosion in Developing Countries.* Longman Development Studies, ed. D. J. Dwyer. London and New York: Longman. Blaikie calls this attitude "the colonial conception of land management."

16. Brokenshaw, D., D. M. Warren, and O. Werner. 1980. *Indigenous Knowledge Systems and Development.* Lanham, MD: University Press of America.

17. Wiersum, K. 1982. "Tree Gardening and Taungya on Java: Examples of Agroforestry Techniques in the Humid Tropics." *Agroforestry Systems* 1:53–70.

18. Social Forestry Team (SFT). 1985a. *Studi Kasus Social Forestry Berbagai Aspek Tentang Hubungan Interaksi Masyarakat Dengan hutan di Jawa Tengah.* Jakarta: Perum Perhutani dengan yayasan Ford; 1985b. *Studi Kasus Social Forestry Berbagai Aspek Tentang Hubungan Interaksi Masyarakat Dengan Hutan di Jawa Barat.* Jakarta: Perum Perhutani dengan Yayasan Ford.

19. The use of the male pronoun is justified in this case: apart from two of the externally recruited social forestry program COs, the SFC has no female forest rangers or guards.

20. See Read, T. 1988. "Field Report: Java Social Forestry Program Units I, II, and III." April-May.

21. Ibid.

22. See Read, T. 1988. "Reflections on Selected Pilot Project Sites." Java Social Forestry Program. May.

CHAPTER TWELVE

Community Participation for Conservation Area Management in the Cyclops Mountains, Irian Jaya, Indonesia

Arthur Mitchell, Yance de Fretes, and Mark Poffenberger

IN MANY DEVELOPING countries, traditional land tenure is an important factor in rural development, including the sustainable exploitation and management of forests. However, local land-tenure issues are often overlooked in forest management planning, as most unsuccessful development activities reflect. Respect for traditional land tenure and the rights of indigenous communities, together with community participation in management, is essential if forest management is to benefit, rather than displace, forest communities.

Traditional shifting cultivation that entails slash-and-burn forest clearance by forest farmers is the greatest cause of tropical deforestation worldwide, both quantitative and qualitative, accounting for 16 million hectares of the estimated 20 million hectares of forest converted from its original state worldwide each year.[1] In Southeast Asia, now thought to have the greatest rate of forest loss, farmers are clearing at least 8.5 million hectares annually.[2] All available lowland tropical forests will soon be altered in some way except those protected in nature reserves, and those areas will be increasingly pressured by communities in the vicinity of reserves. This rapid deforestation, coupled with growing population pressures and accelerating development, reflects the difficulties forest agencies confront in managing vast land areas. Policing efforts have essentially failed to protect forest lands or respond to the needs of communities traditionally dependent on forests. Economically viable and culturally acceptable alternatives to current land-use practices are necessary if forests are to be protected and managed sustainably.

The primary objective of the Indonesian Social Forestry Program (ISFP), is to develop alternative forest management systems based on local community participation.[3] Since 1986, the Ford Foundation has been working with the Ministry of Forestry, the Provincial Government of Irian Jaya, the World Wildlife Fund (WWF), and the Irian Jaya Rural Development Foundation (YPMD) to establish a social forestry project on the periphery of the Cyclops Mountains Conservation Area. This is one of a series of pilot project sites in Indonesia where indigenous communities and the forestry service are attempting to establish collaborative management systems for state forest lands.[4] In 1984, WWF prepared a management plan for the Cyclops Mountains Conservation Area, a protected forest ranging in elevation from sea level to approximately 1,880 meters and located west of Jayapura, the capital of Irian Jaya (Indonesia's easternmost province, formerly Netherlands New Guinea).[5] The reserve was established to protect the flora and fauna of its tropical rainforests and to provide a water catchment for Jayapura, the villages surrounding the reserve, and Lake Sentani to the south. The protected forest thus ensures a clean and adequate water supply for the area's growing population of about 100,000 people. Although the reserve officially includes approximately 31,600 hectares, field work during management planning led WWF to recommend increasing its size to 36,800 hectares and creating a new boundary in consultation with communities along its periphery.[6] The management plan also proposed a system of buffer zones, or low-intensity use zones, between agriculturally developed land and protected forest. These zones were to be managed by and for the benefit of local communities, which view forest access as a traditional right. While the buffer zone concept has been discussed in Indonesia for over a decade, the Cyclops Mountains plan represents one of the first attempts to establish community-managed zones within and around the periphery of a nature reserve.

In Indonesia, the boundaries between state forest land and tribal land have never been clarified. Thus, the Cyclops Mountains pilot project provides the opportunity to stabilize reserve boundaries and to develop a new process through which local governments and forest-dependent communities could agree on land-use management methods and responsibilities. In this chapter, we discuss traditional government, tribal land tenure and land use, and their effects on community participatory management for the Cyclops Mountains Conservation Area. An important issue is how tribal land-tenure security and community participation can be promoted through social forestry.

TRADITIONAL GOVERNMENT AND CONSERVATION

Irian Jaya is Indonesia's largest province and, although sparsely populated, is culturally diverse, with more than 250 linguistic groups, each with its own relationship to its natural environment expressed through its culture. Around the Cyclops Mountains, there are four main indigenous linguistic groups with different origins and traditions, although their traditional social structures are similar (see Figure 12.1).[7] The social forestry program currently involves three of these linguistic groups. The Sentani people live in the vicinity of Lake Sentani, the Moi are centered around the village of Maribu, and the Tabla live along the northwest coast of the Cyclops Mountains. Indigenous communities have several kinds of leaders in the following hierarchy: lineage leaders *(kepala keret)*, clan leaders *(koselo)*, traditional leaders *(ondoafi* or *ondofolo)*, and heads of tribal councils *(dewan adat)*.

One means for rural community development in Irian Jaya is through the *dewan adat*, or tribal council, which deals with many cultural issues, including land tenure. The councils can potentially influence local people very positively, but they have also been used for personal profit and political aims and consequently are not always respected. At the village level, most land disputes are settled by the *ondoafi*, in his capacity as spokesman for several clan leaders. The *ondoafi* is traditionally responsible for managing the natural resources and controlling the use of communal lands, as well as providing for orphans and widows in the community. Unfortunately, in some cases they have abused their authority by selling communal land for personal profit, although the land is intended to be held in common by the clans under the *ondoafi's* leadership and any land transfers must be made in consultation with the clan leaders.

The government recently established the *dewan adat*, usually based at the regency *(kabupaten)* or district *(kecamatan)* levels, to help initiate and coordinate village development activities. As the *dewan adat* is a recent institution imposed by the provincial government, more traditional forms of local decision making still prevail, and the *ondoafi* have greater influence at the village level than do the leaders of a *dewan adat*, who are appointed by the provincial government. In 1984, the *dewan adat* for the Jayapura regency, based at Sentani, agreed to let the Forestry Department manage the Cyclops Mountains, which are tribal lands, as a nature reserve. The agreement was signed by almost all of the *ondoafi* as members of the *dewan adat*, yet there are still people who sell or rent tribal communal land, both within and outside the reserve, to immigrants. This indicates that the authority of the *dewan adat*, as a relatively new institution, is not well recognized and perhaps not well respected. However, given the provincial government bureaucracy, the *dewan adat*, if strengthened, could be the most effective liaison between the government agencies that promote development activities and the local people they are intended to serve.

In the Cyclops Mountains, as elsewhere in New Guinea, tribal stories concerned with descent, beliefs, and taboos are closely connected to the forest, its animals, and land. Fortunately, conservation is a value inherent in most of the traditional beliefs reflected in these stories. Tabla

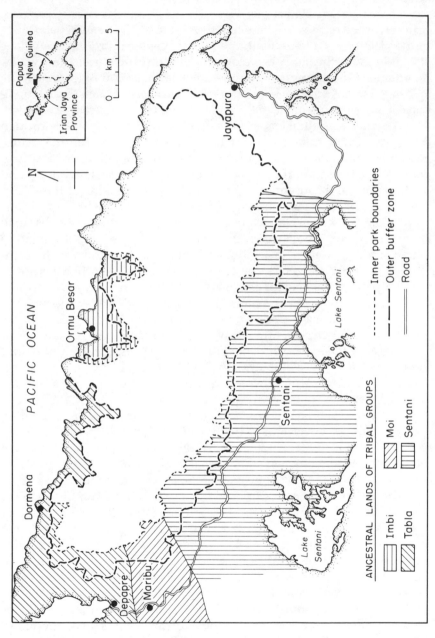

Figure 12.1. Cyclops Mountains Nature Reserve and tribal areas

people and other tribal groups believed they were descended from a large flightless bird, the cassowary. Some also believe that disturbing a species of bird, the wagtail *Rhipidura*, will stunt the growth of their children.[8] One of the Moi clans, the Banundi, do not hunt lorries because their myths trace the clan's origins to these small parrots; each clan has a similar relationship with its own "species of origin." Moi people also do not eat hornbills (*Rhyticeros* sp.) because they believe that its meat will make them weak.

The Sentani and Tabla people respect the peaks of the Cyclops Mountains as a resting place for their ancestors and rarely enter very far into the mountains. Traditionally, the Tabla people and the neighboring Imbi to the east divide the mountains above their villages into three general zones based on land use: an upper zone (over 400 meters above sea level) for collection of building materials and hunting, a middle zone (400 to 300 meters) for certain agricultural activities such as cash crop cultivation, and a lower zone (below 300 meters) for housing and subsistence gardens. Local people largely adhere to these zones without the imposition of government conservation regulations.

TRIBAL LAND TENURE AND OWNERSHIP

Land status in Irian Jaya differs greatly from other regions of Southeast Asia. In Java, for instance, most land has clear boundaries and is under either private or state control and here other Indonesian social forestry experiments have been tried with some success. In contrast, almost all land in Irian Jaya is claimed by tribes as their land right *(hak ulayat)*. In neighboring Papua New Guinea, this type of customary land tenure prevails over 97 percent of the country; absolute ownership lies with the clan or kinship group, which also retains control over its use and transfer.[9] Clan households receive a piece of land for subsistence needs, and their right to the land is held as long as the land is used for growing crops. When no longer in agricultural production, such areas revert to communal ownership.[10]

Very different systems prevail in other parts of Southeast Asia. In the Philippines, almost all land belongs to the government or private individuals, and tribal land rights are complicated and often disputed. On private lands, a tribal group must have an agreement with the land owners; on government lands, they must deal with the Bureau of Forest Development (BFD). The BFD has made various agreements with tribal groups, such as issuing farmers one-year certificates which can be converted into twenty-five-year leases.[11] However, the way in which farmers perceive "their longevity on the land they cultivate influences their willingness to participate in an agroforestry project far more than any legal document they may or may not possess."[12] In Thailand, the land similarly belongs either to the government or to private individuals; there is no recognition of tribal land. Farmers cultivating government land must obtain an agreement and pay a royalty. The term of agreement depends on the crop rotation, commonly twenty to thirty years. Land-tenure problems in Irian Jaya, because of Indonesia's strong centralized government (which maintains that all land belongs to the state) and the importance of tribal land rights in Irian Jaya, will require solutions that compromise between the state land control of Thailand and the Philippines and the recognition and support of tribal rights by Papua New Guinea.

Four different tribal groups claim the Cyclops Mountains through ancestral inheritance. Government land development projects, including protected nature reserves on tribal land, must consider local knowledge and perceptions of land rights. Traditional land ownership is based on the "first cultivators" principle: those whose ancestors first opened a certain piece of land may claim the right to that land. As the number of descendants of the early cultivators increased, the number of people claiming rights to the same piece of land also increased. As a way to mitigate land disputes and reduce tension among the people, tribal, rather than private, land rights are held by a village community (*yo*) or by a clan (*yoho*). A *yo* may be divided into several plots called *yoho* or *imeah*, each held by a clan and controlled by its *koselo*. Supposedly, land is managed by the traditional leader (*ondoafi*) to protect the community's interest, a function known as *holei nyarei*, which literally means "to look after and feed." Land managed by traditional leaders cannot be sold or rented without the consensus of the tribe's clan leaders, the *koselo*.

In principle, the Indonesian government, through its land reform laws (*Undang-undang Agraria*) recognizes traditional land rights (*hak ulayat*) so long as the tribal community in question still recognizes its customary law (*adat*) and is using and managing its land. In the case of tribal people surrounding the Cyclops Mountains, particularly the Sentani community, this is often hard to demonstrate: the recent influx of immigrants into the community and the influence of development have made traditional land rights more difficult to substantiate and defend, and thus have weakened traditional land-tenure security, which in many areas is ambiguous at best.

Although land rights generally remain strong in most of Irian Jaya, which currently has few, if any, competing demands on land, clear, precise boundaries of tribal lands rarely exist. It is not uncommon for different tribes, or clans within the same tribe, to claim the same piece of land. This creates problems of land use and is a continual source of conflict, sometimes resulting in injury or loss of life. Often there is no mitigating institution through which opposing groups can discuss their disagreements and identify land boundaries without clan warfare (*perang suku*).

The government established the *dewan adat* partly to provide a forum for resolving tribal land disputes.

ENHANCING TRIBAL LAND-TENURE SECURITY THROUGH SOCIAL FORESTRY

Since the Cyclops Mountains reserve was established in 1978, shifting cultivation, illegal logging, and hunting have continued. Land sales to immigrants along the reserve's southern boundary have increased and have weakened tribal control of land in some areas, particularly those closest to Jayapura. Also, particularly in the Sentani area, indigenous communal lands have been leased, through unwritten agreements, to immigrant tenants. These immigrants, mostly from the mountainous interior of the province and from South Sulawesi, have done most of the land clearance, which in some areas has extended inside the reserve's boundaries. Such land transfers, coupled with loss of indigenous control, pose the greatest threat to the Cyclops Mountains reserve. The social forestry project is primarily intended to stabilize the reserve boundaries and minimize land clearance by identifying and strengthening tribal ownership and responsibility for land management, as well as to develop a new process through which local governments and forest-dependent communities could agree on income-generating alternatives to slash-and-burn cultivation.

A number of problems also arise regarding ambiguities of land tenure in surrounding villages. Most land around the reserve boundary has been claimed by local tribal groups, although usually there is little evidence of land ownership. When the land is sold to outsiders, however, or when a clan sells land under unorthodox procedures, rightful ownership becomes a question of dispute. Because there are few clear boundaries between the land of each tribe or clan, it is difficult to determine community responsibilities for management. These land-tenure problems are complicated by conflicting interpretations of reserve boundaries by several government agencies and local communities.

To improve forest management, traditional land tenure and management should be legitimized, particularly on lands bordering the reserve, and local clans will need clear title to their communal lands. Local groups and the forestry service must agree on how the community should manage land for their benefit and in support of conservation objectives. Local forest farmers who are involved in the social forestry project have obtained the right to use communal land through their *ondoafi*, and all tenants who are practicing shifting cultivation on communal land have been encouraged to plant tree crops among their subsistence, annual food crops. In this way, tree crops can increase the long-term value of communal land to the indigenous group.

The Cyclops project began with the selection of a ten-member social forestry field team comprising mostly young men from the three pilot-site villages: Yawena, Sentani, and Maribu. Field staff were placed in communities where they knew the tribal institutions and language; usually they had been born and continued to live in these villages. These staff members underwent training in November 1986 to increase their knowledge and problem-solving abilities as community organizers. Training emphasized the use of discussion group methods and practical field exercises and particularly stressed the understanding of formal government forest management systems, indigenous tribal resource management institutions, and the integration of agroforestry practices in collaborative management programs. Training also involved field exercises in the use of rapid sketch mapping techniques, group interviews, and other diagnostic methods for understanding community forest management needs. Procedures for helping communities formulate forest management plans and formalize them with government agencies were also reviewed. After completion of the four-week training program, the field staff returned to their sites and began discussions with tribal leaders and clan members regarding forest dependency patterns and land-use needs. Senior staff from the provincial forestry service, the Irian Jaya Rural Development Foundation (YPMD) and WWF were responsible for field cooperation and supervision. After more than a year of field work, a follow-up workshop was held for field staff and selected traditional leaders to assess progress, identify the problems hindering implementation, and formulate work plans for each of the pilot sites. One of the most useful aspects of the workshop was the involvement of community leaders. In addition, WWF funded two seminars, in January and June, 1988, in Jayapura at the governor's office and Cenderawasih University. The seminars gave various government officials and local people the opportunity to discuss implementation of the reserve's management plan, particularly regarding social forestry.

To better understand how the social forestry field staff approached implementation in their communities, it is useful to review the case of three pilot sites for the Cyclops Mountains: Yawena, Sentani, and Maribu. Yawena is discussed in greater detail, but typifies, with some modification, the approach used in all three existing sites and that proposed for possible future sites.

Yawena

The village of Yawena is on the northwest coast of the reserve, about 95 kilometers from Jayapura. Access is either by foot trail or by boat. The village, with a population of about 900, is inhabited mostly by Tabla people and comprises two neighborhoods, Doromena and the smaller Wambena.

The majority of the people are farmers who also fish, hunt, gather, and harvest sago palm (*Metroxylon* sp.) as the staple of their diet. Level arable land is severely restricted to a strip only about 40 meters from the sea. From there, the land rises steeply in a series of ridges. Gardens are planted on a rotational basis, and most land under 300 meters elevation is either active or fallow. Fallow periods between crops usually last about seven years, sometimes less. Mixed crops include cassava, taro, sweet potatoes, and a variety of other vegetables, while tree crops include mango, nutmeg, clove, lime, jackfruit, coconut, and betelnut. Some of these tree crops, particularly mango, nutmeg, and betelnut, are abundant, but marketing of surplus is difficult as there is no road connection; produce must be carried out or taken by boat, which is dangerous and infrequent during the northwest monsoon from September to January, the time when mangoes are harvested. This village's relative isolation slows the influx of immigrants, and tribal land control is stronger than in the other two sites. Traditional resource management divides responsibility for terrestrial and marine resources among the clans.

The community has had periodic contacts with forestry department staff, but there has never been an agreement between them regarding the boundaries of government and tribal lands. When the two social forestry field staff for this site first began discussions with the community, village leaders questioned whether a "buffer zone" agreement would meet the village's needs. These concerns formed a basis for discussions of current land and resource use patterns and community needs. Using sketch maps and small format aerial photographs, the community organizers helped the community to assess its current land-use systems, which indicated that the community needed to maintain a strip of coastal land rising to approximately 300 meters elevation for traditional mixed gardens, fruit tree crops, and sago groves. It was agreed that this land would be maintained as an intensive-use zone, while a low-intensity zone, generally between 300 and 400 meters, was designated for selective timber cutting for village needs and logs for canoes, as well as for hunting wild boar and collecting firewood, rattan, and other forest products. As the discussions proceeded, the community increasingly supported a clear agreement with the government regarding their tenurial land status. Tribal leaders knew that neighboring communities to the south had begun selling ancestral lands to immigrants, and the Tabla people feared an erosion of land rights in their own area unless their tenurial status was clarified and legally established.

Tribal leaders made a number of recommendations to the field staff regarding demarcation of reserve boundaries. It was agreed that the reserve's outer boundary would be at 300 meters elevation, but that the boundary would be marked at 500 meters, which designated the inner boundary of the reserve, or the strictly protected zone. By January 1988, the villagers had marked two and a half kilometers above their village, supported by the forest service, and boundary marking will continue east to the next village of Yongsu. Because natural boundary markers (*e.g.*, boulders, ridges, streams) were used as much as possible, the boundary is not fixed at a constant elevation. Every ten meters, the villagers planted a *gayang* (*Inocarpus* sp.) fruit tree and between the trees planted a variegated shrub known locally as *puring* (*Codiaeum* sp.) and ti (*Cordyline* sp.); the villagers obtained and planted the seedlings themselves. The brightly colored *puring* and ti shrubs are common property boundary markers elsewhere in Irian Jaya and Indonesia. The forestry department ordinarily uses heavy concrete posts to mark boundaries, but in this area a "living boundary" planted by the people themselves was considered more appropriate. What is important, regardless of the type of marker used, is that the community understands and respects the boundary, and that they have a voice in deciding where the markers are placed.

The community and field staff also assessed current and prospective land-use needs in the buffer area and lands closer to the village. The community's population is growing slowly but will require future agricultural expansion and increased cash income. Participants also discussed intensification of existing land-use patterns, including means to increase the productivity of cocoa, mango, clove, and nutmeg and to improve access to markets. Community organizers help establish forest farmer groups for cocoa cultivation below the 300-meter outer boundary of the reserve. A nursery was established and several plots were cleared and planted with cocoa. Such intensification of cash crop cultivation is expected to reduce pressure on the reserve's forest at higher elevations.

Oblique aerial photograph enlargements, at a scale of approximately 1:8,000, have proven to be both inexpensive and very effective in identifying current land-use patterns and stimulating dialogues with communities regarding their existing and future land-use requirements (see Chapter 6). With the use of a standard SLR camera and a light aircraft, aerial photographs can be produced in a few days, greatly accelerating the identification and negotiation process and providing a good basis for determining appropriate land-use zone boundaries.[13] Once boundaries have been agreed upon, a formal map will be drawn up with an accompanying contractual agreement, stipulating the responsibilities of the tribal community and the forestry department for the joint management of the buffer zone area. The tribal council, *dewan adat*, will be responsible for ensuring that its members follow the terms of the agreement. According to existing plans, the low-intensity buffer zone agreement would run for an initial period of twenty-five years and would be renewable, provided the terms of the lease were met. Similar agreements between the forest department and all tribal groups living around the reserve, if implemented, would establish a community-managed zone around much of the strictly protected zone, thereby transferring responsibility for land-use monitoring to tribal councils and greatly reducing the need for policing by forest service staff.

Sentani

The Sentani area, located at the base of the steep southern slopes of the Cyclops Mountains, encompasses four social forestry plots: Pos Tujuh, Yakele, Kemiri, and Yofiwi. Sentani is about thirty-five kilometers west of Jayapura and access to markets is very good. The two sites, each with its own forest farmer group, are spread across an area from Kemiri in the west to Ifar Gunung and are along the south-central boundary of the reserve where land-use pressure is very heavy. Land ownership and tenancy are complex, as is the pattern of land use. Most of the land is still controlled and claimed by Sentani people, but some land has been sold to immigrants, mainly from South Sulawesi. Also, several hundred people from Irian Jaya's interior highlands, mostly Dani and Ekari, have been resettled by the Social Affairs Department and by mission groups. Highland migrants have cleared most of the new gardens within the reserve and along its boundary; some rent land from the Sentani and others do not, perhaps not understanding that land is not "free for the taking." This creates conflict and also causes serious problems for forest protection. In past years, the forestry department placed concrete boundary markers in the area, but they are universally disregarded or misunderstood. There was, apparently, insufficient consultation with local people when the markers were placed.

Gardening, logging, hunting, and land clearance are practiced on communal clan land under the control of the *ondoafi*. Tenants orally agree to pay or give part of their harvest to clan leaders. Sentani people do not intensively use the forest within the nature reserve; they mostly use level land far from the reserve for their gardens and do not clear the mountain slopes. They do collect some forest products for building material and canoes, and also hunt. Their main staple is sago, found in the lowlands around Lake Sentani, where they also fish. Unlike the Sentani people, the Ekari and Dani depend on sweet potatoes as their main staple and require rather large gardens for shifting cultivation. A lack of education and marketable skills drives them to grow crops for subsistence and sell the surplus for cash.

The Sentani community organizers have begun to implement an agroforestry scheme for their area that involves intercropping fast-growing annuals with longer-term tree crops such as candlenut. Highland people who are now working lands owned by Sentani clans are forming forest farmer groups together with the Sentani. Tenants will continue to grow quick-yield crops but they and the Sentani will maintain new tree crops on the same plots. The profits from the long-term tree crops would go to the Sentani landowners, while the Dani and Ekari will have continued use of the land. Boundary identification and stabilization will require that tenants restrict their expansion of shifting cultivation and that Sentani landowners enforce their customary land control more strictly.

Maribu

Maribu, a village just southwest of the Cyclops Mountains reserve and about 45 kilometers from Jayapura, is made up of several neighborhoods composed mostly of Moi-speaking people. Other inhabitants are recent Javanese immigrants who arrived through the transmigration program begun in 1964, who either rent land from the Moi or own land originally provided by the government (2.4 hectares per household) after compensation to Moi landowners. However, almost all the land thus provided to transmigrants has been sold to nontransmigrants and planted with cash crops such as cloves, cocoa, oranges, and coconuts. The original transmigrants often become laborers and are paid monthly by the new landowners, although they still occupy the houses given them by the government. Sometimes this situation drives them to practice shifting cultivation for subsistence. Land ownership and customary land transfer procedures, which ordinarily require the clan's consensus, are eroding in Maribu. For example, an *ondoafi* recently gave away about fifty hectares to his son-in-law, an immigrant from the highlands, and 100 hectares were sold to land developers in Jayapura, the proceeds of which were not distributed among clan members. Thus, compared with the other sites, land tenure and ownership is very complex in Maribu and it is often difficult to determine who owns a particular parcel of land. As customary land rights remain strong among the Moi, this is a common source of disputes.

Local cultivation is similar to the other sites, but there is more land available outside the reserve. Like the indigenous people of the other sites, the Moi eat sago as the main staple of their diet. Most of the village gardens and tree crops are across the road from the reserve, which is relatively far from settlements. Some local people have small cocoa and clove plantations in Maribu Tua and Dosai; other plantations are owned by immigrants, some of whom live in Jayapura. In the nearby villages of Girirejo and Sabron, however, logging and gardening are fast approaching the proposed reserve boundary. Also, some of the reserve's most important lowland forest is inadequately protected from small-scale loggers, who receive permission from the local *ondoafi* and forestry service officers to take timber from the forest, contrary to regulations. It is particularly important that the reserve's boundary be identified and stabilized in this area as logging pressure increases in the future.

Community organizers in Maribu have collected data on land use, ownership, and leasing at five plots identified for social forestry. A nursery was established to germinate matoa fruit (*Pometia* sp.), rambutan (*Nephelium* sp.), durian (*Durio* sp.), petai (*Parkia speciosa*), and mango (*Mangifera* sp.) and cocoa. Four forest farmer groups were formed and the main social forestry plot for Maribu, Alang-Alang Joy, has been planted. Proposed zoning is similar to that for Yawena but at lower elevations, and some of the boundary has been identified. Although the forest reserve area near Maribu is not currently threatened, a boundary must still be marked to avoid future infringements.

CONCLUSIONS

Despite clear progress since the beginning of social forestry field work at the end of 1986, the Cyclops Mountains project has been hindered by problems resulting largely from unclear agency responsibilities, which affected coordination by forest department staff and, consequently, the initiative of field staff. Heavy bureaucratic involvement, which may be inherent in any government project, made project management cumbersome and unnecessarily complicated. In spite of two well-organized and productive training sessions for field staff, the lack of coordinated supervision and follow-up to the training led to increased apathy among the initially enthusiastic field staff.

The provincial forestry department now recognizes the need to restructure the social forestry program in Irian Jaya. Essential for a simplified and improved structure is the assignment of a full-time social forestry coordinator endowed with greater responsibility for local decision making by the National Social Forestry Working Group in Jakarta. Many agroforestry projects have failed largely because of the ambiguity of project staff roles *vis a vis* the project and the community.[14] The forestry department is now giving greater attention to clarifying field staff responsibilities and procedures. In spite of a difficult first year, however, the field staff made progress with community organizing, nursery and agroforestry plot establishment, and reserve boundary identification.

The social forestry program is now attempting to stabilize the Cyclops Mountains reserve boundaries through control of encroachment, land sales, illegal hunting, and logging. Here again, many problems could have been avoided had the local people originally participated actively in determining the boundaries.

By contrast, more immediately effective grassroots conservation and forest management projects have been started in the Arfak Mountains Conservation Area, also in Irian Jaya, and in Papua New Guinea.[15] Bureaucratic involvement in the project is low and Hatam tribal people in the Arfak Mountains have organized themselves into village communities for identifying boundaries and developing an agroforestry buffer zone. The people see the importance of actively participating in forest management and decision making if they are to secure their land tenure in the mountains. This experiment in community participatory management of a conservation area has moved much faster than that in the Cyclops Mountains, primarily because enthusiastic project personnel in the Arfaks have sustained its momentum, whereas the top-heavy bureaucratic inertia and lack of follow-through in the Cyclops stifled individual initiative. Yet, while the involvement of Jakarta and provincial officials has slowed project implementation, it has succeeded in placing local tenurial issues on the agenda of senior planners and enhanced their awareness of the need to respond to the land claims of communities when planning new forest management systems.

It would be useful to consider establishing village councils for land management in the Cyclops Mountains. A village council should consist of the tribal leaders, people already involved in social forestry, farmers, and landowners. By following tribal beliefs, traditional laws, and field experience, and with the advice of government agencies, the village councils could manage the periphery of the reserve through social forestry. In the villages where traditional laws and beliefs remain strong, people still respect the natural environment, making conservation practices easier to implement than in immigrant settlements. The authorities should recognize the *ondoafi*, tribal land rights, and the *dewan adat* with its traditional laws, and their land management roles should be precisely defined. In this way, land transfers involving illegal logging and shifting cultivation may be effectively controlled and long-term strategies for establishing a community-managed reserve periphery could be developed.

The Ministry of Forestry and the Directorate General of Forest Protection and Nature Conservation (PHPA), which has the legal authority to manage reserve areas in Indonesia, need to expand their efforts, especially for lands far from villages or near immigrant settlements. The PHPA could focus on land management in areas occupied by immigrants or no longer belonging to tribal people.

If communities are to support social forestry and conservation efforts, tribal lands must have clear title as communal or clan land, with acknowledged owners and specified boundaries. This will help prevent the *ondoafi* or other council members from selling communal land. Communal or clan lands that will be used for intensive agroforestry production could be managed as "private" land by individuals from the tribal community for a specified period, and a certificate or agreement could be obtained. The aim is to eliminate future problems when cash is obtained from trees or their fruit. If the land is still fully communal, care must be taken to formulate clear produce-sharing agreements. Land allocated to individual households could be considered as community property under temporary private ownership, and not allowed to be sold or transferred outside of the local tribal community. If the land is then no longer producing or being managed, it would revert fully to communal tribal land.

The ultimate success of the community-managed areas of the Cyclops Mountains will depend on the management capacity of the tribal organizations, the extent to which land-use agreements reflect community needs, and the establishment of good communications between the community and the forestry department based on mutual incentives. The pilot project, although still at a very early stage, has tried to consider these needs. A key aspect of the program is to strengthen tribal management through recognizing and using indigenous institutions and land-use systems. Initially, the project's design did not sufficiently allow for the cultural differences between Irian Jaya and Java, where an earlier model for social forestry had been successfully developed. The tribal people of the Cyclops Mountains are not landless, but are in danger of losing the long-term security and economic potential their land affords them if the current trend toward land sales continues. An early error was the misidentification of community members with whom dialogue and cooperation would be most effective; these have now been identified as the clan leaders and *ondoafi* rather than groups of farmers.[16] These leaders have traditionally controlled access to tribal lands and are still responsible for the sale and leasing of land to immigrants.

The field worker's role as community organizer, initially the most important, is to help the community formulate its proposal outlining the functions of their managed buffer area. This helps ensure that the tribal community's perspective is central to all future discussions. Training field workers in the functions of traditional legal systems *(hukum adat)* related to natural resource management and in diagnostic techniques based on intensive community participation enhances the field staff's understanding of local perceptions. Finally, the formulation of legally binding agreements that provide land-tenure security for the tribal community should provide a strong incentive for long-term cooperation with the forestry department. Once an umbrella land-use agreement is achieved, programs can be developed to help the tribal communities intensify indigenous agroforestry systems, particularly export commodities such as cocoa, coffee, and cloves. Such agricultural development economically benefits the tribal community, secures their land tenure, and reduces pressure on the forests of the nature reserve.

NOTES

1. Myers, N. 1980. *Conversion of Tropical Moist Forest.* Washington, D.C.: National Research Council.

2. Ibid. Kartawinata, et al. 1981. "The Impact of Man on a Tropical Forest in Indonesia." *Ambio* 10(2–3):115–119: Myers, N. 1987. "Trends in the Destruction of Rain forests," in *Primate Conservation in the Tropical Rain Forest,* Monographs in Primatology, vol. 9, eds. C. W. Marsh and R. A. Mittermeier. New York: Alan R. Liss, Inc.

3. Poffenberger, M. 1986. "Social Forestry in Irian Jaya: Possible Program Directions," mimeograph. Jakarta: Ford Foundation.

4. Poffenberger, M. 1988. "A Community-Managed Buffer Zone for a Nature Reserve, Indonesia," in *Saving the Tropical Forest,* eds. Judith and Russell Gradwohl. Washington, D.C.: Smithsonian Institution Press.

5. Ratcliffe, J. B. 1984. *Cyclops Mountains Nature Reserve, Irian Jaya, Management Plan, 1985–1989.* World Wildlife Fund Report. Bogor, Indonesia.

6. Ibid.

7. Ibid.

8. Pugu, A., and D. Iryani. 1984. "A Brief Survey of the Current Impact of Local People on the Cagar Alam Pegunungan Cyclops," mimeograph. WWF/IUCN Project 1528/Universitas Cenderawasih.

9. Eaton, P. 1985. "Customary Land Tenure and Conservation in Papua New Guinea," in *Culture and Conservation: The Human Dimension in Environmental Planning,* eds. J. A. McNeely and D. Pitt, pp. 181–191.

10. Weinstock, J. A. 1984. "Tenure and Forest Lands in the Pacific," working paper. Honolulu, Hawaii: East-West Center.

11. Aquino, M. R., et al. 1987. "Mounting a National Social Forestry Program: Lessons Learned from the Philippine Experience," working paper. Honolulu, Hawaii: East-West Center.

12. Seymour, F. 1985. "Ten Lessons Learned from Agroforestry Projects in the Philippines," unpublished mimeograph.

13. Killimayer, A., and H. Epp. 1983. "Use of Small Format Aerial Photographs for Land Use Mapping and Resource Monitoring." *ITC Journal* 1983–1984; Fox, J. M. 1986. "Aerial Photographs and Thematic Maps for Social Forestry." *ODI Social Forestry Network,* paper 2c (May).

14. Seymour, "Ten Lessons Learned from Agroforestry Projects in the Philippines."

15. Craven, I., and Y. de Fretes. 1987. *Arfak Mountains Nature Conservation Area, Irian Jaya, Management Plan 1988–1992.* World Wildlife Fund Report. Bogor, Indonesia.

16. Hamilton, L. A. and J. M. Fox. 1987. "Protected Area Systems and Local People" (paper presented at Workshop on Fields and Forests, Nov. 17–21, Xishuangbanna, Yunnan, China).

CHAPTER THIRTEEN

The Growth of the Philippine Social Forestry Program

Christopher Gibbs, Edwin Payuan,
and Romulo del Castillo

THIS CHAPTER DESCRIBES the early evolution of social forestry in the Philippines. In 1971, for the first time, public programs for forest occupants were introduced that were not simply punitive. These programs are still evolving, but their early history represents a valuable case study in how a public agency responds to the need for structural change. This chapter focuses particularly on the years since 1981, when a working group was formed within the Forest Management Bureau (FMB, then known as the Bureau of Forest Development) of the Ministry of Natural Resources, to guide that agency's dealing with forest inhabitants. The working group's actions prompted a period of analysis and experimentation intended to reshape the FMB's structure and programs, largely on the basis of field experience. The working group provided a forum for discussing plans of action, program progress reports, evaluations, and program revisions. Evaluating the working group's effectiveness as a catalyst for change requires an analysis beyond the scope of this chapter. It is clear, however, that the working group has contributed to the development of social forestry in the Philippines, and may afford valuable lessons to others.

BACKGROUND AND FORERUNNERS

Since the enactment of the Spanish Maura Law in 1894, the Philippine state has claimed approximately two-thirds of the country's area as public forest land. Similar legislation was enacted during the American colonial period. In 1975, the Revised Forestry Code claimed all lands with a slope of 18 percent or more, including mountainous land above 600 meters, as part of the public domain and placed it under FMB jurisdiction. Under that legislation, unless these hilly lands were subject to legally recognized claims before 1975, they cannot be alienated from the public domain. Subsequent legislation further eroded forest occupants' rights to the land base they depended upon. In part, this legislation was intended to strengthen state rights over the Philippine rainforest and to control unofficial incursions into the forest. However, an unanticipated effect of the legislation was the erosion of forest occupants' long-term interests in sustainable land management. Forest residents came to be labeled as "squatters" by public officials, regardless of the length of their occupancy, and were further stigmatized as *kaingineros*, or slash-and-burn shifting cultivators, regardless of their farming practices. Such actions encouraged the Philippine government to stereotype occupants of public land as ignorant and destructive and to seek to regulate their actions with force.[1]

The need for regulation was reinforced by evidence that the rainforest was rapidly disappearing, largely due, it was believed, to the *kaingineros*. Statistics on the extent of forest cover in the Philippines have long been regarded as unreliable due to the lack of a periodic national inventory, the high rate of illegal logging, and the vested interests of officials who saw the size of the public domain and the public forest as a primary source of their power. In 1971, however, officials estimated that the forest was shrinking at a rate approaching 172,000 hectares per year, and the Kaingin Management and Land Settlement Regulations were implemented as a result. By 1975, these regulations were incorporated into the Forest Occupancy Management Program, which authorized forest occupancy by permit and regulated the forest land-use practices of farmers. Forest occupants were required either to be relocated where continued cultivation would not adversely affect the public forest, or to remain in place and not expand their clearings. Those who chose to remain were further required to undertake forest protection activities in accordance with the FMB's plan.[2] This program also included a census of forest occupants to identify the population of the public domain; however, more than ten years later, this census is still largely incomplete and official estimates invariably understate the population within public forest boundaries.

In 1978 a second program was started, said to be inspired by a similar program in China and called the Communal Tree Farming Program. This program was intended to establish tree farms or plantations in every Philippine city or municipality and to promote reforestation through cooperation between government agencies, local communities, and the private sector. In 1979, a third program was added based on the Burmese *taungya* system and called the Family Approach to Reforestation, in which the FMB entered into short-term contracts with families to establish tree plantations on public land. These families were allowed to interplant the same land with agricultural crops until the trees were well established; then they would move on to new sites and repeat the process. Participants were paid in installments an amount for each seedling tree surviving after two years and three years, and a lump sum at the designated end of the program.

None of these programs performed especially well and by 1981 the total area covered by all three was only 33,000 hectares. The various reasons for their lack of success have been analyzed elsewhere,[3] but the creators of these programs clearly faced considerable obstacles. While these obstacles were generally seen at the time as technical and regulatory, it slowly became apparent that social, economic, and institutional obstacles might in fact be more important. Technical and regulatory issues received greater attention largely because the problem was perceived to be one of deforestation and the solution to be a responsibilty of forestry. Forestry organizations in the Philippines and throughout most of Asia had evolved to protect the state's interests in forests as sources of raw materials and revenues through exploitation. While forest protection had improved foresters' skills in policing, exploitation had developed their skills in engineering and silviculture. As a result, foresters' first proposals for solving the problems posed by *kaingineros* involved terracing or agroforestry, limiting forest occupants' freedom of action, or resettlement to areas where actual forest was exhausted. Philippine forest administrators also realized that as forests and the forest industry shrank, they could more firmly base their legitimacy on a custodianship, not of the actual forest, but of public forest land.

By the end of the 1970s, agricultural productivity and self-sufficiency in rice, the major staple food, had increased tremendously. However, food production increases were concentrated in the irrigated lowlands, where technical and credit support were accessible and market infrastructure was highly developed. In more marginal areas, including the rainfed uplands, "green revolution" technologies were not applicable. Although the expertise to improve production was lacking, the need to develop uplands agricultural systems was recognized, and the Ministry of Natural Resources realized that its continued jurisdiction over public forest land depended on expanding its programs to include the livelihood activities of forest occupants who could reasonably be described as upland farmers: if it failed to do so, it might be forced to share control of the public forest with other agencies. At the same time, the environmental consequences of deforestation and inappropriate agricultural systems in the uplands became more widely recognized. Foresters once preoccupied with trees had to acknowledge the effects of deforestation, hydrology, and soil erosion. The pressure for change arose primarily from the downstream costs of upland mismanagement, most notably on the shortened lifespan of reservoirs, poorer hydrological regulation of rivers and streams, and heavier silt loads in estuaries and coastal zones. Once again the convenient culprit was the *kainginero*. The costs of land degradation borne by uplanders themselves were only rarely recognized. The forester, as public land manager, was portrayed as fighting a losing battle against an expanding population of slash-and-burn farmers. Deforestation was only rarely discussed in terms of the mismanagement of timber concessions and, although illegal logging was acknowledged, its scope and impact were not well understood.

Certainly the uplands population was growing quickly in the 1960s and 1970s, a fact appreciated by people who lived and worked there. However, research and official estimates did not begin to indicate the full extent of that population growth until the 1980s. Using census data, the population of upland municipalities in 1980 was estimated to be 14.4 million, almost 30 percent of the national population at that time.[4] This research also indicated that some upland areas had been rapidly colonized in the 1950s and 1960s, exemplified by migration from degraded upland areas with relatively dense populations, such as in the Central Visayas, to more sparsely populated upland frontier areas, such as Northern and Central Mindanao. In some upland areas, such as the Cordillera Mountains of Luzon, immigrants confronted tribal communities reluctant to lose ancestral lands to lowlanders and violent conflicts resulted. In other areas, such as Mindoro and Palawan, indigenous peoples retreated when faced with competition for land from immigrants. Finally, while income levels of upland people have rarely been analyzed, upland farm households began in the late 1970s to be identified as a significant poverty group in the Philippines. In addition, provinces with significant proportions of public forest land were poorly provided with public social, health, and infrastructure services.[5]

By 1980 the Philippine uplands and the upland population were significant issues in national development policy, but current information was inadequate to define new policies and programs to tackle the apparent problems. Equally important, the public programs of the late 1970s to control slash-and-burn farmers on public lands and to promote reforestation through local initiatives had not been successful. This lack of success was usually attributed in public debate to the FMB's lack of resources, but there was a growing realization that the success of public programs, especially those concerned with poverty, depended on the full participation of the target population in both planning and implementation. The conventional approach to program development came under attack for its failures, especially in rural development.

In conventional program development, researchers provided data to planners, who designed cost-effective projects for administrators to implement through large public bureaucracies. After a period of implementation, the project was evaluated and, if necessary, amended or replaced. This "blueprint approach" appealed to professional development planners, but rural development projects suggested a more inductive learning approach in which actors learned to make programs respond more intimately to beneficiary needs and to build competent organizations to make the programs work.[6] This prompted the FMB to establish the Upland Development Working Group in 1981 to guide a learning approach to social forestry. The working group in turn provided a forum for steering the evolution of the Integrated Social Forestry Program initiated in 1982.

THE UPLAND DEVELOPMENT WORKING GROUP

The working group's major purpose was to guide an old organization in a new direction and to evolve a new structure. The old structure may have suited the regulatory and protective forestry practices of the FMB and a small number of concessionaires, but it was inappropriate for social forestry implemented by families and small groups with the indirect support of a public agency. Such a structural change required creative experimentation, which bureaucratic structures typically discourage. The creation of the working group was, therefore, a major departure for the FMB. The working group's designated chairperson was the director of the FMB, but he rarely participated in working group affairs directly and the effective leader was a deputy director. Members of the working group were all volunteers and included key FMB staff responsible for programs that were the forerunners to social forestry, or who headed FMB units such as the legal and planning divisions, which were likely to be instrumental in shaping new policies and programs. In addition, the working group contained an almost equal number of individuals from outside the FMB. These included academic social and management scientists from the Institute of Philippine Culture at Ateneo de Manila University and from the research center at De La Salle University, forest scientists and ecologists from the University of the Philippines at Los Banos, and representatives from nongovernmental organizations working with upland peoples. Finally, there was a Ford Foundation representative who helped the working group to coalesce and obtain funding for an experimental program.

The working group first decided to become familiar with the field experiences in social forestry of the governmental program initiated in the 1970s. Very early on, the group visited alternative types of projects and discussed their performance. This exercise was enormously valuable in giving central and field staff from different FMB divisions the chance to discuss social forestry issues as a group for the first time. These discussions typically took place in the field and included academics with different backgrounds, program beneficiaries, and community leaders. Both a fresh look at familiar subjects and a process of team building emerged. The academic members began to put themselves into the bureaucrats' shoes and the bureaucrats began to put themselves into the shoes of their clients. Discussions were also held with members of other agencies who had gone through similar processes, most notably the Philippine National Irrigation Administration.

Following this familiarization period, a consensus began to emerge on an appropriate work plan for the working group. The first task would be a detailed analysis of the FMB's three main social forestry programs of the 1970s: Forest Occupancy Management (FOM), Communal Tree Farming (CTF), and the Family Approach to Reforestation (FAR). The participating academic institutions would write the analysis, with the direct involvement of the FMB units responsible for the respective programs. This task would test whether the academics and officials could jointly write constructive criticism of programs in which the officials had a vested interest or become critical but mutually supportive partners in a learning approach to restructuring a public agency. The analysis was to identify lessons learned and it was presumed at the outset that many of these lessons would be negative. In preparing their reports the academics and the officials again went to the field and discussed programs with the intended beneficiaries. Both partners were forced to look hard at activities that could have been safely ignored from an office in Manila. The entire working group discussed these reports both in progress and after completion to ensure that experience gained was aired.

Since this initial task was considered a success, the working group agreed to adopt a longer-term strategy and to seek financial support for a multi-year program to proceed in three stages. In the first stage, teams of academics and FMB staff would analyze a broad spectrum of completed social forestry projects, including projects initiated by nongovernment organizations (NGOs) and the private sector. The analysis would be comprehensive but focus particularly on issues of local organization and management, participation of beneficiaries, and the role and structure of the supporting agencies. The projects would be selected to represent a geographic and cultural cross-section of the country. The results of this analysis would be used in the second stage to design a series of FMB pilot projects. The pilot projects would form the focus of an intense participatory learning exercise from which, it was hoped, the form and function of a new generation of social forestry projects would emerge, including a new and more appropriate structure for the FMB division working with forest occupants. It was agreed at the outset that any new roles and tasks defined for FMB social forestry would be based on experimentation and feedback from the pilot projects.

In this regard the working group owed a lot to the example of the Philippine National Irrigation Administration (NIA) and its Communal Irrigation Committee, an innovator in social learning since 1979.[7] Following the NIA example, the FMB learning process was to include intensive documentation by pilot project social scientists. The working group was to receive monthly documentation of the implementation process. The documentation was intended, not to provide standard monitoring reports, but to indicate issues and problems encountered by implementors and to stimulate discussion of how to resolve them on a program-wide basis as standard agency procedure.

The third and final stage of the project would establish a broad program based on the experience of the pilot projects, implemented by an agency with new experience of how to work in decentralized ways, and following guidelines and procedures tried and tested in the field. The heart of this approach was to build capacity from intense interaction between program managers and field staff, facilitated by social scientists as intermediaries. The FMB's focus was to shift from solving technical problems by blueprint approaches to creating a decentralized capability for working with people who occupied and cultivated public land. Technical problems would undoubtedly arise in implementing programs, but these would be addressed in the context of overall capacity building, not as primary objectives. The aim was to prevent the program from being perceived as a watershed management or agroforestry project judged principally by its cost-effectiveness in halting soil erosion or promoting fast-growing tree species on farms. The approach would also avoid the premature creation of a new national program without a foundation based on effective experience.

THE INTEGRATED SOCIAL FORESTRY PROGRAM

Despite the working group's cautious, step-wise approach, in 1982 a Social Forestry Division was established in the FMB to implement an Integrated Social Forestry Program (ISFP). Existing units and programs were terminated and their staff and resources pooled in the new division. The program was to be managed by an executive committee composed of ten government ministers and the director general of the National Economic and Development Authority under the chairmanship of the minister of natural resources. This committee was supported by an equally complex National Secretariat. The evolution of this program between 1982 and 1986 has been documented well by Aquino et al.[8] The ISFP's achievements include the creation of new land-tenure options designed to increase the tenure security of forest occupants, expansion of public land areas eligible for settled occupancy, the development of "bottom-up" approaches to agroforestry farm planning, and the development of an active research and program-support group.

The establishment of ISFP in 1982 was in some ways a premature attempt to create a national program when the reasons for the lack of success in the 1970s were still unclear and the capacity and resources for a major new program were unavailable. However, the political pressure on government for a high-profile approach to upland development was considerable. There were public demands from environmentalists for sustainable management of the public forest, from social workers for improved standards of living for upland peoples, from indigenous peoples seeking political autonomy, and from military analysts concerned about communist insurgency in the uplands among the most economically disadvantaged provinces. Confusion also existed among upland communities over the array of earlier FMB projects and parallel programs offered by other government agencies. Further, a growing sense of urgency over the shrinking resource base and growing population pressures forced planners to rapidly implement more intensive land management schemes.

The government responded to these pressures in a conventional way by drawing up a blueprint for a national program with few details of how it was intended to operate. As a result, the working group was drawn very quickly into the process as the research and program-support component of ISFP. The working group's immediate problem was that it had adopted an alternative approach to program development and a timetable for action that would, almost certainly, deliver results more slowly than the ISFP leadership required. Nevertheless, ISFP and the working group began to move ahead simultaneously, and the results of the first two stages of the working group's program were fed into ISFP as directly as possible. In consequence, many of ISFP's national initiatives resulted from experimentation in the working group's pilot projects in Luzon, the Visayas, and Mindanao. For example, working group methods for rapid community appraisal, community organization, and process documentation became standard procedures in ISFP. Also, new ISFP tenure arrangements, such as certificates of stewardship and communal forest leases, were monitored and evaluated most intensively in the pilot project communities and later amended in ISFP in the light of that experience. As a result, the working group became a testing and steering mechanism of ISFP, not in the slow and purposeful way initially planned, but out of necessity, driven by an existing program's need for direction.

The working group's activities influenced ISFP in three areas: site selection and introduction of the program to new communities, provision of tenure security, and agroforestry development. With respect to site selection and the promotion of ISFP, the pilot projects demonstrated that the social characteristics of a potential site were at least as important as the biophysical factor. Site selection was therefore to be on the basis of certain reasonable social and biophysical criteria. Upland communities and sites were so diverse, however, that social foresters needed economical and rapid ways to diagnose these critical differences before introducing the substantive elements of the program. Similarly, organizing upland communities required greater skills and more intensive interaction than most FMB programs; working group pilot projects provided guidelines for these tasks. Building local organizations also required a focus, most commonly improvement of tenure security. Lack of tenure security was the obstacle upland people most commonly perceived as blocking their development initiatives. While the tenure issue remains only partially resolved, individual and communal tenures renewable for periods of twenty-five years are now a standard feature of ISFP.

The working group's interaction with ISFP was probably weakest in the area of agroforestry techniques. In the Philippines, as elsewhere, upland agroforestry systems research is very limited. Social foresters have few technical tools relative to the enormous variety of circumstances they confront. Upland farmers in the Philippines can be characterized by the diversity of the lands they use, their limited access to resources, including credit and marketing infrastructure, and their attitude to risk. Under these circumstances, agroforestry extension agents must be able to offer inexpensive agroforestry techniques that are either viable under an array of conditions or are specifically tailored to a few and produce predictable results relatively quickly. The research investment required to identify such innovations is significant, and, so far, has not been made. Since it was assumed in 1981 that the FMB would keep abreast of technical agroforestry developments without special incentives, the working group did not become deeply involved in technical research at the outset. Instead it used its experience with social and organizational issues to fill a vacuum in FMB skills. This may have been an error since relatively few technical tools are now available for improving upland agroforestry systems and the performance of alternative tools, both ecologically and economically, remains largely untested.

WORKING GROUP'S CONTRIBUTION

Since 1982 the working group has provided a critical forum for thinking about the evolution of ISFP. Its effectiveness in guiding the restructuring of social forestry agencies and programs cannot be fully evaluated, but its contributions are significant. The working group has stimulated a high level of discussion about social forestry issues and programs. These discussions have involved project beneficiaries and participants from governmental and nongovernmental organizations at all levels, from headquarters to field staff. Discussions take place openly and include government "insiders" and academic and NGO "outsiders," creating an environment where issues could not be ignored or suppressed even if they created discomfort. Because the forum was well informed about field-level implementation, it was expected that issues would be addressed as they arose.

Among the "outsiders," the social scientists provided the monthly documentation reports, supplemented by summaries of issues and case studies of particular sites. These methods have become standard for social scientists contributing to the analysis of development programs, but the documentation reports were a source of stress for the working group. Some of the group's members found it hard to digest the sheer volume of reports, the level of detail, and their frequency. Delays in report submission also resulted in outdated information. Further, while reports raised field-problem issues, it was often difficult to resolve problems from Manila. The working group responded by creating a special team to analyze the field reports and prepare summaries along with policy recommendations for administrative staff and tactical recommendations for field staff. The reports also contained a great many observations critical of FMB procedures and performance and, despite the FMB members' initial willingness to examine their actions self-critically, the constant stream of criticism created considerable tension at times. However, the FMB remained remarkably open to this process and the nongovernmental participants learned progressively how to avoid confrontations with officials. More subtle communication problems arose between academic policy analysts, who were themselves learning about social learning processes, and senior public officials who had come to expect from junior staff succinct recommendations for action, not endless questions. At times FMB officials probably felt the academics raised questions merely in order to be contracted to answer them.

Despite this periodic tension, the working group functioned actively until political tension, foreshadowing the revolution of February 1986, became overwhelming. This continuity was accomplished by the exemplary leadership of the FMB's deputy director, the persistence of the chief of the FMB's Social Forestry Division, and the conviction of the members of the working group as a whole that they were working on a topic of social, economic, and environmental significance. An important additional factor was the flexible funding provided by the Ford Foundation, which enabled the FMB both to begin an experimental program at a time when its overall budget was shrinking, and to hire experienced applied researchers, including a number of social scientists, to augment its very limited research capabilities. This combination of leadership and research capabilities progressively engendered a joint commitment between "insiders" and "outsiders" that kept a very difficult program moving ahead. Working group participation became characterized by a powerful combination of frustration and excitement.

Despite its successes, the working group's approach could be faulted on a number of grounds. Restructuring a bureaucracy through a social learning approach is clearly a long-term process that must be purposefully driven month by month. Few bureaucracies are likely to take such a long and torturous path without strong assurances about its validity. Also, the FMB working group was attempting an approach to structural change with which individual members were themselves unfamiliar; *i.e.,* they were learning about a particular process of change at the same time they were implementing it, which slowed the delivery of research results. Furthermore, this was being attempted within an agency known for its centralized regulatory approach to management. Within a year of its inception, the incremental approach that the working group first adopted, which was designed to build understanding slowly, was overtaken by the establishment of ISFP. As a result, the working group became seen within the FMB as the research arm of ISFP, a program with an immediate need to innovate. Although the working group provided considerable direction to ISFP, that program expanded rapidly under pressure to arrest deforestation and control shifting cultivation; while the ISFP was influenced directly by the working group, it also grew and expanded in directions the working group could not control. The smooth evolutionary path to social learning envisioned at the outset could not be followed.

Since the 1986 Revolution the uplands' priority in the national development policy agenda has waxed and waned slightly. Immediately after the Revolution, members of the working group and others influenced by the process quickly defined a new agenda for expanded upland development. This was followed by a major restructuring of the Ministry of Natural Resources into a Department of Environment and Natural Resources with a new and decentralized approach to resource management. However, expansion of field-level social forestry activities has been constrained by limited resources and an unwillingness to grasp the problem of land reform in the uplands. The activities of the working group and ISFP have created a pool of experience, tools, and talent available to government and nongovernment organizations working on social forestry in the uplands. The bureaucratic desire to control public lands remains strong, even if this means control over a degraded resource. Yet, while some bureaucrats and forest administrators are reluctant to see the transfer of greater management authority to upland communities, political support for the program is growing. As of September 1988, 4.3 million hectares of public forest lands were classified as alienable and disposable and were being surveyed for allocation. In the years since the program started, 10 percent of the conversion forest land has been allocated to 200,000 households under the stewardship program. Political pressures are further accelerating the program even though field staff capacity is limited, and this inhibits the ISFP's ability to address community organizational and technical needs. In the past, FMB efforts have focused on conducting the laborious paracellary surveys required for stewardships. The government has attempted to speed up the process by creating 1,038 new positions, including one social forestry officer and five technicians for each of the 173 Philippine districts (centro), while decentralizing authority for issuing stewardships to the regional level. It appears, however, that many of these staff positions will be filled by existing employees and that few new staff may actually join the program.

An exciting element of the program is the recent increased issuance of communal forest stewardship agreements (CFSA). After years with only two CFSAs on record the FMB issued six more in 1987. The CFSA participants now include a number of indigenous ethnic communities in upland Luzon (including Igorots, Mangyans, and Ikalahan) as well as Islamic and migrant communities in Mindanao. The new leases generally cover from 1,000 to 4,000 hectares. The CFSA may be a more efficient mechanism for empowering local groups with forest management authority, as the agreements require only a perimeter survey for defining leasehold boundaries. This avoids the need for a parcellary survey at the outset of the program and allows the community to arrange household farmlot allocation at a later date. While community management capacity development takes time, organizations like the Philippine Association for Intercultural Development (PAFID), which has arranged many of the recent CFSAs, show that nongovernment organizations can give communities the legal and technical assistance they need to organize and formulate management systems.

As a policy environment supporting individual and community management of public lands grows, the primary determinant of success will be implementing capacity. The working group and the ISFP learned a great deal through the pilot project program, but the demand for field-tested organizing techniques, management methods, and agroforestry technologies is rapidly exceeding existing knowledge. Further, the need for experienced field staff is expanding quickly. While donor agencies and the government are allocating substantial sums to support ISFP's expansion, there are serious concerns that the quality of the early pilot projects will not be maintained under a national program. This is the challenge the ISFP faces as political pressures demand its rapid transformation from localized pilot projects to a national vehicle for public land reform and upland management.

NOTES

1. Lynch, Owen J., Jr. 1987. "Recognizing Undocumented Ancestral Property Rights: A Legal Response to Environmental Crisis in the Philippine Forest." Background Report to World Bank Farm Study, Manila.

2. Aquino, Rosemary M., R. A. del Castillo, and E. V. Payuan. 1987. *Mounting a National Social Forestry Program: Lessons Learned from the Philippine Experience.* Honolulu, Hawaii: Environment and Policy Institute, East-West Center.

3. Ibid.

4. Cruz, Ma. Conception, and Imelda Zosa-Feranil. 1987. Policy Implications of Population Pressure in Philippine Uplands." Background Report to World Bank Farm Study, Manila.

5. Sevilla, Judy Carol D. 1984. "Indicators of Upland Poverty: The Micro-View," in *Uplands and Uplanders*, ed. Charles P. Castro. Quezon City, Philippines: BFD Upland Development Program.

6. Korten, David C. 1980. "Community Organization and Rural Development: A Learning Process Approach." *Public Administration Review* (September-October 1980) 40:5:480-511.

7. Bagadion, Benjamin U., and Frances F. Korten. 1985. "Developing Irrigator's Organizations: A Learning Process Approach," in *Putting People First*, ed. Michael M. Cernea. New York: Oxford University Press.

8. Aquino et al. *Mounting a National Social Forestry Program: Lessons Learned from the Philippine Experience.*

CHAPTER FOURTEEN

Social Forestry in Upland Cebu

Salve B. Borlagdan

UPLAND ENVIRONMENTAL DEGRADATION and widespread poverty are a continuing concern of the Philippine government. Through poor management, 65 percent of all public forest lands have been transformed into grassland and degraded farmland. Although only marginally productive, these upland areas were occupied by an estimated 16 million people in 1987. Further, it is estimated that 80 percent of all uplanders are among the nation's poorest people. Competition for limited resources and problems of forest destruction and soil erosion are further exacerbated by annual population growth of 4.4 percent in the Philippine uplands.

Recognizing the failings of traditional forest management procedures in controlling encroachment, the Forest Management Bureau (FMB), previously known as the Bureau of Forest Development (BFD), began to experiment with new ways of managing occupied upland forests and encouraging reforestation. In 1984, the FMB began three pilot projects under the Ford Foundation-assisted Upland Development Program (UDP) to learn effective ways of involving upland communities in its Integrated Social Forestry Program (ISFP). The ISFP promised to transform the agency's role in the uplands from being rigid and regulatory to being responsive and developmental. To curtail and reverse the problems of environmental degradation and poverty, ISFP seeks to (1) settle upland occupants in their current landholdings by securing their occupancy through individual or communal forest stewardship certificates, (2) assist them in undertaking soil and water conservation measures and adopting agroforestry systems, and (3) create or strengthen upland community organizations that will sustain development efforts. The experience of the Bulolakaw UDP pilot project in Cebu provides insight into problems forestry agencies face in encouraging community management systems. The author organizes the analysis of the Cebu project into three major stages and suggests ways local management capacity may be increased.

THE CEBU PROJECT

Settlers first came to Bulolakaw from neighboring upland villages in the late 1800s, with a second major influx during the Japanese occupation period. The migrants cleared and burned the forest to create their farmland. Community members developed a system for allocating land rights, and strengthened their claims through the payment of municipal land taxes. These actions helped to formally establish permanent settlements in the forest area.

Encompassing 356 hectares within a 3,000-hectare forest, Bulolakaw, a small village in southern Cebu, is situated 18 kilometers from the nearest town at an elevation of 700 meters. It is connected to the outside world by an unpaved road that winds through the hills and forests; no public transportation serves the community. The village is inhabited by ninety-two families who grow corn on the steep, rocky mountainsides for subsistence. Most households also grow vegetables and sell them in a market town twenty kilometers from the village. Off-farm employment is periodically available with FMB reforestation projects, private-sector industrial tree plantations, and local coal mining companies. Young men and women earn cash through employment in the lowlands as house servants, shop clerks, and stevedores.

The village was chosen to be among the three UDP pilot projects on the basis of its extensive denudation. Vast tracts of grassland, greatly eroded hillsides, and acidic soils characterized the farmlands that marked its rugged terrain.

The Cebu project was implemented by two FMB social forestry pilot field coordinators (PFCs). The field coordinators were based in the Bureau's district office, which held jurisdiction over the public forest land surrounding Bulolakaw village. One of the field staff was a woman with a degree in agriculture and the second was a male forester. They were assisted by a survey aide, a clerk, and bookkeeper, and received support from the district and regional forestry offices.

The pilot project allowed the ISFP staff and the Uplands Development Working Group (discussed in Chapter 13) to experiment with a range of interventions in this upland community. Community organizers were used to develop a farmer association, impart organizational skills, improve community resource management capacity, and develop farmers' abilities to secure needed social and agricultural services. Community organizing techniques were used to promote environmentally sound technologies and facilitate the issuance of stewardship certificates.

Establishing an Organizational Base

One of the first activities of the project staff was arranging for a team from the regional FMB office to conduct parcellary surveys in preparation for awarding individual stewardships. Some seventy-two hectares cultivated by forty-five farmers were surveyed in twenty days. This survey identified initial project participants. To encourage stewardship applicants, the PFCs discussed the stewardship system in farmers' meetings. However, because the stewardship system threatened preexisting landlord-tenant relations, many tenants hesitated to apply. Consequently, most of the early stewardship certificates were awarded for lands where no such relationships existed. In retrospect, conducting the parcellary survey before organizing the farmers caused the results to be poorly accepted, and the PFCs had to resurvey all of the parcels.

After the survey, the PFCs mobilized an indigenous labor sharing organization *(alayon)* to help bring a core group of eight community leaders and twenty-six farmers together to form an association, draft a constitution and by-laws, and develop a credit program for farm inputs. Activities were planned at officers' meetings and general assemblies of the membership.

Given a free hand to formulate the organization's mission and statutes, the farmers addressed the community's all-encompassing needs, developed a five-year plan, and drafted the constitution and by-laws subsequently ratified by the general body of farmers who formed the upland organization. The constitution and by-laws provided criteria for membership, including the possession of stewardship as well as residence in the Bulolakaw project area. The core group members were subsequently elected officers of the organization.

Implementing Management Activities

The second stage involved the establishment and implementation of the farm credit input program. Farmers viewed input credit as the primary function of their newly formed organization. The organization dealt with problems of loan payments, issues of responsible leadership and membership, equitable distribution of credit and other resources, and enforcement of agreed guidelines and procedures. Project participants responded in the next years to these problems by reviewing and amending the organization's statutes, observing sectoral groupings of members' participation, and establishing ad hoc committees, caucuses, and trainings as mechanisms for discussion, planning, and resolving problems.

Complaints about the inaccurate depiction of landholdings in stewardship certificates led the farmers' association to pass a resolution requesting a resurvey of the awarded landholdings. Project staff conducted a second series of parcellary surveys and instituted ways to ensure farmer participation, including presurvey conferences with the survey aide, the division of survey work into sectoral schedules, the definition of farmers' tasks and responsibilities during the survey process, actual participation in the survey work, and a system of reviewing maps plotted after the survey.

By late 1987, 92 of the 115 target beneficiaries had been awarded stewardships and 57 of these had become members of the farmer association. Membership increased to 70 with the entry of women (mostly wives of stewardship holders) into the association at the end of 1987. There were fewer farmer complaints over boundaries after the new survey, but the duration of the survey itself and subsequent delays in awarding stewardships gave rise to new complaints.

The management of conflicts about boundaries and the existing system of claims, which involved absentee claimants, was an integral part of the farm security program. Conflicts between project participants were dealt with during the survey process itself, when farmers were required to settle disputes among themselves before the survey was conducted. The project was less successful in helping new stewardship holders gain release from traditional sharing obligations with absentee claimants. While local "landlords" hold no legal right to the land, their land rights are recognized by most community members.

While this stage of the project focused on establishing farm input credits, attempts were also made to implement water supply and health and nutrition projects, and to establish a project library. In planning these activities, project staff helped farmers develop contacts with local government agencies and private institutions. Free clinics and supplementary feeding programs were started with the aid of local branches of the Department of Health and the Department of Social Welfare. The PFCs also stimulated farmers' interest in tree planting through a series of cross-farm visits. They provided both members and nonmembers with tree seeds and seedlings. Ad hoc committees and sectoral group proved to be the effective means of instituting and managing the credit project and these other activities.

Consolidating Management Systems

The third ongoing stage was to strengthen the organization by creating sectoral groups and resolving problems of fund management in the credit project. It also involved a team-building training program among farmer leaders, selection and training of community organizing farmer-volunteers (COVs), and the amendment of the organization's constitution and by-laws. This third stage saw personal contacts between project staff and individual leaders and farmers intensified through "groundworking" activities. PFCs visited farmers in their homes and fields to discuss and demonstrate soil conservation measures. Farmers were encouraged to build rockwalls and plant hedgerows. The farmer's *alayon* facilitated the construction of rockwalls, which were widely adopted. The PFCs also mobilized the sector groups to plan agroforestry activities, including the establishment of black pepper groves, stall-fed goat raising, and multipurpose tree nurseries.

Another early weakness of the program was a lack of technical expertise on the part of the PFCs. Initial attempts to assist farmers in developing agroforestry systems were frustrated by the field staff's limited technical knowledge. Increased technical support beginning in 1987 accelerated the development of a number of agroforestry production systems and generated considerable enthusiasm among farmers.

COMMUNITY PARTICIPATION ISSUES AND LESSONS

Organizational Issues

The primary objective of community organizing in pilot projects was to develop a farmer organization that would sustainably manage local upland resources and respond to community needs well after the BFD's withdrawal from the project site. The three years of experience in community organizing identified a variety of problems confronting upland people, including the need for greater land-tenure security, improved marketing facilities, better access to production inputs, income generation, emergency funds, health and medical services, water supply, and employment opportunities. The project tried to respond to these needs in various ways. Early on, project staff attempted to make available reasonably priced production inputs through a credit project. Later, they helped the organization obtain assistance from other agencies and institutions, as in the case of the water supply project, which depended on links with the municipal government and a university-based water resource center. For employment and livelihood opportunities, assistance focused on helping farmers negotiate with employment-generating entities such as the Southern Cebu Reforestation and Development Project (SCRDP) and the Gypsum Chemical Corporation, which, for about a year, undertook coal mining explorations in the project site.

Upland farmers also wanted surrounding land boundaries clarified. Farmers felt their wider community land rights were threatened by the BFD's reforestation project (SCRDP) in the area, as well as by a coal mining operation and commercial industrial tree plantations. A perimeter survey was therefore conducted to identify and certify the farmer organization's rights over the project area; however, the lack of a clear process to give them formal control over common lands resulted in continuing community concern and insecurity. Since ISFP focused on extending individual stewardship for farmlots, it was unable to respond effectively to communal land management needs.

Another issue involved viability of dividing the project area into sectors, using smaller administrative units for project implementation and management. The centralized structure of the original farmer organization was based on the assumption that the community was homogeneous, but it became clear that two factions existed: a large cohesive group of fourth-generation migrants bound to one another by kinship ties, and a small scattered group of relatively new migrants. Because the new migrants were better educated and more experienced in formal leadership (they also had larger landholdings and were cultivator claimants, not tenants), they were among the first to be elected officers of the organization. Later developments, however, showed that these officers' interests were limited to those of their small group, as indicated by their attempt to monopolize resources provided by the project. Because the farmer organization limited decision making to these officers, it created hostilities with other project participants, particularly regarding repayment of farm input loans. This paralyzed organizational activities for a number of months. Mobilizing nonmembers in sectoral groups stimulated new activities in the agroforestry livelihood projects. The greater motivation of some sectoral groups and the delivery of limited resources to these groups spawned perceptions of competition between sectors, but generally the sector groups had a positive effect by allowing nonleaders to participate more actively in planning and implementing agroforestry activities and generating the broad-based involvement of community members within the program.

The recognition of women as legitimate project participants also became an issue. The Bulolakaw project showed an early bias toward male farmers, who were assumed to be the household heads. Since the land stewardship program and membership in the farmer organization were designed for household heads, women were effectively excluded from direct participation in organizational activities and benefits. Thus, until mid-1987 only three of the ninety-two stewards and four of the fifty-seven formal members of the organization were women. Excluded from direct participation in the organization, the women formed their own group to respond to health, nutrition, and livelihood needs. Their activities revealed to the project staff the great leadership potential of the women, previously untapped by the upland organization. The constitution and by-laws were therefore amended to allow women to become members of the organization. To date, four of seven candidates for community organizing volunteers and two of fourteen candidates for officers in the organization are women.

Farm Tenure Issues

Three aspects of farm security were found to be critical to both the speed with which stewardships were awarded and the feelings of security they inspired among the farmers: farmers' participation in surveys, enforcement of regulations, and legal assistance. The extent of farmers' participation in the parcellary survey was influential in their acceptance of the resulting boundaries. During the first survey, farmers' exclusion from the process caused dissatisfaction with the land boundaries given in their stewardship certificates. Parcellary surveys of all the previously surveyed landholdings had to be redone and the stewardship certificates rectified because of complaints about misrepresentation of the farmholdings. In the second survey process, farmers' direct participation was elicited through the early scheduling of survey work with the cultivators. Coordination between farmers and the survey team was facilitated by presurvey meetings where the survey process and tasks were described and the project area was divided into sectors. The second survey also involved a survey aide directly responsible to the project staff, conducting the surveys, sketching maps, and validating them with the farmers. These arrangements allowed the farmers to resolve boundary disputes and other conflicts themselves, although they lengthened the time required to conduct the survey and issue the stewardship certificates. Other delays resulted from institutional limitations, including the lack of appropriate paper for map reproduction and the turnover of district foresters, which delayed the process of rectifying sketch maps.

Farmers' willingness to observe and abide by the provisions of the stewardship agreement was also important to the success of the program. Violations, such as the continued practice of slash-and-burn agriculture (kaingin), the harvesting of trees and forest products for market purposes, and the burning of reforestation plantations and brushlands, showed a lack of appreciation for the stewardship agreement and emphasized the economic pressures that drive farmers to exploit lands claimed by the state. Farmers cited their resentment of BFD reforestation personnel and their need for new grazing grounds as reasons for burning upland areas. Shifting agriculture and the harvesting and marketing of forest products, on the other hand, were survival strategies, particularly during the lean months, which were exacerbated by a prolonged drought. Project staff have had limited success responding to these violations, but they have held private meetings with offenders and offered to help them replace the trees they had cut. Efforts to mandate the planting of banana and root crops for organization members may improve food supplies in future droughts, and reduce pressures on forest lands.

The third aspect of implementing the farm security component was the BFD's ability to give legal assistance to stewardship holders when their land-use rights were contested by absentee claimants. Experience in the Bulolakaw project showed how the local judicial system could be mobilized against the stewardship holders. In one case, a wealthy absentee claimant filed a complaint against a steward who was his former tenant and had not given the landlord a share of his past harvests. Because the landlord had no legal title to the land, he filed a complaint for breach of contract over the sharing agreement, a personal contract between the tenant and the claimant. The case was dismissed after the tenant apologized to the claimant and swore to resume compliance with the sharing agreement.

In this instance, the project staff documented the case, and contacted a lawyer from the Citizen's Legal Assistance Office (CLAO), but did not attend scheduled hearings in the local branch of the regional trial court. In retrospect, the presence of project staff and the farmers during the hearing to present the case as an organizational rather than an individual issue would have been desirable. As a result of this experience, the farmers decided to add a constitutional provision requiring members to provide moral and financial support in cases where members' stewardships are contested by their former landlords.

Agroforestry Technologies and Extension Issues

Implementing the agroforestry component within the community organizing framework proved the most difficult part of the project. Difficulties reflected weaknesses in planning and extension strategies, as well as the inadequate training given to social forestry technicians. Initial problems in promoting agroforestry technologies reflected the need for better ways to identify more appropriate agroforestry systems. With limited capacity to offer information on agroforestry, the staff began to focus their efforts by promoting soil conservation. Project staff required credit participants to construct rockwalls and use soil conservation measures, but this strategy affected only farmers receiving input credit.

Cross-farm visits to local tree planting and agroforestry showcases were a breakthrough for the project. The visits convinced farmers of the economic potential of agroforestry and encouraged several to request and plant hedgerow materials such as *ipil-ipil (Leucaena lucocephala)* and napier grass, and at least one innovative farmer began keeping bees and established a woodlot. Hedgerow planting was not sustained, however, because of a scarcity of napier grass and the psyllid infestation that reduced the viability of *ipil-ipil*. Later in the program, the anticipated delivery of profitable planting materials led farmer group members to formulate agroforestry development plans by sector. Nurseries were established by three of the four sectoral groups after the distribution of lucrative black pepper cuttings, but planting was slowed by prolonged drought.

Early extension difficulties resulted from the BFD staff's lack of knowledge in promoting agroforestry technologies. BFD technical support to the field coordinators was often delayed and poorly defined. In response, the Upland Development Working Group sought technical consultants from the College of Forestry at the University of the Philippines at Los Banos. Their involvement in the project coincided with the recruitment of a new project field coordinator with a forestry background and a desire to disseminate agroforestry technologies. Improved teamwork between project field coordinators and technical staff allowed for more intensive agroforestry promotion, including on-farm demonstrations and field trials of such planting materials as hedgerows of legumes, black pepper, and tree species useful as trellis material for black pepper.

Project staff continue to seek better ways to disseminate technology. Two means now in operation include a project demonstration farm and the on-farm demonstrations and trials discussed above. Project staff doubt the effectiveness of the demonstration farm, however, and question the sustainability of the technologies applied in the demonstration farm because they rely on subsidized labor. Tree planting and soil conservation technologies, such as contouring and hedgerow planting, were best promoted through personal instruction. Intensive contact with the project staff and the technology itself increased farmers' appreciation for and adoption of technologies.

Project experience shows that different types of agroforestry technologies and activities require different strategies for mobilizing farmers. Sectoral groups composed primarily of *alayon* or local cooperative groups were effective for laborious technologies like rockwall construction; sectoral group livelihood activities, however, tended to create competition and conflicts in the larger farmer organization.

The project staff members now face the question of which social unit should generate and distribute seedlings. Until recently, seedling materials were procured with project funds and distributed to anyone interested. This system encouraged an individualistic orientation and, for most, dependence on the project for seedling materials, leading the project staff to reconsider this approach. The more recently established sectoral group nursery projects were generally well managed and required less staff supervision. Consequently, specialized production groups may be the most effective organizational tool for managing production systems, provided competition does not lead to disruptive conflicts.

IMPLICATIONS FOR PROJECT MANAGEMENT

A number of useful lessons can be drawn from the Cebu social forestry pilot project. It was apparent that starting the parcellary survey program without extensive discussions with community members led farmers to reject the allocated farmlot boundaries; a second survey that intensively involved farmers was generally accepted. Future projects need more time for gaining broad-based farmer participation in public land allocation surveys. A major weakness of the first survey was its failure to consider existing land-control patterns, specifically landlord-client relations. Social forestry program staff cannot assume that because the survey area is designated public land, there are no prior claims or ongoing tenant-landlord relations. In the Cebu case, despite the issuance of stewardship certificates giving cultivators sole rights to the land, many farmers felt obliged to continue to give part of their harvests to local landlords. In the case discussed earlier, where the stewardship holder was taken to court for nonpayment of land rent, the landlord won. Social forestry programs that aspire to more equitable rural tenurial arrangements on state claimed lands must be more sophisticated in their knowledge of local land-control patterns and need to provide lease grantees with legal support to allow them to deal more effectively with village elites who have unofficially controlled forest land use.

The experience of the Cebu stewardship program also indicated that while the issuance of individual stewardship certificates improved the tenurial status of many recipients over their farmlots, these legal mechanisms were of little use in protecting the community's common lands. The villagers of Bulolakaw felt the forests and grasslands surrounding their community were threatened by government and private-sector projects, and consequently were interested in gaining stronger legal control over their common land resources. Future social forestry strategies should include a range of tenurial mechanisms designed for family units, smaller production groups, and larger community organizations to improve the fit between the legal arrangements and the land use systems.

The Bulolakaw project staff, when beginning to organize farmers, assumed that a single farmer association would be sufficient to manage the community's land resource base. They assumed the community was homogeneous. They later learned there was a need to represent a number of factions within the community, including women. Project experience indicated that because women were less dependent on seasonal migration for jobs, their residential stability often allowed them to play more effective roles in overseeing resource management. The pilot project experience also indicated that while the farmer group was a useful umbrella organization for administering land allocation and use, sectoral groups were more effective mechanisms for administering agroforestry production systems and nurseries. Smaller sectoral groups allowed individuals with similar interests, available labor, and capital to plan and implement more intensive land-use activities. It also brought new leaders, especially women, into the land management system, who had not previously been involved in the farmer organization.

To develop sustainably productive agroforestry systems, social forestry project staff need technical expertise and support. Early experiences in Bulolakaw showed that without such knowledge agroforestry activities failed to develop. The pilot project also experienced a lack of direction, with organization members becoming involved with a broad range of community development activities. While the activities were worthwhile, they detracted from the focus on solving land management problems and increasing the productivity of the land-use system.

Conclusion:
Steps Towards Establishing
Collaborative Management

Mark Poffenberger

THE FOREST COMMUNITIES of Southeast Asia possess a wealth of knowledge regarding their environment and how to sustainably manage forest lands to meet their needs. In the past, forest use was often regulated through the allocation of family, corporate, and communal rights, based on customary land laws, religious beliefs, and peer-group pressure. The region's indigenous groups frequently viewed their common forest lands as inalienable resources, under community protection, to be passed from one generation to the next. Over the centuries, forest communities developed social and technological strategies to respond to diverse ecological settings. While the viability of many indigenous forest use systems has eroded substantially over the last century, throughout Southeast Asia customary laws and local management practices continue to play an important role in sustaining forest resources.

During the colonial period, Southeast Asian states began to claim and exploit forest resources on a more extensive basis and colonial legislation strengthened state control over the region's forests. Land legislation based on Western concepts of state and private control either ignored or gave little recognition to the customary rights of forest communities.

By the mid-nineteenth century, state forest agencies began to emerge as the operational mechanism through which governments could assert control over forest lands and exploit them. A century later, as postwar development gained momentum, governments allocated vast tracks of forest land for commercial logging, plantations, resettlement, and infrastructural development projects, with little consideration for the future of the forest and its inhabitants. Government attempts to gain control over forest lands, often undermining the authority of local communities, have contributed to periodic insurrection movements in the Philippines, Northeast Thailand, Indonesia, and Burma from the 1950s to the present.

The acceleration of deforestation during the latter half of the twen-

tieth century indicates responsible agencies are failing to sustainably manage the extensive tracts of forest lands they claim. Continued emphasis on
protection and production, in ways unresponsive to the diverse needs of
nearby communities, has exacerbated tensions between the state and forest
dwellers. Most forest policies continue to be designed for political and economic ends, with little consideration for their impact on forest communities. While those in the cities suffer little from deforestation, forest communities must live for generations with the outcome of exploitative policies.

Forestry organizations have tried to implement national forest laws
and ensure sustained management of much of each nation's territory, but
they are subject to the influence of political, military, and commercial
interests. They are generally constrained by a complex and changing
national policy environment, which often produces laws and regulations
that inhibit attempts to decentralize management and extend greater
responsibilities for forest administration to community groups. Many
Southeast Asian governments are still in the process of extending their
authority further into local communities, thus eroding traditional rights
and responsibilities.

In the past, compulsory resettlement of forest communities has often
been a prerequisite for watershed and park protection strategies, commercial logging activities, and for multilateral bank-funded infrastructural development projects. Such actions are indicative of the low priority accorded
to the ancestral rights of indigenous communities and the growing needs
of migrant groups. At the same time, politicians, in an attempt to defuse
rural tensions and undermine insurgency movements, have sometimes
turned over land to rural families in a haphazard manner, without carefully considering long-term forest management needs and local capacities. The complex, often contradictory, mix of protection, commercial exploitation, and politically motivated conciliatory policies has confused both
foresters and villagers.

Forestry agencies have attempted to respond to the needs of forest
communities by experimenting with "people-oriented" programs over the
past two to three decades, but these efforts have generally failed to slow
deforestation. Forestry agencies, with some justification, are proud of their
long traditions of forest protection and timber production. While these
organizations have abundant knowledge of timber stand management,
soil and water conservation, and silviculture, they have limited experience
working with communities to manage forest lands. Little is known about
how to establish collaborative management systems which bring foresters
and communities together; further, few individuals have the experience
needed to train agency staff in such approaches. The need to facilitate and
formalize community involvement in forest management is only gradually being recognized and has sweeping implications for agency policies,
procedures, attitudes, and objectives.

This book demonstrates that, while some planners, development workers, and foresters in Southeast Asia are beginning to consider decentralized forest management, the political will and capacity to begin transferring authority to forest villages remains limited. If families and communities are to be given a formal role in managing state forests, a number of changes must take place within forestry organizations. Policy makers and development agencies who want to involve communities in forest management will need to work closely with sympathetic foresters to form political coalitions which can lobby effectively for decentralization.

Once forest policy makers are convinced of the merits of joint management with communities, they will need to develop long-term plans for a gradual transition to collaborative forest use systems. Staff reorientation and skills development are a major element in any organization's restructuring. Staff attitudes must change to support community participation in forest use decision making, while knowledge of community forest use practices, problems, and aspirations must be expanded. New skills and capacities will need to be created through training and hiring. To facilitate learning within the agency, staff rotation periods might need to be extended. While staff orientation could be conducted throughout the organization, special attention could be placed on developing staff skills in specialized divisions that focus on facilitating community management systems.

Agency procedures must also change to better serve both staff and community needs. Additional time flexibility in developing forest management plans would facilitate community participation in the planning process. Procedures governing production sharing and allowable land-use practices, species, and agroforestry systems, will need to be revised to be more responsive to community needs and provide participants with stronger incentives for sustainable resource management.

Communication channels between communities and rangers, and operational staff and their superiors, need to be improved to allow information about field-level problems to flow upwards. Forestry organizations need new tools and forums to assess the problems of joint management systems and respond effectively. The Southeast Asian experience indicates that working groups linked to field projects can be useful in providing a forum for learning. Lateral communication between related divisions could be improved, with special reference to the coordination of community-oriented forestry programs.

The legal aspects of transferring management authority to forest communities still require much attention. To provide long-term tenure security, some agencies are developing twenty- to thirty-year rollover leases, while other forestry organizations have found contractual arrangements useful in formalizing joint management agreements. Legal mechanisms need to be designed to protect community interests while providing participants with incentives to achieve such national objectives as soil and water conservation, forest regeneration, protection, and increased productivity. Because of the great diversity of local political, agroeconomic, and ecological settings throughout Southeast Asia, joint management systems may vary widely. In Irian Jaya a small hunting and gathering tribe may require 100 square miles of primary rainforest to meet their needs, while a larger community in upland Java may be able to meet their fuelwood, fodder, and timber needs from an intensively managed 100-hectare agroforestry plot. Thus, legal agreements with forest dwellers should include use rights to an area sufficiently large to sustain the proposed production system, under the management of an appropriate social organization. The best-suited management unit might be a family, clan, tribe, migrant group, sub-village production unit, or small collective or cooperative. Past experience indicates successful local management groups are generally comprised of individuals who share a common economic interest in sound forest management and are willing to invest their time and energy in developing the resource. Groups which build their management organizations on traditional values supportive of sustained environmental use, recognized leaders, and indigenous methods for mobilizing labor and reaching consensus, bring added legitimacy and capabilities to their management institutions.

Forestry agencies also need to develop the capacity to work with rural women. For thousands of years women have played important roles in using and managing forest resources. Women are often the most knowledgable members of the community regarding forest ecosystems. Frequently, women are responsibile for minor forest product collection, nurturing and regenerating productive species, and processing and marketing forest products. In many forest communities, men leave the village for extended periods to seek employment in urban areas, while the women remain to manage the farm and forest and raise the children. In many cases women hold primary responsibility for managing the household budget, and may be the major source of income for the family. In some communities, the superior status accorded to adult males allows them to spend their income on entertainment, while the women must provide social and economic stability for the family. At the same time, due to their lack of mobility, women may suffer more from underemployment. Because their opportunity costs are often lower than men, they may be more interested in investing labor in the development of agroforestry systems. Given that women often spend more time in the forest and are more dependent on its products, they may have stronger incentives to manage it sustainably. The experiences in Java and Cebu (see Chapters 11 and 14) showed that some of the most successful community organizers were female. Yet, while women have great potential as forest managers, current attempts to involve women in collaborative management are woefully inadequate. Forestry as a field is uniformly dominated by men, and gender and disciplinary hiring practices are heavily biased in favor of men. A major reorientation of forestry organizations will be needed to formalize and empower women's roles in forest management. Special programs need to be created to enable women to organize forest management groups and gain access to greater authority and production resources.

Community groups could take over many routine forest management responsibilities, but agencies will still need to support their rural partners by arbitrating disputes, providing legal support to forest keepers, and extending technical and marketing support services. Creating this backstopping capacity will involve a long-term process of structural change, budgetary reallocations, and staff development.

Donor agencies, who have in the past encouraged forestry organizations to work more closely with communities, could play an important role in the future in facilitating this management transition. Many donors still place too much emphasis on the achievement of physical targets and financial expenditures, which constrain opportunities for learning and limit implementing agency flexibility to experiment with alternative management approaches. By relying on relatively short-term, technically oriented projects, donors have failed to help forestry organizations develop long-term strategies to respond to more fundamental institutional needs. Donors need to cooperate more in supporting integrated efforts to build problem-solving capacity through an iterative learning process. Such an approach requires an emphasis on building capacity within forestry organizations and at the village level, setting long-term goals, increasing agency flexibility, and improving relations with rural communities through the extension of greater management responsibilities and benefits. Finally, multilateral development banks could relieve pressures on the region's governments to generate revenues from commercial logging through restructured loans and debt forgiveness programs, allowing forestry agencies to shift their dependence from large-scale commercial logging to sustainable, small-scale forest production activities.

Researchers must also develop new capacities to respond to agency and community needs. More applied research is required to better understand the legal and social ramifications of the management transition. Diagnostic studies should be conducted on a wide scale to assess local management capacities, appropriate agroforestry technologies, and marketing options. Economic studies of the investment costs and returns for small forest enterprises are desperately needed. To increase their effectiveness, participating scientists need a better understanding of agency constraints and operating practices. Most important, researchers need to spend more time in the field learning about problems and opportunities from forest communities and foresters.

Nongovernment organizations (NGOs) could play an important role in encouraging and accelerating the transition to collaborative management by assisting communities to gain access to information regarding new community forestry programs. NGOs could help villagers to organize and establish relations with forest department program staff, and could provide community forest managers with legal aid, technical advice, and marketing support. Some NGOs in Southeast Asia are already pioneering such roles.

While indigenous communities have protected the forests of Southeast Asia in the past, their management capacity has been undermined in recent generations by political, economic, and social changes within the village and the nation. It would, therefore, be unrealistic to assume that many communities would be able to sustainably manage forest resources through a simple transfer of use rights and responsibilities. In many forest communities, traditional methods of access control, usufruct allocation, and conflict resolution have become ineffective or disappeared. With new economic and political forces operating at the village level, traditionally powerful families or newly wealthy factions may attempt to capture community forest management programs for quick profits, creating conflicts and mismanagement. Millions of more recent migrant settlers, through their use and presence on the land, also have justifiable claims on forest resources; however, migrant communities often have little experience managing forest lands.

Many communities will have to develop new methods to administer their forest lands. Representative leaders will need to work with their communities to discuss management issues and reach a consensus regarding management policies and practices. Rules will need to be established to control forest use. Community administrative organizations will need to develop revenue sources through fees, fines, and production taxes to cover administration and protection costs, regeneration needs, and soil conservation measures. Mutually acceptable procedures for deciding disputes and distributing revenues will need to be formulated. Community members will also require a greater knowledge of their legal rights and responsibilities and how to protect them through the judicial system. Finally, to take advantage of new agroforestry technologies and marketing opportunities, management organizations must have better knowledge of this field and its application to their forest resources.

One advantage of joint management systems over the transfer of all forest rights to the community is that they give forest departments the leverage to ensure that the resources will be equitably and sustainably managed, and, if they are not, the authority to intervene and resolve local problems; however, agencies must be supportive if efforts to establish and sustain joint management systems are to succeed. A second argument for joint management is that community participation enables foresters to benefit from the knowledge, interests, and labor of rural people in fine-tuning management practices to fit the unique hydrological, biological, and economic conditions of smaller tracts of forest. The development of micro-management plans allows foresters and villagers to consider micro-climatic variation, soil fertility, vegetative cover, and topographic features in classifying land use for protection, timber, fuel, fodder, and minor forest product needs. While staff and informational constraints on forest agencies have often forced them to designate tens of thousands of hectares for a single use, community involvement would allow for far more detailed assessments of forest resources and management needs.

While progress is being made in developing the procedural and technical tools for a transition to participatory management, many questions and problems still remain. Further, time is becoming an increasingly critical factor. As the forests are degraded and the resource base becomes impoverished, opportunities for developing small-scale agroforestry enterprises will be lost as the soils erode. As natural forest ecosystems are degraded, valuable species are lost and their inherent regenerative capacity declines. Already the Southeast Asian rattan industry is being undermined by a lack of concerted government support and the over-exploitation of natural reserves. Further, as population dependencies on forests expand in the absence of any attempt to systematically determine use rights and control access at the community level, the task of creating local management systems will become more difficult.

Current levels of research, field experimentation, policy study, and financial investment are woefully inadequate in responding to forest management problems. A massive increase in regional and national efforts to decentralize forest management and establish viable controls at the village level will be required if forest use is to be stabilized before the ecological functions and productivity of these important natural resources are lost.

The authors of this book have attempted to illuminate the history of forest mismanagement in Southeast Asia and avenues for solving the growing problems which now threaten the existence of these rich ecosystems. If the process of degradation is not halted, millions of families throughout the region will lose the environment which supports them. They will either have to survive on increasingly degraded forest land or move to urban slums. Their nations will be further impoverished through the loss of natural resources which, if properly managed, could provide substantial national revenues, ensure the availability of water resources, and yield the timber and forest products necessary for long-term development. The earth will lose its richest genetic storehouse and a critical mechanism for stabilizing global climatic patterns. The problem of deforestation is too important not to receive priority in the consideration of international and national agencies. The authors conclude by calling for accelerated and intensified efforts to respond to this crisis through the development of community forest management.

Index

❖   ❖   ❖

Gender Roles in Development Projects: A Case Book
edited by Catherine Overholt, Mary B. Anderson,
Kathleen Cloud, and James E. Austin

"An extremely important reference work... Highly
recommended... "   — CHOICE Magazine

Managing Organizations in Developing Countries:
A Strategic and Operational Approach
by Moses N. Kiggundu

"People like Dr. Kiggundu are extremely valuable
brokers in the process of international collaboration and
assistance."   — Kenneth L. Kornher, USAID

Reforming Public Administration for Development:
Experiences from Eastern Africa
by Gelase Mutahaba

This important study updates practitioners of public
administration on the recent administrative reform
measures taken by Kenya, Tanzania, and Zambia.

Transforming a Bureaucracy:
The Experience of the Philippine National Irrigation Administration
edited by Frances F. Korten and Robert Y. Siy, Jr.

"... an inspiring example of how emphasis on people's
participation and self-organization can lead to a viable
but leaner, more cost-effective organization... "
— Soedjatmoko
Former Indonesian Ambassador to the United States

Women's Ventures:
Assistance to the Informal Sector in Latin America
edited by Marguerite Berger and Mayra Buvinić

"... addresses the subject of women in a manner that
acually reflects the reality of their participation in the
informal sector and microenterprises in Latin America"
— from the introduction

❖   ❖   ❖

Please write for a complete catalog of Kumarian Press titles:

Kumarian Press, Inc.
630 Oakwood Avenue, Suite 119
West Hartford, CT 06110-1529 USA

Tel: (203) 953-0214 ❖ Fax: (203) 953-8579

naya MD + Jeff Fox + Peluso + Korten → Chambers
                                   119 Rul des: Putting the last First
1990

277 - Collaborative Mgmt.

xix - crisis
xv - Bush quote - setting the scene
xxii - failure of outside → in technologies
          paternalism

118 - cits → the bigger picture
236 - Blaikie "received conception of land mgmt"

290 - role of ?

282 - joint mgmt - naive

293 - call for community forest mgmt (conquest / depreciation)